ENCYCLOPÆDIA
OF
SEXUAL KNOWLEDGE

ENCYCLOPÆDIA
OF
SEXUAL KNOWLEDGE

BY

A. COSTLER, M.D.
A. WILLY, M.D.

and others
under the general editorship of

NORMAN HAIRE, Ch.M., M.B.

EUGENICS PUBLISHING COMPANY
NEW YORK, N. Y.
1940

PREFACE TO THE ENGLISH EDITION

THIS book was originally published in the French language in 1933, and had an enormous success. It is now being translated into several other European languages, and I have been asked to act as general editor of the English edition, for which I have written special articles on Contraception, Abortion, and Sterilisation. In addition, I have made a number of corrections, amendments and notes in other parts of the book.

While I am in general agreement with the book as a whole, it must be remembered that a number of authors have contributed articles, and I am not necessarily in agreement with their views in every detail.

In view of the large number of popular books on Sex that have been published in England during the last few years, the reader may wonder why this one is being added to those which have already appeared. My answer is that sexual ignorance is still so general, and the mass of misery arising therefrom so enormous and so appalling, that I welcome all additions to the list of volumes offering a measure of sexual enlightenment, provided that the information be accurate, the exposition lucid, and the book reasonably free from the sloppy sentimentalism and the religious ' gush ' which unfortunately disfigure too many of the books that have been published previously.

The medical man who specialises in sexology sees, every day and all day, unhappy people whose lives are rendered miserable by some sexual maladjustment. A few of these unfortunate individuals are sufficiently divergent in their

sexual make-up from the average for us to class them as
'abnormal', but the vast majority are just average people
whose misery is due to ignorance on the one hand, and to
the stupid sexual conventions, prohibitions, and taboos,
which are accepted and imposed in our society, on the other.

The ignorance is due to lack of proper sexual education.
Children are brought up in ignorance of the phenomena of
sex, and of the interpretation of those phenomena; or worse,
they are deliberately misinformed about them by parents
and teachers who do not scruple to lie to the children in
order to keep them 'pure'. To-day parents and teachers
are beginning to realise the wrongness of this attitude, and
the necessity of replacing it by something better, but even
among those who are intellectually emancipated from the
old views about sex, there is too often an emotional
obstacle which renders them unable to enlighten the young.
They find the task too embarrassing, and they shirk it.

We cannot teach the children properly until we first
provide adequate teachers from among the adults.

It is to adults that this book is directed, in the hope that
it may enlighten them, not only for their own sake, but also
for the sake of the children.

How necessary such enlightenment is, has become increasingly apparent to me during the last year, since I
began holding courses of lectures on 'The Elements of
Sexology' for adult students. So far I have given four
courses of lectures—three to general audiences, drawn from
all walks of life, and one for clergymen and their wives.
In all about a thousand people have attended these courses,
people drawn from all occupations, but principally doctors,
lawyers, clergymen, teachers, and university students; and
about as many women as men. I invited questions from
the students, and particularly asked that questions should
be written and posted to me to be answered at the next

lecture. These letters served to convince me, more strongly than ever, of the necessity for sexual enlightenment. Men and women of fifty and sixty years of age, fathers and mothers, sometimes grandfathers and grandmothers, were ignorant of some of the most elementary facts of sexual anatomy and physiology, to say nothing of the more complicated subject of sexual psychology.

It may be objected that in my capacity as a practising sexologist, or as a lecturer on sexology, I get a one-sided view of sexual misery and ignorance, and am apt to exaggerate their frequency and importance.

But I lead a pretty busy and varied social life too, travelling a good deal, and coming into contact with all sorts of different people, in all classes of society, and in many countries; and, observing them, I find my impressions confirmed and deepened.

If you have the gift of achieving intimacy with the people you meet, so that they will talk freely to you, without embarrassment and without dissimulation, about their sexual lives, you will be surprised at the rarity with which you will find, even among the highly cultured, persons who are well informed about the facts of sex, and at the much greater rarity of persons who are free from some sort of sexual maladjustment. I do not contend that a knowledge of the facts will enable every individual to make proper sexual adjustments, but I am convinced that factual ignorance makes maladjustment infinitely more likely.

It is in the hope, then, of dispelling that factual ignorance, and of rendering happier the sexual lives of its readers, that I commend this book to the English-speaking peoples of the world.

NORMAN HAIRE, Ch.M., M.B.

127 Harley St., London.
April 30*th*, 1934.

SUMMARIES OF CHAPTERS

xi

and fixed ideas. Size of the male organ. The inferiority complex. Technique of defloration. Oriental recommendations. Position recommended by Van de Velde for defloration. Gradual defloration. Difficulties of defloration. Disappointments of the wedding-night and how to avoid them. The art of love requires patience.

BOOK III

PROCREATION

CHAPTER XVI

CHAPTER XVII

CHAPTER XVIII

CHAPTER XIX

and unfavourable days in the menstrual cycle. Absolute certainty not possible. An example.

BOOK V

SEXUAL ABERRATIONS

CHAPTER XXXI

CHAPTER XXXII

CHAPTER XXXIII

BOOK VI

VENEREAL DISEASE

CHAPTER XXXIV

ENCYCLOPÆDIA
OF
SEXUAL KNOWLEDGE

INTRODUCTORY

INTRODUCTORY

CHAPTER I

THE EVOLUTION OF LOVE

Difference between human love and animal heat. Primitive love. Love in the Bible. The Roman and Greek conception of love. Homosexuality. Platonic love. Influence of Christianity. Opposition of love and sex. Love and sex united by the Renaissance. Modern ideal of love. False morality and hypocrisy in the sphere of sex.

' It is without hatred and without jealousy that animals make love in every corner of the earth; in the shade of the big firs or of the flowers in full bloom, on every patch of field, in every mountain gorge, in every cave, in the immense depths of the seas, under the streaming waters of geysers, in the highest layers of the atmosphere. Thus every sunray bathes the entire globe and, during every hour of the day, millions and millions of love scenes. Although at every instant a leaf falls from the human tree to revert to dust, at every instant also germinates a new life whom the joys of love await in its turn.'

MANTEGAZZA.

The two primary instincts of man, the instinct of self-preservation and the sexual instinct, have undergone a profound evolution in the course of millions of years. Nevertheless, the difference between the wild beast gorging himself on his newly-killed prey, and the physical and mental satisfaction of a human being eating a perfectly

[3]

cooked meal in an atmosphere of well-being, in other words the refinement that has taken place in the instinct for food, is not as marked as the change in the sexual instinct, from the animal in rut to human love.

Through evolution this instinct has developed to such an extent that its origin is lost in the fog of ages and almost forgotten. This initial truth—that all love between the two sexes, however sublime its expression, has its root in the primitive sex instinct, as a fragrant flower owes its brilliance to the nutriment which it draws from earth's bosom—this fundamental truth seems to have been lost during the last century and only modern scientific and objective conceptions have, so to speak, rediscovered it. Yet the great souls of all times, from Zarathustra and Jesus Christ to Voltaire and the leaders of thought to-day, have all been perfectly aware of this truth. Voltaire in his philosophical dictionary says that man, who has the gift of perfecting everything with which he is endowed by nature, has also idealised love. And Auguste Forel, the precursor of modern sexology, writes in his classical work *The Sex Question*: ' Love in the primitive sense of the word is the sex-instinct guided by the brain, that organ of the soul '.

This evolution from root to flower, from animal instinct to love, the highest human emotion, has taken millions of years and has often diverged from its course. The ancestors of present-day humanity were gregarious. But animals who live in herds know nothing of the lasting relationship that can exist between two human beings; they live in sexual chaos unless the most vigorous male of the herd becomes dominant. Even the higher animals resemble vegetables in that they seek only to propagate their species, and, impelled by this instinct, are only attracted to the female as such, and do not exercise personal choice. It often happens that several males fight for the same female, but the outcome is decided by brute strength and not by the free choice of a, mate. When, in addition to the sexual instinct, selection, i.e. reason and sentiment, come into play, the first step is taken that leads from the animal form of sexuality in the direction of human love.

But even man has not always exercised selection. The first human beings lived in bands and practised group marriage. That is to say, in a tribe—when herds changed into tribes—every woman was the common property of all the men. The motives which finally impelled man to adopt individual unions has never been explained. But it seems most probable that these first 'marriages' consisted in kidnapping women from other tribes, who then became the property of the ravishers; it would also seem that the transition of man from the nomad life of a hunter to the sedentary occupation of the agriculturist, and the ownership of private property, played a big rôle in the transformation.

In the selection of a partner man only progressed one stage, for even if sentiment and reason played a part it was an insignificant one compared to that played by the element of blind instinct. As Havelock Ellis writes: 'It is only when desire suffuses and irradiates the entire organism, that it can become transformed like a flower into love'; and he defines love as follows:

'Love, in the sexual sense and taken as a whole, is the synthesis of "desire" (in the primitive and undefined sense) and friendship. It is wrong to apply the term in its sexual aspect to primitive and unsophisticated lust; it is equally wrong to apply it to the different varieties and combinations of friendship. There can be no sexual love without desire; but, on the other hand, until the flux of desire has radiated through the organism into its psychical components, or at least into its social and affective elements, there is not yet any sexual love. Desire, that is specific sexual impulse, is undoubtedly the essential and primary element of this synthesis.'

Other authors define love otherwise. Herbert Spencer, for instance, distinguishes nine different factors necessary to love. But all opinions agree with regard to love being a compound of instinctive physical desire and mental attraction. The physical desire in man corresponds to his sex, the mental attraction to his personality; the two elements have an invigorating influence similar to that produced by an induction coil; if either is lacking, there is no question of love.

We have said that selection is but the first step towards the most evolved form of love, because instinct still predominates over mind. The notion of love is indeed unknown among most primitive peoples, who have not even a word for it, whereas ancient semi-civilised races were familiar with it and possessed a large store of love-lore.

In the Bible, love is mentioned in only a few chapters, as for instance in the story of Rachel and Jacob, but sex is continually mentioned. Even in this wonderful love story of Jacob, who worked many long years to win his beloved, desire is more apparent than love in the highest acceptation of the term. Yet desire takes increasingly refined forms. In Solomon's Song of Songs, the beloved one's body, her eyes, her perfume, her voice, her complexion, and the taste of her, are described in the most minute detail so that all the senses partake of her. On the other hand, there is not a word about her mental and spiritual qualities. We see therefore that even instinctive love can be ennobled and made to differ appreciably from the brute possession of prehistoric times, by being changed into a rich sensuality, which thrills the whole body and senses, instead of being limited to the genital organs.

This evolution of sensuality, already far advanced though one-sided, reached its culmination in the classical period of Greece and Rome. Even if the spiritual element was incomplete, since the Greeks and the Romans denied woman a spiritual life of her own, their love was nevertheless spiritualised, and the sculpture of those times shows a refinement of the sexual instinct. Despite their refusal to concede woman a soul, the Greek representations of feminine beauty imply the possession of one.

Thus, while ennobling sexual love, the Greeks ignored love as we understand it; woman in their eyes was partly a procreating machine and partly an instrument of pleasure. True, the myth of Orpheus holds an echo of a more abstract sentiment which is reminiscent of love, but that is almost the only instance in ancient Greece.

Once civilisation has attained a certain standard, mind and body can no longer be separated, and sensuality reaches the stage when it must have spiritual co-operation. As the Greeks did not acknowledge the existence of a feminine soul, the synthesis of physical and spiritual love, mixed with the ideal of friendship, could only be realised between men. Thus we find in Greece a cult not only tolerated, but even officially glorified and idealised, that of homosexuality. ' True love among the Greeks was homosexual ', writes Havelock Ellis; that is because this form alone permitted the fusion of physical and mental attraction which we call love. This expression of Eros was the outcome of Grecian civilisation, the development of a spiritual ideal. Since woman was excluded, this sexual compromise was the only one possible.

The conception of woman held by Plato's contemporaries is therefore diametrically opposed to our notion of platonic love. Of all philosophic ideas this is perhaps the one which has been most misunderstood. When contrasting a worldly

Eros with a heavenly one, that is spiritual love, Plato did not think of human love, but of the ideal love of beauty, truth, goodness, of the ideal of superhuman perfection. Plato's metaphysical conception therefore refers not to concrete individuals but to an abstract idea. The expression ' platonic love ' should therefore not be applied to a relationship between a man and a woman.

In short, we may say that, on the whole, antiquity knew a refined form of sensuality but not the love in which both the physical and spiritual co-operate. A turning point in this development was the birth of Christianity, which placed the soul and all spiritual values at the centre of life, and on this foundation built a new belief in which the soul dominated the body.

In fact, sexual ideals were driven from one extreme to the other. Spiritual love was exalted and carnal love deprecated. The asceticism of the monks deprecated all physical contacts as impure and sinful, and regarded the sexual act as an evil necessary for the perpetuation of the species and nothing more. St. Augustine's crudely expressed opinion, *Inter fœces et urinam nascimur* (we are born between excrement and urine), became a byword intended to deter people from being damned by carnal love. ' I am not a lover, but a worshipper ', sang the troubadour, and woman, who hitherto had been merely a brood-mare and a plaything, was now idolised and placed on a pedestal. Whereas the lovers of antiquity were interested only in her nether parts, mediæval lovers saw only her lofty brow, and in each case to half a woman could offer only half-love.

' This spiritual love has a distinctly religious stamp and finds its highest expression in the cult of the madonna. This is the time of an exaggerated idealisation of purely spiritual love, of a delicate and pale love which does not want to possess. Its base is æsthetic and it despises sensuality. The cleavage thus made between sexuality and love lies at the root of some of the most difficult problems of modern times.' (Stekel's *La lutte des sexes*.)

Not before the dawn of the present epoch, i.e. before the Renaissance, do the two parts of mutilated love become welded into a whole. As the Renaissance discovered the forgotten works of antiquity, and sought to apply them to the present, so spiritualised love became associated with the body of woman, who, leaving Heaven, came down to earth, no longer as a slave, but as a complete human being who henceforward takes her place in sexual life.

' More than a thousand years passed before men found worldly love beside its heavenly counterpart. In the Renaissance of thought, love stands among the most beautiful monuments of the fifteenth century. The road was indeed long from the sublimated madonnas of religion to the magnificent women of the Italian Renaissance, as every road is long which rejoins the highway after much meandering. The art and the literature of the fifteenth century are the work of new men, who knew individual love and brought back to humanity, back to woman, the desire which for so long had gone astray. To these men a woman is no more a means of satisfying carnal lust than she is a medium of procreation; she is neither a dumb servant nor a devout nun, neither is she the " devil incarnate " of the early centuries of Christianity; she is a human being endowed with all the finest qualities.' (*The Sexual Problems of Youth*, Totis.)

The modern ideal of love includes both a physical and a spiritual attraction between the lovers, who are thus fused in a harmonious and indivisible whole. In a love that is worthy of the name, body and mind, heart and brain, co-operate with the sexual organs so closely that, if one is lacking, the word love becomes a misnomer: the spell of Eros no longer works and one is back in the Middle Ages.

To-day light has dissipated darkness. But a heavy cloud still befogs sexual relations. Traditional beliefs, vestiges of morals bred from asceticism, the economic dependence of woman on man, which establishes unequal standards of chastity for the sexes, still favour deceit and hypocrisy, and place distorting glasses between man's eyes and nature.

In this book we have endeavoured to combat not only those beliefs and their terrible consequences, but also the deceit and hypocrisy that burden the physical and spiritual relations of men. In every sphere of sexual life the scientist's part is to clear the ground, to tear the veils from false modesty, and to make way for a natural outlook on natural phenomena. We shall not shirk our task in spite of the possible protests from the Pecksniffs and the Leeches. So long as our readers receive a solution to their problems, we are content.

It is indeed regrettable that, even in our time, he who tries to solve these problems should find himself so handi-capped. It is sad that humanity, after having found the synthesis of body and mind, should cover it with such a thick veil. Theoretically our civilisation acknowledges the union of spiritual and physical love, but in everyday life it disowns them and hides them behind a mask of hypocrisy. True, a young man is no longer asked to risk his life for his beloved, but woe betide the maiden who dares to state that she is physically attracted by a young man. Sexual instinct has theoretically been reinstated, but it is still regarded as ' impure, low, bestial '; one admits that man possesses this instinct with the reservation that it is a remnant of the animal in him. Havelock Ellis has very truly asserted that man's sexual instinct cannot be

compared to animal instinct, and that on the contrary it
is the refinement of the latter which changed the animal
into man:

'There is no animal in which the sexual instinct has grown
so refined, so developed, so versatile, so permanently
active, so far and high reaching, as in the human animal.
The sexual activity of man and woman does not belong to
the so-called inner part of ourselves which is supposed to
degrade us to the level of the brute, but to the better part
which determines our intellectual possibilities and the
formation of our ideals. True, it is mostly ignorant and
uneducated women who consider sex beastly and animal,
but as those women are the mothers and teachers of the
human race, such gross ignorance must be done away with
as soon as possible.'

Our intention is not to laud love to the sky any more
than to trample it under foot. Love is not a mystic
adoration nor is it a bestial indulgence; it is the attraction
of one human being towards another, the impulsion of his
ancestral instinct under the guidance of his highest sentiments. It is more than an endocrine function, but it must
not be considered an aspiration to an unreal abstraction.
Its kingdom is neither Heaven nor Hell, but the good earth
on which we live and on which we wish to remain.

CHAPTER II

DESCRIPTION OF THE MALE AND FEMALE GENITAL ORGANS

Description of male genital organs: (1) The external organs, (2) the internal organs. The physiology of erection. Composition of the seminal fluid. Description of the female genital organs: (1) The external organs, (2) the internal organs. The female germ cell. The cause of menstruation.

IN this chapter, we make no pretensions to give a detailed description of the male and female genital organs. We mean simply to call the attention of our readers to certain anatomical and physiological facts, a knowledge of which is indispensable to those who wish to understand the following chapters.

Let us begin with a description of the principal male organs. We may distinguish between the internal and the external organs, i.e. those situated inside and those situated outside the abdominal cavity.

The external genital organs of a man include the male member, known as the penis, and the two testicles. In order to understand the part played by the former, a description of the latter will be necessary. The testicles are glandular, egg-shaped bodies, situated in the scrotum, a pouch of rough skin, the epidermis of which is dark and studded with hairs. A connective tissue divides the scrotum into two compartments, each of which contains a testicle to which it acts as a protecting envelope. Behind and above each testicle is an elongated and flat organ which is called the epididymis.

The testicle, when fully developed, is from 4 to 4.5 centimetres long and about 2 or 2.8 centimetres thick. Its weight varies from 15 to 26 grammes. The left testicle may be slightly larger than the right. These two glands are a sort of laboratory, where, from puberty to extreme old age, the principal elements of the semen, the spermatozoa, i.e. the male reproductive cells, are produced.

The testicles and the epididymis are traversed by a multitude of small canals called seminiferous tubes, whose function is to carry the sperms. They are extremely fine tubes, only a small fraction of a millimetre in diameter. Owing to their numerous and intricate convolutions, they form a network of considerable length: for the two testicles this length is more than fifteen hundred metres. This tubular system leads into a larger tube called the vas deferens. This tube is from 30 to 40 centimetres long and performs the function of collecting the secretions of the testicles and of the epididymis and transmitting them to the internal organs. It acts as a kind of connecting link between the external and the internal parts of the male genital apparatus. The contractions of the muscles in its walls cause its contents to flow further forward.

The penis acts as a channel for the semen, which brings about the fertilisation of the female cell by the male cell. It is a long, thin organ, elastic, extensible, and without hairs on its epidermis. It is situated immediately above the testicles; its length varies in different individuals and depends on whether it is in a state of rest or in erection. When in a state of rest, it averages 9 or 10 centimetres in length, when in erection from 14 to 16 centimetres. In addition to its fore part, which hangs freely, there is a posterior portion. At its extremity, the penis has a thicker portion, the glans, traversed at its summit by an opening, the urinary meatus. The base of the glans, which is called the corona, is separated from the rest of the organ by a furrow called the neck. The glans is covered by a cutaneous fold which does not adhere to it and which is called the prepuce (or foreskin). The prepuce is a continuation of the sheath of the epidermis, enveloping the entire organ. It serves as a protection for the very fine skin of the glans, this latter being very richly supplied with nerves. Normally, the orifice of the prepuce is sufficiently large, and the prepuce itself sufficiently elastic, for both to be easily pulled back. It is only then that the glans becomes visible. Circumcision, a custom practised chiefly by the Israelites and the Moslems, consists in removing the prepuce. The operation, however, is also performed for exclusively hygienic reasons, for the prepuce favours the accumulation of secretions and residues capable of creating a centre of infection.

The penis is composed of two cavernous bodies, in very close contact with each other. The urethra, which is used for the emission of urine, also receives two tributary ejaculatory canals which, as we shall see, transmit to it the secretion of the seminal vesicles.

The penis is composed almost exclusively of cavernous tissue, that is to say, of spongy vessels which dilate and become turgid as a result of the influx of blood which characterises erection.

In its usual state, the penis is flaccid and not prepared for sexual intercourse. It is erection that gives it its elasticity and its rigidity. It is then enabled to deposit deeply in the female organ the semen which it emits, and its function is favoured by the fact that it has a slight upward curve which corresponds to the curve of the vagina. Under normal conditions, the volume of the penis in erection is about the same as that indicated by the dimensions of the vagina. There exist, however, considerable individual differences, which may disturb the harmony of sexual relations and even render impregnation in the normal manner impossible.

Copulation is made possible by the erection of the male member, a phenomenon produced by an influx of blood to that member. As soon as the excitement which has produced the erection brings about its normal result, that is, an emission, the blood recedes from the cavernous bodies, leaving them empty.

Let us now explain briefly the internal genital organs of a man, their appearance and their functions. We have seen that the vas deferens carries the secretions of the external organs to the internal organs. In fact, despite the proximity of the testicles to the penis, the semen, before being ejaculated in the course of the sexual act, makes a long journey, during which it becomes enriched by elements which are indispensable for the accomplishment of its mission.

The products of the testicles first pass into the two pouches situated between the bladder and the large intestine, called the seminal vesicles. These organs are from four to five centimetres long and about one centimetre thick. The principal function of the seminal vesicles is to furnish the semen with supplementary products. It is their secretion, a glutinous mass of a yellowish colour, which gives the semen its viscous appearance.

The seminal vesicles discharge their contents into the urethra in the neighbourhood of the prostate gland, an organ shaped like a chestnut and measuring from 2.5 to three centimetres in thickness. It is situated above the anus, and from there can be felt with the finger. The prostate is composed of a number of glands separated by a connective tissue. The secretions of these have the appearance of a milky liquid, and contain an element with a characteristic odour, called ' spermine '. The prostatic secretion is projected into the urethra at the moment of copulation. Its rôle is to stimulate the activity of the spermatozoa.

Let us devote a few words to the products of the male genital organs which contribute the fertilising elements. We have seen that the liquid in question is a complex one, composed of the secretion of the testicles, of the epididymis, of the seminal vesicles, of the prostate, and also of certain accessory glands. On being emitted from the urethra, the semen has the appearance of a thick, opaline liquid, with a penetrating odour. It contains albuminoids, salts, and the element which we have already mentioned, and which gives it that peculiar odour, which some compare to that of musk and others to that of chestnut flowers. If we examine a drop of semen under the microscope, we see that it contains filiform bodies. These are the spermatozoa, which measure from 1/50,000 to 1/60,000 of a millimetre in length. The spermatozoon is composed of an egg-shaped head, an intermediate segment, and a kind of tail, called the flagellum. It is by means of the flagellum that the spermatozoon moves forwards in the seminal fluid, after the manner of a fish which propels itself in the water by means of its tail. The spermatozoa are not motile until contact is made between the secretions of the seminal vesicles and those of the prostate. As long as they remain in the testicles and in the epididymis, the spermatozoa are inert, and they do not attain their maturity until they pass through the excretory canals of the testicles and the epididymis. The spermatozoa retain that motility after entering the vagina and propel themselves through the orifice of the uterus towards the ovum.

The semen ejaculated during a sexual act averages about three cubic centimetres. As there are 60,000 spermatozoa in every cubic millimetre, the number of spermatozoa ejaculated in the course of the sexual act is about 260 millions.

The motility of this multitude of fertilising agents is extraordinary. Under the microscope they may be seen moving incessantly with extreme agility, crossing each other's paths, coming into contact with each other, rushing in all directions and then coming back again. Each one of them is capable unaided of impregnating the ovum, the female reproductive cell, but only one performs that function, while the others, being no longer of any use, perish.

The female genital organs also consist of external and internal ones. We shall first describe the former, i.e. the vulva and the vagina.

In the lower part of the abdomen of a woman there is a vertical opening called the vulva. This is composed of the large lips which, when opened, disclose the small lips or nymphæ. The large lips bulge slightly and are covered with hairs. In virgins they are usually approximated. The small lips, which are about thirty millimetres long, about fifteen millimetres wide, and from three to five millimetres in thickness, become narrower towards the front, and are joined together at the base of the clitoris.

The clitoris is the chief seat of voluptuous sensation in the woman; it possesses a very rich network of nerves, and is particularly sensitive at its termination, where there is a glans, which moves more or less freely between the upper parts of the large lips. The part most sensitive to excitement is the lower side. At that spot it requires only a very slight touch to produce excitement. It is, in a sense, a

[17]

miniature penis. It should be noted, however, that the clitoris is not capable of a genuine erection like the penis, although it is richer in nerve ends and more excitable.

Immediately behind it is the urinary meatus. Finally, in the folds of the vulva, near the entrance to the vagina, are two small glands, called vulvo-vaginal glands, which secrete an oily liquid which serves the purpose of facilitating the penetration of the male member. The vulva serves as external orifice to the vagina, an organ which is from eight to twelve centimetres long and about four centimetres wide. In virgins the vagina is more or less closed, a short distance from the vulva, by a membrane called the hymen, which offers resistance to perforation, the resistance varying in different individuals. The hymen is usually broken during the first coitus, the breaking in most cases being accompanied by a slight hæmorrhage.

The vagina, the walls of which are very elastic and provided with many folds, extends as far as the neck of the uterus, which connects it with the womb. We now come to a description of the internal organs, the uterus or womb, the two tubes or oviducts, and the two ovaries. The uterus is a hollow, pear-shaped organ, consisting chiefly of muscular tissue, and is situated between the large intestine and the bladder, the largest and most important part of it lying in the abdominal cavity. The narrow part is inserted into the vagina, forming the uterine neck mentioned above.

The uterus, which is adapted for carrying the embryo, communicates by its upper part with the tubes, which are two ducts, from twelve to fourteen centimetres in length and from two to three centimetres in diameter. These originate in two lateral openings situated in the upper part of the womb, and each one terminates in a bell-shaped portion with fringes, called the funnel. This portion branches towards the ovaries, two glands placed inside the abdomen, one to the left and the other to the right of the womb. Each of these glands, which are almond-shaped, is estimated to contain a million ova, i.e. female generative cells. Of this enormous number, only a few hundred reach maturity.

The ova are found in small sacs called follicles. Every four weeks a follicle, called the graafian follicle, comes to maturity, sometimes in one, sometimes in the other ovary. The fluid that it contains flows out, carrying the ovum with it into the abdominal cavity. In the neighbourhood of the funnel the ovum is caught up and carried through the tubes in the direction of the womb. This process is accompanied by a congestion of the whole genital apparatus. A number of small blood-vessels break, thereby causing a more or less marked hæmorrhage which finds an outlet through the vagina and is known as the ' monthlies ' or the menstrual flow, a process that we shall describe in detail in the chapter dealing with sexual maturity in women.

The tubes are formed in such a way as to favour the downward movement of the ovum; they are coated with a ciliated epithelial tissue, which continually vibrates in a way which may be compared to the movements of the walls of the intestines. The direction of these vibrations is towards the uterus.

An important part in the process of impregnation is played by the uterine wall. This consists of mucous membrane containing numerous glands and adapted to receive the fertilised ovum. In order to insure success in the enormous task of making a nest for the egg, the mucous membrane goes through a preparatory process every four weeks and undergoes important changes. If the preparatory processes prove useless owing to the lack of a fertilised ovum, the waste products of the mucous membrane are expelled with the menstrual flow.

From this description of the genital apparatus of both sexes, it becomes evident that there is a striking analogy between the various organs. In fact, the glandular organs, the testicles, in a man, correspond to the ovaries in a woman, for both secrete generative elements. The tubes which convey the ova in a woman resemble the vas deferens which receives and transmits the spermatozoa. The penis corresponds to the vagina, since both are agents of copulation, and so constructed as to accommodate each other. Finally, the female genital apparatus, as we have seen, possesses a kind of penis, one, however, which plays only an indirect part in the act of impregnation.

BOOK I

BOOK I

CHAPTER III

SEXUALITY IN CHILDREN

Two primary instincts. Fallacy of believing children lack a sexual instinct. Sexual instinct present from moment of birth but manifests itself in different forms. Auto-erotism. Pleasurable sensations derived from stimulation of certain parts of the body. Mouth, anus and genital region. Infantile masturbation. Non-interference on part of parents advocated. Harmless except when excessive. Most trouble caused by parental threats. Sleeping arrangements. Danger of allowing children to witness coitus. Healthier outlook of country children. Games with sexual significance. Homosexuality in children, a normal phenomenon. Table showing rate of development.

Two primary instincts accompany man throughout his life: that of self-preservation and that of sex.

While the instinct of self-preservation, which impels us to seek food, is in evidence from the moment of birth, it was formerly believed that the sexual instinct was not awakened in man before puberty.

This opinion was still widely held at the end of the last century; and, on the whole, no one thought of questioning it. No specialist had had the idea of enquiring whether the sex instinct is innate in man, and if so, in what form it manifests itself up to the age of thirteen or fourteen years. If we assume that children are 'pure angels', that is to say, sexless beings, the sexual instinct must apparently descend on them like a bolt from the blue, when they feel the first stirrings of it. Such a hypothesis, however, is contrary to all experience and incompatible with all the physiological laws which govern the development of man.

Human growth does not take place by fits and starts. The sexual instinct is clearly innate, although it manifests itself during childhood in a form different from that which it assumes in adults. These are the considerations which have led some modern sexologists to maintain that the sexual life of man begins at birth. Strange as this may sound, it is none the less true that in practice it is irrefutable. All experts to-day agree that the sexual instinct is in evidence even in sucklings.

It is essential, however, clearly to define the meaning of the word ' sexual '. When associated with the idea of a very young child, the word may appear surprising, or even shocking, to certain susceptibilities. For example, if mention is made before a mother who has not been well instructed of the ' sexuality ' of her baby, she may very well shudder with horror. This is because, with her, the word ' sexual ' immediately calls up thoughts of sex and sexual relationships. But in speaking of the sexual instinct of children, we do not refer to the sexual orgasm. Science has given the word ' sexual ' a much wider connotation. It means, in the case of children, the tendency to seek pleasurable sensations—a tendency which, at first sight, seems to be free from any erotic element, but which as it develops clearly assumes a sexual character.

Now this urge to seek pleasure, like the urge to eat food, is innate in every human being. In the infant these two primary instincts are to some extent combined, for the satisfaction of hunger is one of the chief sources of physical gratification. ' He who sees a satiated child sink back from the mother's breast ', says Freud, ' and fall asleep with reddened cheeks and a happy smile, will have to admit that this picture remains typical of the expression of sexual gratification in later life.'

In fact, sucking the breast not only satisfies the hunger of the infant, it brings him an intense joy which he will soon seek to arouse *independently of the nutritive function.* One of the favourite occupations of an infant consists in sucking his own thumb. When doing this, he seems completely detached from all that surrounds him, the blood goes to his cheeks, and his pleasure is clearly reflected in his eyes.

This urge to experience pleasurable sensations may seek satisfaction in the most unexpected ways. When the child is being taught to control his excretory processes, he discovers that retention gives rise to a painful sensation which is not lacking in a certain degree of voluptuousness. Defecation after retention becomes a source of pleasure, and many children quickly learn to appreciate this and to provoke it, despite the disapproval of their parents. It is not uncommon to hear young mothers complain that their child obstinately refuses to pass its motions, preferring to soil the bed in its own good time. The mother little suspects that this delay is intentional on the part of the child in order to procure the maximum of pleasure from defecation. Freud remarks that educators are not far from the truth when they call children 'little savages'. The association of pleasure with such a physiological function may seem paradoxical and inspire repulsion, but it should be remembered that fæcal matter is not an object of disgust to the child. He sees in it an intimate part of his body, he is proud of it, and his mother does not find it easy to inculcate in him ideas of cleanliness. All these manifestations of sexuality in the child have only a vague connection with the sexual life of the adult. The fundamental difference, as we have pointed out, lies in the fact that in the child these sensations are not produced in the genital zone. But this lack of differentiation in the erotogenic zones is not surprising if it is remembered that, even in adults, voluptuous sensations may be aroused in several different parts of the body. In the woman, especially, there are many such zones. We shall have occasion to study this phenomenon in detail in other parts of this work.

In the child, it is the orifices (the mouth, the anus, and the external genital organs) and certain parts of the skin, e.g. the thighs, the shoulders, the armpits and the buttocks, that constitute the principal sources of enjoyment. The genital parts, however, soon establish their supremacy, and specialists have shown that infants often practise a mild form of masturbation. This infantile masturbation is not identical with the conscious masturbation of the adolescent or the adult, because it is free from any association of ideas and not accompanied by erotic images. In fact, for the child, masturbation is not a makeshift, but a means of satisfaction which is an end in itself. The second characteristic of infantile sexuality is known as auto-erotism, which, according to the definition given by Havelock Ellis, is 'a spontaneous manifestation of the sexual impulse, not directed towards a sexual object', or, according to the psycho-analysts, '. . . directed towards the subject himself'.

It is said that these infants who masturbate are an exception*. The truth is these exceptions are comparatively common, as any mother could testify, if she took sufficient notice. But in most cases she does not dare to believe her eyes, although the phenomenon is natural and perfectly inoffensive.

*Editor's Note.—It would be truer to say that infants who do *not* masturbate are an exception.—N. H.

The causes of infantile masturbation are often purely mechanical. ' The overflowing of secretions, the washing and rubbing of the body, and certain accidental excitements such as the wandering of intestinal worms in little girls ', impress on the child the pleasurable sensations which these erotogenic parts of the body are capable of producing, and these sensations awaken in him the desire for their repetition. In the case of boys satisfaction is obtained by rubbing with the hand; little girls more frequently press the thighs close together.

The following case of masturbation in a little girl is quoted by Professor Garnier:

' A little girl, not quite one year old, continually wanted to be placed on the ground or on a chair, where she would immediately begin making movements with her abdomen and legs. An experiment was made by placing her on a stool. She immediately set about making continuous movements backwards and forwards in keeping with her habit, and went on in this way for about two minutes; then, falling on her back, she twisted herself convulsively, and emitted a number of little shouts. When she recovered she again took up her favourite position and was about to begin once more but was prevented, whereupon she gave way to anger and tears.

All specialists who have studied sexuality in children have borne witness to the existence of infantile masturbation. The celebrated Viennese psycho-analyst, Dr. Wilhelm Stekel, in particular, has made some interesting observations. We quote his conclusion:

' In the simplest form of mastubation the child holds its hand on or near the genital organs. In addition the contraction of the thighs and the legs proves to the physician that the child is experiencing the first stage of masturbation.

'There exist two types of infant masturbators. The first experience a slight but permanent irritation; with the others, masturbation is more pronounced and may be carried so far as to produce an orgasm. . . .

'Since children are usually enveloped in long clothes, and cannot get their hands near their genital organs, it is by the rhythmic movements of the body that parents will know that masturbation is being practised. The baby makes vigorous movements with its abdominal muscles, raises or lowers its legs, or else presses its thighs one against the other. Respiration becomes more rapid, the child stares vaguely ahead, its eyes become almost glassy and its cheeks flushed; it sighs or even stops breathing until the orgasm is produced.

'Parents are nearly always unaware of the nature of these manifestations, and even when describing them fail to realise that they may be one of the various forms of masturbation.

'When they are a little older and begin to speak, children who masturbate often make such exclamations as "There 'tis", "It's coming", or "It's come", expressions which are usually wrongly interpreted by the parents.'

* * *

These, then, are the chief manifestations of the sexual instinct in very young children. We now propose to examine briefly the way in which parents who care about the physical and moral health of their children should react to these phenomena.

Thumb-sucking is one of the most harmless activities. In most cases, the child gives it up of his own accord, so that the intervention of the parents is not necessary. When carried beyond a certain point, however, thumb-sucking may develop into an abuse which demands the attention of the parents. Madame Alice Balint, in her remarkable work, *The Psychology of the Nursery*, emphasises the point that thumb-sucking is a form of satisfaction which tends to make the child too independent of his surroundings. As long as he is sucking his finger, he has no need of anybody, and when he retires into this ' shell ', we have no means of making him come out of it. One might compare the child who has become addicted to thumb-sucking to the drunkard who finds in alcohol the refuge which makes him forget all the troubles of his daily life. But it is not by violent methods that one can best succeed in making the child give up the habit. Madame Balint's advice is rather to seek to amuse the child at the moment when he begins to indulge in these practices. The educator should try to divert the little one by offering him another and more inoffensive source of pleasure. Evidently, much must be left to the discernment of the person concerned with the education of the child. If the latter is in the habit of sleeping with his fingers in his mouth, it would be imprudent to divert him at that moment and disturb his sleep.

With regard to masturbation in children, it is, as we have said, essentially inoffensive, in any case not more dangerous than finger-sucking. The great majority of experts agree that infantile masturbation has no consequences, either physical or psychological. It is important, at all costs, not to smack the hand of a child who masturbates, for since the child does not understand what wrong he has done such punishment might give rise to a trauma and have serious consequences. The advice we have just given with regard to thumb-sucking holds good for masturbation.

But the chief precaution is to see that the child does not sleep in the same bed as the mother. Quite apart from any considerations of comfort and hygiene, and from the danger

[29]

ENCYCLOPÆDIA OF SEXUAL KNOWLEDGE

of the mother suffocating the baby under her own body, the innocent caresses which are exchanged at such a time may later on have certain effects on the child, which are beyond the scope of this chapter. At present, we merely wish to emphasise the fact that excessive demonstrations of affection are capable of profoundly influencing the emotional life of the baby. The innocent little angel which the child is commonly supposed to be is, despite his innocence, very sensitive to sensations of an erotic nature. This statement will no doubt shock certain parents, but they should nevertheless take note of it, in the interest of the little ones who are dear to them.

It is never advisable to let two children sleep in the same bed, even when they are of the same sex. Every psychiatrist knows of innumerable nervous troubles which analysis attributes chiefly to the effect of too great an intimacy between children, either of the same sex or of opposite sexes. Certain forms of play inspired by such intimacy do not justify alarm at the corruptness of children, for they are merely evidence of childish curiosity with regard to sexual matters, and that is a perfectly natural phenomenon.

Some parents even go so far as to perform the sexual act in the presence of the child, whom they believe to be asleep but who is not. Children are sometimes very light sleepers; in any case, they are very keen observers, and the memory of scenes such as those to which we have just alluded may leave an indelible impression on their unconscious mind. These children will not fail to interpret the sexual act as a form of ill-treatment or an abuse of power; in the words of Freud, 'for them the act will have a sadistic implication'. For instance, a little girl, eighteen months old, on seeing her father kiss her mother, protested violently and cried out: 'You mustn't hurt Mummy'. Psychoanalysis maintains, moreover, that such an impression

[30]

received in early childhood contributes greatly towards the development of sadism in a bisexual person in later life.

Some, while admitting the possibility of this hypothesis, will perhaps reply that it is extremely rare that our memory goes back further than the fifth year of life. This is perhaps true of the conscious memory, but analysis has shown that, apart from our conscious memory, there exists an unconscious memory which goes back to the cradle. And it is precisely these memories which have always been buried that continue to influence our actions.

Parents should bear this in mind when they indulge in familiarity before their children, on the assumption that the latter do not understand. Anatole France says somewhere that children are unrecognised geniuses: they take possession of the world with superhuman energy. Nothing can equal the force of their first impulses, their first psychological experiences.

*   *   *

The powers of observation possessed by children are generally under-estimated, so that little thought is given to scenes of sexual intimacy witnessed by them and the consequences that such scenes may have upon their mental life. It is precisely for this reason that we think it well to quote several examples dealing with this problem. The three first are taken from Professor Liepmann's book *Youth and Sexuality*, which consists entirely of confessions made by his pupils of both sexes concerning their earliest memories of a sexual nature. It is interesting to note that all these accounts have one point in common, i.e. that the erotic spectacle produced a very painful impression:

' . . . Unfortunately,' writes one of the students, 'as a result of our economic condition, which did not permit us to have more than one bedroom and a kitchen at our disposal, I was soon to receive another revelation.

[31]

'With my own eyes, I saw my parents perform the " act ". For me it was a horrible moment; I pulled the bed-clothes over my eyes and stopped up my ears. . . . I wished I was ten miles away.'

And here is what was remembered by a young woman student:

'. . . We lived in lodgings, which generally consisted of one room only. Thus it happened one day, when I was four years of age, that I surprised my parents in the act of copulation, and I screamed with terror. The sight made a profound impression upon me, and I still seem to have it before my eyes.'

Another girl tells a similar story:

'We slept in the same room as our parents. . . . Every night I heard the same thing take place, the thing that I had not thought possible, and I was ashamed, yes, I was ashamed of my parents. All this made me like another being. I suffered terribly. Suddenly I began to have sensual dreams which greatly excited me; I became pale and my eyes had dark rings around them. I considered myself a degraded creature because I was already familiar with these things. I regarded all other children as pure and myself as unworthy to mix with them.'

And in *The Psychology of the Nursery* Madame Balint gives us an account of a little girl who slept in the same room as her parents and wet the bed every night, except during the week when her mother had her menstrual period. The eminent psychologist observes that micturition as well as defecation may be an expression of infantile sexuality. In this way the child simply imitates in his own way, so to speak, the acts of his parents.

*   *   *

To illustrate the interest that a normal human being evinces in sexual matters, from his earliest childhood, we shall record a few observations made by various psychologists, which illustrate in a striking manner the child's preoccupation with the subject. We shall deliberately avoid referring to the questions which every child puts to its neighbours at the age of about five or six years, or even earlier, and which bear witness to his sexual curiosity. We shall have occasion to speak of them when discussing sexual enlightenment.

The penis, even in very little children, assumes a special significance; the child attaches more importance to it than to any other part of its body and makes it an object of pride. In this connection, Madame Balint tells a very characteristic story about a little boy. One day, his parents received a visit from a young officer who had just been promoted in the military school, and was inordinately proud of his new sabre. The little boy observed him with jealous eyes for some minutes and then, wishing at all costs to show that he also possessed something precious, opened his pants and said: 'I've got a thing to make pee-pee, too'.

Another child was informed that he was to be operated upon for rupture. In his presence, his parents carefully avoided the word 'cut', and explained that his rupture had to be 'mended'. Before going to the clinic with his mother, the child seemed to be very frightened. Finally, pulling out his penis, he asked: 'Has this got to be mended too?' When his mother reassured him, declaring that 'this' was in good order and did not need to be mended, the child immediately became calm and allowed himself to be taken to the clinic without showing any anxiety.

Naturally, little boys cannot understand that it is possible for anyone to have sexual organs different from theirs, and when for the first time they see a little girl naked, her sexual organs seem to them like a scar. They often imagine that she has been deprived of the penis by way of punishment.

Little girls become aware of the true state of affairs much more readily, and it arouses in them a sense of inferiority. They become jealous of boys and envy them their penis. When a little girl is in the presence of a little boy and both are naked, the girl feels ashamed, and in order to explain her imperfection, she may exclaim like the three-year-old girl we quoted, ' I used to have a thing, like you've got, but I lost it'. Others console themselves with the thought that the penis has not yet grown on them, and that their inferiority is only temporary. The little girl from the infants' school mentioned by Léon Frappier apparently wanted to apologise to the governess who was helping her to unbutton her clothes when she said, ' You know, I haven't got my penis yet'.

The mother of a girl of two relates how, after the birth of her second baby, a boy, she surprised the little one in her bath improvising a male sexual organ with the thermometer. She was quite obviously jealous of her brother's property.

Jealousy sometimes gives way to admiration, as in the case of the girl who, on seeing a boy playmate passing urine, exclaimed, ' How handy that is'.

Particularly illuminating are the following words of a child concerning the relation which exists between nutrition and sexuality. A little girl of three and a half was surprised in the act of masturbating. Not wishing to frighten her, the mother asked gently, 'What are you doing?', to which the child, in her naïve frankness, answered, ' I'm feeding it'.

* * *

We now pass on to those games of ' father and mother ' which vary considerably, but which always consist, more or less, in a manipulation of the genital organs. It makes little difference whether the partners are brother and sister, of the same sex, or of opposite sexes.

These games are usually played during the period between early childhood and puberty. The sexual life of children is continually developing and assumes many different forms, beginning with the auto-erotism of infancy. The child, seeking a form of sexual expression, indulges in original experiments, or allows himself to be guided by such external influences as the behaviour of animals, the actions of his parents or of neighbours, or by an 'example' given by one of his comrades.

One must neither under-estimate nor over-estimate the importance of these games. In some children, those who are very sensitive or subject to psychological disturbances, they may occasion severe traumas which disturb the freedom of their whole sexual lives. In others they may have no influence at all. Everything depends on a number of factors which are decisive in any given case.

On the whole, we may say, however, that in children whose psychological and physical constitutions are perfectly healthy, such games, even when carried to great lengths and practised for a long time, may have no harmful result at all. This applies especially to children brought up in close contact with nature, in the invigorating air of country districts. Amongst peasant children such games are much more common than in large cities, and the parents do not see anything alarming in them.

The following example, supplied with other similar ones by Dr. Grassel, is taken from the German periodical *Zeitschrift für Sexualwissenschaft*:

'The sexual life of the individual, or rather that which gives the impression of it, begins very early, generally about the third year (in the country). A couple of ladybirds or flies performing the sexual act may arouse the curiosity of the child. The example of dogs, bulls and cows, etc., does the rest. In addition, the sight of the naked body of a playmate or of a little sister, in her bath or elsewhere, provides food for thought. With country children, whether those of peasants or of the country squire, it is common, from the age of three or four, to see attempts being made to play at " papa and mama ".

' My brother and I were one day on the top of a hay cart that we were unloading. Peasant children, boys and girls, passed us singing merry songs. My brother then drew my attention to a curious spectacle. The children were diving into the hay-stacks, two by two, but without getting out of our sight, and lying one on top of the other in close embrace. When we disturbed them they got up without seeming in any way troubled and went further on as merrily as they had come. I expressed my astonishment to my brother, who lived in the country, and he told me that children forget all that unless they are punished, in which case these things become fixed in their memory.'

We have already said that these games are especially common in the country. It must not be imagined, however, that they are the exclusive privilege of peasant children, for the streets of big cities offer numerous examples of this sort of thing, against which Dr. Stekel takes pains to warn mothers in his work on sexual enlightenment. The following account of a student, quoted from Liepmann, is of first rate documentary interest:

' We were five children (four boys and one girl, the youngest of us all). I myself was the second and my elder brother was two years older than I. He and I spent our childhood practically without supervision, as my mother always had so much to do with the three younger ones. Until my ninth year, the only rule imposed on us was that we had to be home by eight o'clock every evening. On Sundays, we even had the right to run about the streets until nine o'clock. It was at the age of four that I had my first sexual adventure. My brother, who at that time was six years old, I remember well, took the little girl from next door, herself six years of age, and in the dark unbuttoned her drawers and with the tips of his fingers began to play with her sexual parts, which, by the way, was a thing that many of our playmates used secretly to do. We called it the "game of little father and little mother". The little girl, moreover, permitted all this; she stretched herself out on her back and seemed to derive great pleasure from the process. But the affair was discovered that same evening, because the little girl was not able to button and unbutton her drawers by herself. The mother became suspicious, questioned the child, and then came running to tell my own mother about it. My brother and I were severely scolded on this occasion, for which we took revenge on the little girl by calling her a "tell-tale". But this did not prevent my brother from getting hold of another little girl with the same object in view and continuing the practice until, in his fourteenth or fifteenth year, when he was learning his trade, he had real sexual intercourse for the first time.

'My parents frequently got wind of it and each time it meant a terrible drubbing for him. But he none the less persisted. As for me, I took part in the game only once. Afterwards I abstained for fear of being punished, although I still had at the tips of my fingers the agreeable sensation of softness and warmth that was procured in this way. We had no ulterior motive in doing this; we sought nothing except the digital sensation and we did this simply to follow the example of others. I may add that this little game seems to me to be still quite common in our part of the country. Only a few days ago, I found a boy of seven and a girl of five at midday on the granary staircase acting in the same way. When I asked them what they were doing there they replied, smiling: "We are having some fun". When I remarked that such things were not allowed and that if their parents got to know of it there would certainly be a hiding in store for him the little scamp replied in a daring way: "My father can't mind as he does it to my mother". It is true that his father (a factory hand) is a rather tough specimen, but at the same time I do not think he observes so little restraint in the presence of a young boy.'

To conclude this part of the chapter, devoted to games of a sexual character, games which may have profound repercussions on the emotional life of the subject, we think it interesting to quote a long fragment from the confession of one of Dr. Stekel's lady patients. The author of this account gives evidence of such sincerity that her story has several times been compared to the *Confessions* of Jean-Jacques Rousseau. Before letting Miss A. (twenty-one years of age when this account was written) tell her own story, it is worth while drawing the attention of our readers to the fact that the practices revealed in this document are of an exceptional character, and all generalisation should be avoided. At the same time, we hasten to add that none of those concerned are to be considered perverts. It is an extreme case, but one which, on the whole, cannot be considered abnormal:

'At the beginning, I must make statements that I learned from hearsay.

'I was an eight-months baby, ugly and under-developed. On being christened, I was given a girl's name although one of the doctors in attendance considered I was a boy, and despaired of my life. My first companion, in the first year of my life, was a big collie whose eyelids I used to pinch, until one day my mother became aware of what I was doing, through the whining of the poor animal, and smacked my hands. I cried a great deal, especially at night, as I always wanted to be carried. My " squawking " drove my father to give me a so-called " sleeping-draught " every night. I often got my hands smacked because I had a habit of putting them under my clothes and playing with them. On one occasion I also bit my mother's breast although I had not been breast-fed. For this I was soundly cuffed. It gave me intense pleasure to pull out the hair or whiskers of men, but my greatest fury was displayed when I had to go to " tea and rum ", which meant going to sleep. The first curses I heard were " You are a cockerel " and " You are a knave ". I first learnt to walk when I was twenty months old, at which time my tongue wagged more freely. Once when I had seen my mother washing herself I blurted out, " Anna's got hair too, but on her head ", saying which, I caught hold of my head. The first thing I learnt to say was " O ho ". Once a couple of lovers were kissing each other, being unaware of my presence. I cried out " O ho ", whereupon the two broke away from each other in terror, not knowing that I was such an *enfant terrible*. Up to the age of two years, I had to sleep in the bed with my parents. And once I told all our relatives that my father had said to my mother, " When Anna has gone to sleep, I'll come to you ".

' My first playmates were a five-year-old girl and a little boy, Richard, some six or seven years of age. We were a great deal together. My parents had a bedroom, a study and a kitchen. I was often in the care of my great-aunt, who was quite fifty years older than I. One day I was playing with Richard. My aunt was in the habit of going to sleep when she was with us and we were forced to play in the kitchen so as not to waken her, or else she became very angry. I wanted to know how one could tell whether a child was a girl or a boy. I had been told that it was by the ear-rings. But when a child comes into the world it has no ear-rings. Then I was told it was by the nose. I was satisfied with this answer, but I soon discovered that something was being kept back from me. While playing I waited for an opportunity to solve the mystery. All at once Richard expressed the desire to urinate. The required key hung far too high for us children and we did not dare to disturb our aunt when she was sleeping. Then I conceived the idea of lending him my chamber-pot. I sat near him on a stool waiting with well-acted cold tranquillity to see what would happen. To tell the truth, he seemed rather embarrassed about it despite his seven years, but necessity knows no law and after many entreaties on my part he finally decided to avail himself of my offer. When I saw his penis, which was quite an unexpected sight, as I had always thought that boys were made the same way as girls, I was highly delighted. "What have you got there?", I cried. "By jingo, I must have that too". Thereupon, I seized him firmly by the penis while he stood there crying and confessing that he could not urinate unless I let him go. So I modestly turned my back to him while he urinated. But I hoped afterwards to go on with my object lesson. But my great-aunt coughed and this rudely disturbed us in the middle of our fantastic game. I had a presentiment that I was going to be given a suitable lesson. She appeared in the doorway and the flaming look in her eyes betrayed the fact that she had overheard us. Richard found things too hot for him, and went home as quickly as he could, leaving me to my fate. I had to bear the brunt of it as soon as he had shut the big door. My great-aunt yelled, "You good-for-nothing wretch! You whore!

What have you done? Wait, I shall tell everybody about it and they shall all know what a wicked girl you are. You begin early. Nobody who gets to hear of it will ever give you his hand when you go to school. Your teacher will never so much as touch you again. And you must confess it all when you go to school. None of your schoolmates will sit next to you when they hear what you have held in your hand ".

' Reduced to tears, I begged for forgiveness and defended myself by saying that I only wanted to let him " do a wee-wee " and there was nothing wrong in that. Richard and I went each his own way and from that day our friendship became much less intimate. I never could forgive him for having left me in the lurch, and for the fact that, owing to my kindness, I had had to listen to such terrible things being said to me. To-day when I occasionally meet him two voices speak in my heart. One of them says: " Look the other way and be ashamed that twenty years ago you were so intimate with him ". The second says: " What is the reason that we are so completely estranged and that after so many years we have become so stiff and reserved, each one looking furtively at the other, while the next moment we look on the ground?" From that day, both in work and in play, we have been stiff and reserved.

' My grandfather was a business man who lived at the back of a large house and had at his disposal two big sheds, a little garden and a lovely summer-house, that we children, his two youngest boys of eight and nine respectively, and I, a nine-year-old girl, made use of when we played at husband and wife. Every day, I would promise to marry one of them when we were big—one day it would be Arthur and another day Alfred. Our favourite amusement (especially mine) was to play doctor. I of course was the patient and let them unbutton my clothes and examine

me all over, the examination being especially directed
to my genital organs. One day we were in the summer-
house, where there was nothing except a small table and
a leather sofa. The roller blinds had been left down
and it was quite dark, as it had been a summer's afternoon.
We had been left alone, for something always detained
my grandfather and my great-aunt when they wanted to
spy on me. I was playing with Arthur, my favourite
uncle, with Alfred, and with a boy named Rudolf, who was
at that time at least fourteen years old. "We'll play
doctor to-day", I suggested. I laid myself as always on
the sofa. As usual, they undid my clothes, lifted my dress
up, and seized my genitals. I quietly let them do all this
but I didn't look at any of the boys. I stared up at the
ceiling. Then the eldest (Rudolf) unbuttoned his trousers
and wanted to lie on me or bend down over me—I don't
know which. I was panting for breath, I was terrified and
began to beg and cry, declaring that he should not do
anything to me. I wouldn't lie down any more, I wanted
to sit up. I would give him a kiss but insisted that he
should not do anything to me and that he should let me
sit up. All in vain. They held me fast. It seemed to
me that our genital organs were touching and I became
attentive. Finally he let me go but questioned me closely
to make me tell him what my parents did when they were
married. I began, in my terror, to tell him all that I could
think of and in the end I said that they had also kissed.
He laughed at me and said, "You have forgotten the
chief thing. They also did what I just did to you". I
was deeply grieved. "Oh, no, they didn't do anything so
horrible", I said. "That is a sin and God sees everything.
My father and mother were not so wicked as that." Both
the younger boys then opened their trousers and said,
"If you don't let me put my wee-wee in too, I'll tell Auntie

and you'll be thrashed". So I quietly gave myself up to
my fate, laid myself out on the sofa, spread out my legs,
held up my dress convulsively, but took pains to watch
how first Arthur and then Alfred brought their members
nearer. But they remained in contact with me for too
short a time for my liking, because with every touch I felt
something strange—a delightful experience. In the end
I managed to free myself with a kiss. But throughout
the whole scene, which must have lasted a very long time,
for we spent some hours in the summer-house, I anxiously
watched the door for fear my great-aunt would come in.
From that day I often sat with Arthur behind a plank
in the lumber-house. We used to sit down on the ground
and promise each other that we would be husband and
wife when we were big. He would earn a lot of money
and I should have a big apartment, servants, fine clothes,
and so on. We used to embrace and kiss whenever we
came near each other. I was always glad when he paid
attention to me. If I heard the slightest noise, down
would go my clothes at once, and we would talk about
school. Alfred always had to be our child, and we would
often tell him to run away and play and not disturb us.
If Arthur was not there when I came I used to play with
young Alfred, who always complained bitterly because
I preferred Arthur. He also loved me; he also wanted
to marry me when I was big. Arthur could do anything
with me. He often surprised us when I thought he had
gone for a walk. One day when I had been nasty to him
he told his grandfather about it. "I love you too, Alfred,"
I said; "to-day you shall play with me." (It was a pity
that he had blue eyes. Arthur, being my mother's brother,
had big black eyes.) In his happiness, seeing that I gave
him all he wanted, he presented me with all his playthings
when it was time for me to go away. I took them all

[43]

and had quite a load to carry. Although my people said it was nasty of me always to take Alfred's toys, he always cried when I was not there and got scolded by his grandfather. From Arthur I never took anything. I was very fond of him, and even as a girl of fifteen I wept bitter tears (my first, I believe) when he went to the Naval School. Before leaving he said to my mother, in a knowing way, " If I haven't learnt anything at school, you will find that Anna is a fine girl ". I found it quite natural to take things from Alfred. But if he surprised me in a tête-à-tête with Arthur it cost me my favourite toys, for I had to give them to him as hush-money, carrying them out behind my mother's back. They consisted mainly of hares and cats made from rag, which I always used to take to bed with me even when I was a comparatively big girl, putting them around my neck and absolutely refusing to sleep in any other way. In the early morning I was usually lying on the poor toys. For a month all went well. Nothing was suspected and we could give ourselves up to our love, undisturbed. But one day I quarrelled with Arthur. I knew that he smoked cigarettes on the quiet, and in my rage I told his father, my grandfather, about it. My great-aunt undertook to make the complaint in my name. He was thrashed severely, but he took revenge on me by saying something about our games in the summer-house. Scarcely daring to breathe, I went into the house with my great-aunt. She looked at me threateningly but didn't say a word. I felt that a storm was brewing. Arthur said to me: " I've told Father about you. You're going to get it from Auntie Laura ". Finally she broke the silence: " And now will you tell me what you did with Rudie? I'll say nothing about the other things, they don't matter so much ". " Nothing," I said . . . " I gave him a kiss." . . . There followed another

scene like the one that had taken place four years before.
" You worthless wretch, if you don't hurry up and tell me
what you did I'll give you to the next policeman." I began
to cry and stammered out, " He wanted to put his wee-wee
in mine. Please, dear auntie, don't be angry, I'll never
do it again. Give me a kiss ". I wanted to fall on her neck,
but she pushed me from her. "Shame! You little demon.
I'll give no kiss to such a little whore. Get away from
me. Get away. (So saying she pushed my hand away.)
Such a wicked girl can stand alone. What a disgrace.
If Rudie tells any more people everybody in Grandpa's
house will know about it. Now, when your father hears
about it he'll never want to touch you again. When the
head-mistress hears it you'll get a bad mark. You'll get
sent away from the school; you'll have to go to a reformatory
and you'll end up in prison." I was desperate. That
was too much. I cried and begged for mercy all the time.
"Don't tell. Please don't tell." She said neither yes nor no.

" Please, dear Auntie Laura, don't tell anybody."

"Oh, yes, I shall. I'll not say anything to your father,
but I'll tell your mother."

' With chattering teeth I entered the house and went to
bed, the personification of innocence, and as if butter
wouldn't melt in my mouth. The following afternoon
I was with my mother and my aunt in a restaurant. My
aunt took advantage of the occasion and said: " I always
guessed as much, as I told you, when she is alone with the
boys, but whenever I said anything R. (my grandfather)
stopped me and now you see the result ". But I didn't
fail to notice that my mother, instead of punishing me,
turned her head the other way and suppressed a smile.
She only said that I was not to do it again, which I solemnly
promised. I was angry with Arthur and our friendship
was broken off.

The time was approaching when I was to be promoted to the fourth class, and I also had to make my confession. I was suffering like a martyr. I endured the pains of Hell. How could I tell all about it? However, it went off all right. I stood and stammered out: " I have acted in an unchaste way, alone and with others ". It was over! And after a mild warning I obtained absolution.'

* * *

Many experts, amongst them Malinowski, Ivan Bloch, Hammond and Godard, state that among primitive peoples these games are quite common and that the parents do not disapprove of them in any way. Some ethnologists have noted that in the course of these games there are distinct tendencies to coitus.

We have seen that children do not generally attach much importance to the sex of their playmate. This indifference may be explained by the well-known theory, defended by many sexologists, that up to the age of puberty every child is bisexual, i.e. possesses both heterosexual and homosexual tendencies. It is only with genital maturity that the sexual character of the child becomes definitely determined.

Obviously, this theory is not accepted by all authorities on the subject. The school of Magnus Hirschfeld, for instance, opposes it energetically, as we shall see in the part of this work dealing with homosexuality.

Those who support the theory base their arguments on anatomical observation. Until the third month the embryo possesses the rudiments of both male and female genital systems and it is only later that one of them degenerates. Vestiges of the organs belonging to the opposite sex, however, never disappear completely. For instance, a man possesses nipples, and a woman a clitoris—which is nothing but a rudimentary penis.

In children, this bisexuality is much more pronounced than in adults, and it is only during puberty, following the reaction of certain glands, that the feminine characteristics in a man and the masculine characteristics in a woman are completely eliminated. It is easy to understand, therefore, how a little boy may become deeply attached to a schoolmate or a male teacher, and a little girl to a girl friend or a school-mistress.

Examples of this are abundant, but we shall content ourselves with quoting a few of the more striking.

One of the pupils of Professor Liepmann, otherwise sexually normal, writes as follows:

'. . . I also remember distinctly that when I felt any affection, especially for one of my schoolmates who was already fifteen years old when I was only nine, I used to like to imagine him being thrashed on the buttocks, and myself being thrashed on the buttocks by him. That thought was enough to produce an erection. That is why I called the penis the sentimental barometer. This will perhaps seem incredible. To-day I am myself surprised at such a definition occurring to a child, but it is none the less true.'

Affection of a very high degree and not without a sexual element is admirably illustrated by the following passage from the charming *Psycho-analytic Diary of a Young Girl*, the authenticity of which is guaranteed by Professor Freud:

' November 8th.—There is a wonderful young lady who comes skating; she makes eights and other beautiful figures. When she goes to the dressing-room she leaves a marvellous perfume behind her. Will she be married some day and does she know everything? She is pretty and always throws her hair back when it falls over her forehead. I should like to be as pretty as that. How happy I should be then. But unfortunately I am dark and she is fair. If only I could find out what her name is and where she lives? To-morrow, I must go skating again: I prefer to study during the night.

' November 9th.—I am quite agitated; she didn't come skating. Perhaps she is ill?

' November 11th.—At last. To-day she came. My goodness, how beautiful she is.

' November 12th.—She spoke to me. I was standing by the door and suddenly I heard someone behind me laughing and I knew at once that it was she. She came along and said: " Shall we go skating together? "—" Oh, please ", I said. And we crossed our hands and skated together. My heart leapt up to my mouth and I wanted to say something, but I couldn't find anything sensible to say. When we got to the door a gentleman was already there and greeted her; she greeted him, and then said " Good-bye " to me. I asked very quickly, "When? To-morrow?"—"Yes, perhaps", she cried. Perhaps . . . only perhaps . . . If only it were already to-morrow.'

The biographies of any number of famous men and women describe love affairs of this kind, which, as we have seen, are perfectly normal phenomena of sexual development. It would be a mistake if parents, when confronted with an affair of this kind, were to become alarmed and imagine that their child was incurably homosexual. But all this holds good only for the early stages of puberty. After that games cease to be games and we have to deal with sexually mature persons who must be considered as such.

We have already said that among primitive peoples and peasants the first sexual expressions of the child are not considered offensive. The bourgeois population of large towns, where life is infinitely more complicated, interpret such manifestations in a much more tragic manner. Parents fear the effect such activities may have on the psychological development of their children. We can only say of all these dangers which threaten very young children and even infants that the same principle applies to them as to adults: everything depends on the predisposition of the individual, on his psychological stability and his character. An event which in certain people will provoke a serious trauma or even a disease may have no effect on others.

Even parents who know their children very intimately cannot discover with scientific exactitude what is taking place in the young minds. We therefore advise all mothers and fathers, even when their child seems gifted with unusual emotional stability, to deal tactfully with him and spare him any distress. One should never use violence in delicate cases, never have resource to threats and never terrorise. The dangers which may result from such treatment are infinitely greater than those which the child is likely to encounter when left to himself. That is why the only intelligent method consists not in punishing but in forestalling.

CHAPTER IV

SEXUAL ENLIGHTENMENT

Sexual curiosity in children. Their efforts to find out how babies come. Lack of belief in cabbage and stork stories. Necessity of enlightenment at an early age. Parents or teachers as sexual educators. Danger of sexual ignorance and half-truths. Primitive superstitions. Dr. Max Hodann's experiment with school children.

INTELLECTUAL activity, which awakens early in every child, manifests itself by an intense curiosity for every phenomenon of life, even the most ordinary; this curiosity also extends to sexual matters. In his famous work on sexual education, Havelock Ellis very aptly remarks that the problem which puzzles most children's imagination is precisely 'how do children come into the world?'

It would be quite stupid to condemn as 'immoral' this curiosity of the child concerning sexual matters. In fact this inquisitiveness is but one of the first manifestations of human mental activity, which is precisely what put man above beast and made a civilised being of the primitive barbarian. The child's sexual curiosity is really a reflection of the unquenchable thirst for knowledge which possesses people, whether it be from a purely speculative interest, that is knowledge for the sake of knowledge, or from a practical one, the harnessing of nature's mysterious forces. The question of the origin of our presence in this world is not merely a matter for a metaphysician's hypotheses; it puzzles the child from the time that he begins to think.

From his earliest childhood he asks his parents innumerable questions bearing on that delicate subject. Volumes could be filled with curious and revealing instances recorded by educators as well as by psychologists who have specialised in the study of the child's psyche. We shall here quote only a few which we selected as being particularly typical.

The father of a little boy of five remarked that he was going to the cinema on Sunday afternoon, whereupon a guest of the family inquired whether he would be taking his son with him. ' No,' answered the father, ' I have no such intention, because they only present love stories.'— ' Then, how do you expect me to learn what love is? ' asked the child. ' And, you know, it interests me very much.'

One might, of course, contend that love was not the only point of interest for the boy, and that therefore this instance is not very convincing; but the very way in which he made the remark showed clearly that ' the question of love ' had already been for some time in his mind.

The subject which whets most childish curiosity is, as we previously remarked, that of knowing how children are born. To such questions the majority of parents usually give the well-worn answers: ' they come out of cabbages ', ' the stork brings them ', and so forth. The child listens to those explanations, and although he may sometimes appear satisfied with them, in reality he suspects to some extent that his query is being evaded. In her book which we have already quoted in the preceding chapter, Mrs. Alice Balint, the author of *Psychology of the Nursery*, relates the case of a nurse who no sooner arrived in a certain family than she was taken aside by the five-year-old boy and asked: ' You *will* tell me truly where babies come from, won't you? ' That boy had obviously been putting the same question to his parents without receiving a satisfactory answer. The parents were greatly astonished when the nurse reported the conversation with her young charge; they thought that he had long ago forgotten the subject.

Experience has shown that stories of the cabbage and the stork are not blindly accepted by children. Even if they appear to give satisfaction for a time, it is not long before an elaborate investigation is instituted to verify them; the children watch at the window for the arrival of the stork, and when, after several days of expectation, they do not see it coming, doubt seizes them; they resume their endless questioning; they ask, for instance, whether the stork brought them dressed or not, how it knew the exact address, and whether it can turn the handle of the door, and so on.

A three-year-old boy, the son of a Berlin porter, having asked all the regular questions and received the customary answers, one day said to his mother:

' Now I know that children grow in their mother's tummy. You thought I was silly enough to believe that before I was born I was at the bottom of the lake; but then I would have caught a cold. And how could the stork have brought me? You said that it dropped me down the chimney; but then I would have been all sooty and I would have hurt myself badly in falling.'

This strictly authentic case shows how often our little ' innocents ', even as early as that, can detect their parents' fibs. This youngster's questioning shows with what close reasoning he refuted his mother's story once his little street comrades had taught him the truth. One must not think, however, that his doubts were due to that revelation; on the contrary, it is because he already doubted that he so readily accepted the information given by the other children.

Another instance. A little girl about four years old

happened to be present when a friend of her mother's was taken with the first labour pains; she watched the general excitement, and was not taken away until the doctor arrived. When going to bed in the evening she said to her mother: ' Tell me, Mummy, is it the stork or the tummy? ' Greatly surprised, her mother confessed: ' Well—er—it is the tummy '. Upon which the little girl exclaimed: ' Now I understand, but I don't see how you managed to swallow me '.

This particularly amusing anecdote shows the cunning with which a child can express its doubts on the story which the grown-ups have told it.

Very often children embarrass their elders by asking them how it is that only married women have children, and not unmarried girls.

*   *   *

The foregoing instances amply illustrate the fact, which nobody ignores in practice, that children's curiosity is definitely turned towards sexual questions. That is why the problem of sexual enlightenment has to be faced from the earliest childhood. Should children be told about this aspect of life or not? As recently as the beginning of this century, the great majority of parents answered in the negative, on the plea that a child's innocence must not be sullied at an early age, and that there would be time enough later on for him to learn all that he need know. It was also said that the child had better learn the truth from his playmates, because he would lose his respect for his parents if the latter discussed such questions in his presence or with him.

This erroneous opinion has since been so vigorously and competently refuted by scientists and educators that we need not go over that ground again. We shall assume as a matter of principle that a judicious initiation can only be of advantage, and that so far as the parents' authority is concerned, nothing shakes it more than a child's conviction that he has been deceived. We shall refer to this question further on in this chapter.

This is how a Hamburg clergyman, Pastor F. Mahling, expressed his opinion on the necessity of an early sexual initiation:

' I am all in favour of absolute frankness, because I think that to hide natural matters under a cloak of deceit may be far more harmful than to reveal the truth. Nobody has ever yet been corrupted by truth, whereas the damage done by prevarication is notorious. We therefore advocate the enlightenment of the young. The question is to know how and when this enlightenment should take place.'

We must not think that the initiation of a child into the natural mysteries of life is not an infinitely delicate task.

Educators will be helped in this task by the freshness of the child's mind, which is always attracted by the sublime and the marvellous, and which, provided it has not been warped by a hypocritical upbringing, will regard the miracle of the perpetual renewal of living beings as something quite natural. He will see in that a manifestation of Nature's all-powerful forces. If this miracle is revealed to him in suitable words inspired by sound wisdom and the respect born of love, the child will see in human nature a wonderful phenomenon and a source of joy, without associating it in any way with lust and vice. Parents whose culpable negligence allows such an association to take place in the soul of their child are actually criminal, as an American physician, Dr. Goodchild, did not hesitate to declare at the beginning of the century, when he protested emphatically against the custom of launching young men into the excitement and the temptation of a city without having prepared them any more than if they were going to live in Paradise.

Although sexual enlightenment is necessary, it nevertheless, as we remarked above, calls for a great deal of tact and
delicacy. That is why a responsible educator should himself
undertake this task, otherwise it will inevitably be performed by an incompetent person whose cynicism and
grossness will besmirch the child's soul. And in this way
parents who endeavour to keep their child ' pure and
innocent' by hiding from him the essential functions of
human life will bring about an exactly opposite result.
The enlightenment will take place outside the home, and
the mystery of procreation will be revealed by the ' smutty '
stories of better informed playmates, depraved servants, or
pornographic writings and pictures.

The following example of one of these atrocious methods
of enlightenment was related by one of Professor Liepmann's
girl-students, in whose case the effect was aggravated by
perverse tendencies which induced in her a morbid and
lasting frigidity.

' When I was about nine years old I was first enlightened
by a thoroughly depraved maid, who having experienced
every possible form of love and lust, and thereby caught
various diseases, besides having a child, felt inclined on the
strength of it all to protect me from the same misfortunes.
She was a self-appointed sexual instructress. I no longer
remember clearly the details. I only know that she always
pictured woman as an innocent lamb, and man as a devouring
monster, who sought only to satisfy his lust without caring
whether his indulgence brought disaster to the woman.
Her sexual advice was summed up in the following few
words: " I can only tell you one thing: beware of men.
Before you've had time to give them a dirty look they have
given you a baby ". As she had detached herself from
those monsters while still retaining a violent sexual appetite,
she used to approach other girls, her fellow maids, and the

little girls entrusted to her care. She did not fail to attempt intimacy with me, but the only effect was to make me feel degraded and nauseated and to induce in me an indescribable repulsion for everything concerning sex.'

We apologise for writing at such length on questions which to many people will appear hackneyed. But there are still so many who do not sufficiently realise the damage done by the ignorance and hypocrisy that still prevail in modern educational methods, that we do not think it is wasting time to emphasise some points. It is not so long ago that an author like Alphonse Daudet wrote: ' As regards young boys, they learn all they need in the streets and the newspapers; as regards young girls, they must certainly not be taught physiology; I can only see disadvantages in this new notion; such truths are dirty, they destroy illusions, they frighten and repel the mind and warp the nature of young girls '.

Unfortunately, such an opinion is still far commoner than one might believe. Havelock Ellis was right when he answered such Puritans by saying that their contention is tantamount to maintaining that it is superfluous to supply fresh water to the inhabitants of a town, since they can drink from the street puddles.

We repeat, a child's introduction to the world of love must at all costs be dissociated from the notion of filth and sin, lest he develop fixed ideas about sex which will influence the whole of his adult life.

* * *

The danger of ignorance, which we have just mentioned, is particularly great in the case of girls, especially when they are taken unawares and unprepared by menstruation. Edmond de Goncourt in his *Chérie* gives a classic description of the fear which overcomes the girl who does not understand the origin of the blood that stains her underclothing. A famous gynæcologist of the last century, Tilt, prepared a table of statistics of the onset of menstruation in a large number of girls; it shows that twenty-five per cent. were unprepared, and that, out of that number, thirteen per cent. were so frightened that they had a nervous attack, while six per cent. thought that they were wounded and washed themselves with cold water. The health of the frightened ones was badly affected.

Engelmann writes:

' Girls without number become ill at the time of puberty through fright, nervous excitement, and exposure to cold. What is more natural for a young girl, surprised by the sudden and inexplicable flow of blood, than to try to stop the hæmorrhage which she in her anxiety thinks is due to a wound? This being so, it is natural that she should apply cold water compresses; a few even try to staunch the blood by taking a cold bath, as did a young girl who eventually became an enlightened mother after suffering for years from the consequences of her mistake. This terrible warning was not wasted; remembering her own experiences, she gave her children instruction, such as few children have the good fortune to receive, on the personal care essential to a woman's health during the monthly period.

' The terror of the uninitiated girl at the sight of this inexplicable hæmorrhage is such that she frequently regards it as a punishment for having masturbated and harboured impure thoughts. She often sees no other solution than suicide. Dr. Stekel cites the case already quoted in the preceding chapter of little Anna. Every time she questioned her mother about the origin of children, she was told: " You don't need to know. Those are dirty things with which you must not pollute the purity of your little soul ", etc. Anna had no inkling that she herself, her mother and her little brothers owed their existence to those " dirty things ", the nature of which remained a mystery for her. Always closely chaperoned by her governess, she never even had an opportunity to discuss the subject with her friends. One day, in the course of a gymnastic lesson, she noticed that climbing up a pole gave her " a pleasant sensation "; then she found that she could induce the same sensation by pressing her legs tightly together. She would have mentioned it to her mother, but she vaguely suspected that her discovery was not unconnected with the " dirty things ". One day little Anna woke up and saw bloodstains on her sheets and nightgown. She immediately concluded that she had defiled herself with those dirty things, and fallen ill. God had punished her, and her mother would learn that Anna was an abject being. She decided to die, and going to the kitchen, turned on the gas. She was rescued at the last moment, after she had already become unconscious.'

A child's reactions are not always so violent, but the crisis through which it passes when the mystery of sex is unexpectedly revealed to it is always extremely grave. The cases of brides running away from their husbands on their wedding night because they had not been prepared for the event are exceptional nowadays; but it frequently happens that a woman goes into marriage with completely mistaken ideas. How many marriages are rendered unhappy by the wife's frigidity and the husband's dissatisfaction as a result of faulty sexual enlightenment?

The ignorance of young girls on the subject of childbirth has sometimes odd consequences. In Alsace, for instance, it is the custom to tell girls that a mother is delivered through her navel. There are many other legends dealing with the same subject. For example, if a peasant woman becomes pregnant, it is because she thought only of her navel and neglected the rest of her person. Physicians have met many girls who thought themselves pregnant after a kiss or a passionate hand-pressure with a man.

Some people might believe that instances of that in the twentieth century are, if not actual fabrications, at any rate greatly exaggerated. Almost every doctor, however, can testify to the contrary. On the other hand, a practitioner is often consulted by girls who, although they have been seduced by some unscrupulous individual, have only a vague idea of sexual matters.

Dr. Totis in his book on sexual education quotes the following cases:

' I clearly remember a fourteen-year-old schoolgirl who one day came to my consulting-room, with her books under her arm. She explained that she had come to me, a gynæcologist, only after a long struggle with herself, and because she had noticed, on her parts, sores which were hurting her. Upon examination, I was amazed to find a combination of gonorrhœa and syphilis; moreover, she was four months pregnant. Yet that girl had no idea of her condition, although she had not menstruated for four months.

' Another time I was visited by a sixteen-year-old flapper, who complained of " something that moved inside her ", and as there had been several cases of cancer in her family, she had come to consult me on that account. That " cancer " was a six-months-old fœtus. Although they frequently discussed medical matters in her family, nobody had troubled to explain to her the female cycle or the other phenomena of sexual life.'

Whether a child is kept in ignorance or told lies, the result is the same in that the parents lose their child's confidence. In this connection the statement of a pupil of Professor Liepmann on the manner in which he was sexually enlightened is singularly edifying. We quote below a short but apposite excerpt:

' Then one day we happened to speak of how children came into the world. He (my playmate) said that children came out of their mother's abdomen. I refused to believe it and asked my mother; she was obviously horrified and told me some story about God sending children, but she insisted on knowing who had told me. Instinctively I sensed danger for Arnold, but I had to confess. Mother rushed to Mrs. B, my friend's mother, and Arnold was caned. That was an excellent lesson for me, and never after could my mother claim that she had her son's whole-hearted confidence.'

The same applies to the method already mentioned of telling half the truth, to present an unattractive mixture of fact and fiction in a hopeless attempt to embroider the sublimity of Nature's manifestations. Besides the dangers already indicated, this method has a distinct drawback in that the child is not content with half-truths and tries to find the real truth in practice as well as in theory. Freud and several other scientists have published interesting works on ' infantile sex theories '. It appears that children who have either not been enlightened at all, or only incompletely, evolve their own theories concerning the origin of human life. These theories always have some elements in common. They believe that a baby comes out of the mother's body either through the navel or in the process of defecation, or they imagine that the man's share of procreation consists in raping the woman with violence. The majority of children think, besides, that there is no anatomical difference between man and woman. Children's sexual phantasies are innumerable, but for the most part they are variations of the ones which we have just mentioned.

The system of ' half-initiation ', where the unreal is blended with reality, lends credence to the infantile sexual theory and strengthens the children's beliefs. A distorted sexual picture, which is the subject of dreams for many years, naturally influences the child's future sex-life. The adult will want to realise his childish phantasies. The scientific analysis of a large number of sexual aberrations has traced the origin of the abnormality to an early childish belief. The coprophagist, for whom sexual satisfaction is associated with the partner's excretions; the homosexual who is repelled by the opposite sex because he always imagined that a woman possessed a penis; the sadist who is a slave to his theory of rape; all these unfortunates suffer from the consequences of childish misconceptions due to faulty sexual enlightenment. And they will remain under that influence without finding the way to a normal sexual life.

Sexual enlightenment ought to be regulated by the same principle which prevails in the courts of justice, the judge being conscience and a sense of responsibility for the child's future, and the motto: ' The truth, the whole truth, and nothing but the truth '.

This truth should be revealed to the child, not all at once but gradually. The process of sexual enlightenment must be systematic and adapted to the child's intellectual development. It would be absurd to mention to a three-year-old child the danger of venereal diseases. Most parents, unfortunately, see in sexual enlightenment a brutal act, delicate and painful in the extreme. On the contrary, sexual education should be spread over a number of years, and keep in step with the sexual development of the subject. Sex should not be a special topic, a forbidden chapter of pedagogy, but part and parcel of the child's general education.

When should it begin? The answer is simple: when the child starts asking questions. So soon as it shows inquisitiveness in sexual matters the child's curiosity must be satisfied lest it try to satisfy itself in a roundabout way, as we described above. The time to begin a child's sexual education depends therefore on the child; but under no pretext must it be postponed later than its sixth year. A normal child will have begun long before then to ask questions about certain parts of its body and the way its brothers and sisters arrived; if it does not, it has certainly sought information somewhere else.

With regard to this outside source of information, it may be interesting to quote here some statistics published by the Berlin Institute of Sexology, which show in a striking manner that, although generally accepted, the principle of sexual enlightenment is far from being universally applied.

These statistics prove that, out of a large number of cases recorded, the sexual enlightenment of boys takes place mostly between the tenth and the twelfth year (60 per cent.); 15 per cent. between 7 and 9; 20 per cent. between 13 and 16; 5 per cent. before 6 or after 16.

The enlightenment of girls takes place approximately one year later than that of boys, but the result is very much the same. Three per cent. of the cases, however, had not been enlightened until the time of betrothal, and 6 per cent. claimed that they had not been enlightened at all.

Even more interesting are the statistics bearing on the source of information. In only one per cent. of the cases had the parents been the sexual educators of the child concerned; 70 per cent. of the answers to the questionnaire read as follows: ' By schoolfellows, friends, playmates, an elder brother or sister, a prostitute, a maid, a nurse, a waitress ', and so forth.

Eighteen per cent. answered ' through reading books and looking in the dictionary or the encyclopædia '; 3 per cent. had learned ' the facts of life ' in the Bible; 2 per cent. by observing animals.

A few of the answers were particularly vivid: ' I was initiated in an altogether repugnant way by playmates ', writes one; ' by grown-ups who talked to me in the street ', says another; ' when seven years old, I attended a delivery ', declares a third; ' when I was eight, two senior schoolfellows showed me how coitus was performed ' and ' I was enlightened when I visited a museum booth at a fair ', state two others.

*　　*　　*

As for the method of education, concrete and obvious questions always call for equally concrete and obvious answers. Illustrations taken from Botany and Zoology of the fertilisation of plants and animals can be resorted to, but enlightenment based exclusively on flowers and chickens will soon bore the child and leave its curiosity unsatisfied. Outside sources of information will then be sought and the parents will have missed their aim.

Sexual education requires a great deal of tact on the part of the parents. Whether the father or the mother should act as the educator depends partly on the child's sex; it is preferable as a rule for the father to teach the son, and the mother the daughter; but the choice also depends on the ability of one or the other to adopt a suitable tone. Some parents realise the necessity of judicious enlightenment, but cannot adopt the right attitude, or else lack pedagogic qualifications, the deficiency being due to the effects of their own faulty education. This being the case, they would be well advised to call upon the family doctor, a relative, or a friend, endowed with better educational gifts. Nevertheless, whenever possible, the parents themselves ought to undertake this noble task for their children.

Children will always be grateful for this enlightenment, as the statements of two of Professor Liepmann's pupils show:

[63]

' I was born in 1909, the first child of my parents. Apart from a few vague notions and an obscure intuition, my enlightenment dates from the period which was known as that of the " loft-rats " (before and after the war). I went to the country with my father and there I had occasion to go into a stable where I admired a very young calf. When I asked the puerile question: " Must one open the cow's belly to let the little calf out? " my father showed me the way in which calves are born. " Was it the same for me with mother? " " Yes ", my father answered. In this way I was enlightened. I did not acquire a fuller knowledge of sexual matters (ovaries, testes, coitus, etc.) until I began my biological studies at school.

' Contrary to Miss X, I consider it very helpful to illustrate sexual education by similes borrowed from zoology.'

The other statement is even more characteristic:

' Even when very young the stork story struck me as being a fairy tale; I couldn't understand why things should not happen with babies in the way they did with animals. I expressed this opinion to my father, who immediately enlightened me in the most discreet and dignified manner.

' I thought it quite natural that unmarried ladies should have no children since my unmated animals did not have any progeny. The knowledge that I could always obtain very precise information from my father prevented me from paying much attention to the jokes and insinuations of my schoolfellows.'

Another much discussed question is whether sexual education should be given in school. The most logical answer, of course, would be that both school and family ought to co-operate in the matter. There are many arguments in favour of at least partial sexual enlightenment being given by the school. It would be preferable for schoolchildren to learn certain matters in a scientific way from their masters during school than to pick them up inaccurately during play-time. Most school-boys around the age of thirteen know the essential facts of life but in a confused way. To them it would therefore be of great advantage to acquire a positive knowledge of sex and sexual diseases instead of fumbling in semi-darkness. Dr. Max Hodann instituted an inquiry among school children between 13 and 14 years of age, and we think it interesting to quote his published results. To begin with, here are a few of the questions in sexual pathology which children asked him:

1. Can one treat (cure) venereal diseases?
2. Are venereal diseases harmful to fertilisation?
3. Can a woman live if her uterus is removed?
4. What is locomotor-ataxia?
5. What is the origin of leucorrhœa?
6. Has a growth any relation with the ovaries? (Has a tumour of the ovary any relation with the ovary itself and does it influence the sexual life of the woman? It appeared later that a woman in the questioner's family had had an operation.)
7. What does an infected breast mean? (This referred to a wet-nurse's inflammation of the breast.)
8. Can a woman live without a uterus?
9. What is a miscarriage, and how does it happen?
10. What is impotence?
11. What is indecency?

To discuss these questions, especially those relating to sexual pathology, requires a knowledge of the genital organs in man and in woman. This gives rise to a number of questions. Girls naturally showed a particular interest in menstrual matters:

12. What does it mean when menstruation does not come?
13. How does it come, and what have boys instead?

14. Can menstruating girls of thirteen or fourteen have children?

15. Why did I not menstruate this time?

16. When is a woman ready for impregnation?

17. How is it that a thirteen-year-old girl menstruates and has not a child at the same time?

18. What is ' change of life '?

19. How is it possible that the feminine organ is large enough to let a baby go through?

20. If a girl has a premature delivery, can she survive?

21. If the mother dies before delivery, does the baby live?

22. What is induced labour?

23. Does the baby die if it requires an operation to deliver the mother?

24. Can a seven-months baby live?

25. Can one have intercourse four weeks after delivery?

26. How is it that negroes do not need midwives?

27. How is one impregnated?

28. How is impregnation effected? (This question betrays a certain shyness at expressing oneself on the technique of coitus which is the real object of the query. The teacher must be tactful enough to satisfy the inquirer without causing embarrassment.)

29. How is it that there are women without children?

30. Can women with a venereal disease bring forth children?

31. Why has one a brown streak on the body?

32. Why are women's breasts different from men's?

33. Why have men not breasts like women?

34. Why do men not give birth to children? (The child is trying to understand the division of sexual labour, procreation and pregnancy.)

35. Has a non-impregnated woman milk? (Then came the

correlated question from a town child: ' Why has a cow always milk? ')

36. Why has one hair on the abdomen?

37. How does hair grow on the head?

38. Why do women who sell their body have no children?

39. What is a ' tart '?

Then come repeatedly questions about twins, triplets, quadruplets and delivery.

40. Is it pleasant? (meaning sexual pleasure).

41. What happens when a man and a woman cannot get apart? (This question may be due to observing domestic animals and insects, some of which remain connected after coitus, or to overhearing the facetious query of an adult. One sees there the imaginative process which takes place in a child's mind on hearing a casual remark which it takes literally.)

There is no doubt that many questions were put in order to obtain a competent opinion on matters which were already guessed at.

The number and variety of these questions form a strong argument in favour of sexual education in the school. But in most countries the inclusion of sex subjects in the school curriculum would require a complete educational reform, the analysis of which is outside the scope of this chapter. This is why we have limited ourselves to sexual education within the limits of the family.

To conclude, we quote an extract from *Egyptian Ethics*, by Amelileau, in which an Egyptian father gives a lesson on sex to his son about three thousand years ago. It shows to what extent our civilisation is behind that of certain peoples of antiquity:

' I gave you a mother who bore you, a heavy burden, for your advantage, and without leaning on me; when at last you were born, she took on yet another burden and for three years you held her breasts to your mouth. Your excretions never repelled her and did not make her say: "What am I doing?" When you went to school she took regularly every day bread and home-brewed beer to your teacher. When, in your turn, you marry and have a child, bring it up as your mother brought you up.'

CHAPTER V

THE 'SINS OF YOUTH'

The sexual instinct in evidence from moment of birth. Experts disagree over connotation of term ' sexual '. Infantile urge to obtain pleasurable physical sensations. Auto-erotism. Onanism. Sexual habits of adolescents. Lack of understanding in parents and teachers. Statistics. Masturbation in animals. Group masturbation. Unconscious masturbation. Methods of masturbation. The ' godemiché '. Psychological masturbation. Day dreams. Night dreams. Erotic dreams. Hygiene.

IN the two preceding chapters we have endeavoured to give a brief survey of the sexual life of the child up to the age of puberty, a much discussed subject and one which has always given rise to the most heated scientific controversies. While the Freudian school maintains that the sexual impulse is in evidence from the moment of birth, many experts object to the word sexual being applied to practices in which they see nothing but innocent forms of play. The question, therefore, as we have already said, resolves itself into a dispute over the interpretation of certain terms, and once it is admitted that the sexual instinct may take the form of a striving or urge towards physical pleasure, the solution of the problem no longer presents any great difficulty.

One thing is certain. Whether we call it the sexual impulse or not, the child's need to obtain pleasurable sensations remains vague for a long time and the means it employs are extremely varied. Any part of its body may become the centre of its emotions, and the erotogenic zones are not localised. Moreover, the need of a partner in these forms of play is often not manifested until very late. The distinction between the sexes is not realised at this stage. Any other child may become a partner in these sexual games (playing ' papa and mama ', or ' doctor '). The child does not quite know how to deal with its playmate: whether to look at his neck, tickle him under the armpits, hit him on the buttocks, or touch his genital organs.

Apart from these games for two or more players, the child seeks from the earliest age to obtain pleasure through its own body. For this reason it is no exaggeration to say that sexual life during childhood and early youth is dominated by *auto-erotism*. For this term, we are indebted to Havelock Ellis, who used it for the first time to describe solitary and spontaneous sexual phenomena. But it has since been adopted by many experts and its meaning has become somewhat modified, so that to-day it is used chiefly to imply the direction of the sexual impulse on to one's own person. This definition in itself clearly shows that masturbation merely constitutes a kind of subdivision of auto-erotism, since the manifestations of this latter may be independent of masturbatory practices. But let us hasten to add that the word masturbation itself has been greatly extended beyond its original meaning. If we go back to the Latin derivation we find two ideas, that of the *hand* and that of *defilement*. But most modern experts use this term to indicate solitary sexual practices of the most varied forms, even those in which the hand plays no part at all. Psychologists even speak of psychological and unconscious masturbation, which leads us very far from the original acceptation of the word.

We must now devote a few words to the term *onanism*, the most common synonym of masturbation. It is generally believed to have originated in the name of a biblical character, Onan, but according to the account given in the Bible, the sin of which Onan was guilty was not masturbation, but *coitus interruptus*. Onan, in order to obey his father, Judah, and to conform to ancient Hebrew custom, married his brother's widow. But, not wishing to have a child by her, he intentionally allowed his semen to drop on to the ground. It is therefore not correct to attribute the practice of masturbation to Onan, though the word onanism is to-day universally accepted in this latter sense and it would be pedantic not to recognise this meaning.

In addition to these two terms, there are others which have been coined by various experts; for instance, Professor Hirschfeld's '*ipsation*', or the less known '*autism*'. There also exist expressions which are not scientific and are therefore all the more employed, such as 'the solitary vice' or 'the sin of youth'.

The latter expression emphasises the fact that these practices are peculiar to the adolescent. This leads us to make a clear distinction between masturbation prior to or simultaneous with puberty, and the masturbation of the adult. If we have not included the study of masturbation in the part of this work devoted to sexual perversions, it is precisely because we have in mind the sin of youth, as it is called. Masturbation in an adult who has the opportunity for normal sexual intercourse, is evidence of a deviation in the instinct, which may, in certain cases, be considered abnormal. This does not apply to masturbation during puberty—as we shall endeavour to prove in the course of this chapter.

Since we recognise the existence of the sexual instinct during the first years of childhood, we are not astonished to see that the awkward attempts of very young children to produce pleasure change, take more concrete forms, and develop into more or less regular habits. The develop-

ment of the sexual instinct may be said to guide the normal
individual, if not towards the systematic practice of
masturbation, at least towards some attempt at it. To
such an extent is this true, that all the experts who have
devoted themselves to these thorny problems, have produced
figures which prove that the large majority of human beings,
if not all of them, have practised masturbation at least once
during their lives.

Before we quote some of these statistics let us denounce,
once and for all, the hypocrisy of those who have condemned
masturbation and described it as a sin and a vice. To
designate masturbation at a certain period of life perverse
would mean condemning one of the most natural tendencies.
' Let him that is without sin cast the first stone.' This
phrase from the Gospel may be applied to those parents
and pedagogues who, lacking comprehension of the most
elementary kind, show excessive severity in their dealings
with the children whose education is entrusted to them,
the moment the least suspicion of this kind arises in their
minds. In the next chapter, when discussing in more
detail the consequences of masturbation, we shall see how
injurious is this violent campaign and how much more
dangerous than the habitual practice of masturbation.

We quote a few figures, collected by various sexologists,
on the incidence of masturbation:

	Percentage
A Russian enquiry among children of school age	60
According to Meirowsky (an enquiry among students)	71
According to Meirowsky (an enquiry among doctors)	90.7
According to Marco (an enquiry among 450 adult criminals)	85
Marcuse (Munich)	93.3
Deutsch (Budapest)	96.7
Professor Duck	90.8

Rohleder (an enquiry among 275 pupils, of whom 248 replied affirmatively)   90.1

Dr. Dukes (an English school doctor)   90–95

Dr. Searley, Springfield (an enquiry among 125 American students)   85.3

Dr. Hirschfeld, Berlin (an enquiry among 500 persons)   96

Dr. Desider Hahn (an enquiry among 200 workmen)   96

Brockmann, America (an enquiry among 232 theological students)   99.3

Professor Young (an American urologist)   100

Berger   100

Thus, according to the last two experts, every man and every woman without exception has masturbated. This is what Berger says: 'Masturbation is a practice which is very widespread, and in which 99 per cent. of young men and young women indulge at some time or the other, while the hundredth, the " pure " person, as I am in the habit of calling him, does not confess the truth'.

And Stekel says: 'Everybody masturbates. To this rule, there is no exception, if we take into account unconscious masturbation'.

It is not without interest to note at what age these practices most frequently begin. The statistics which seem most trustworthy are those of Dr. Hirschfeld, who based his observations on the replies given by 500 persons:—

Age. (years)	Percentage.
4	0.25
5	1.8
6	1.8
7	2.3

Age. (years)	Percentage.
8	2.8
9	3.2
10	5.3
11	5.4
12	15.0
13	13.7
14	15.5
15	11.4
16	9.8
17	4.6
18	2.5
19	1.6
20	1.5

In other words, before the twelfth year, 22.9 per cent. of all children attempt masturbation for the first time; 44.4 per cent. of all cases date from the period between the twelfth year and the fourteenth; after the fourteenth year, the figure is 32.7 per cent.

The statistics supplied by these experts practically tally. All those who have studied masturbation realise that it is not an exceptional phenomenon. Let us now examine, in the light thrown by statistics, the frequency with which masturbation is practised. Physicians have noted many cases of individuals who masturbate four or five times a day. Such cases are certainly morbid, but the annals of medicine contain records of extreme cases in which the figure is much higher. 'One of our patients,' writes Dr. Hesnard, 'twenty-three years of age, masturbated sixty times a day, and never slept except with the penis carefully placed near an electric circuit connected with a bell, so that he would be wakened in case of an erection.' Normally, if masturbation has not become a sexual perversion, its frequency may vary from two to three times per day to once every fortnight; on the other hand, it may be practised only once a month or once every two or three months. Professor Hesnard says that during his long career he has met only seven men and five women who had masturbated only once during their life and had never repeated the act. Of the five hundred persons concerned in his enquiry, 61 per cent. masturbated less than twice a week and 39 per cent. twice or more than twice a week.

There is also much variation in the length of time during which a person is addicted to the habit. In most cases it is about four years, though often only one or two years. On the other hand, it may be considerably longer, even a lifetime. With these statistics before us, it is almost superfluous to ask once more whether masturbation is an unnatural and an abnormal phenomenon. It is the law of the majority that determines what must be considered normal, and since nature provides the stimulation for this practice, which is often spontaneous and unconscious, how can we consider it unnatural? But, having made this statement, it is important to emphasise that it is only the masturbation of puberty, which is a substitute for normal sexual intercourse and of a provisional nature, that may be considered inoffensive. Those who have reacted against the stupid prejudices which are called up by the practice of masturbation, and, going to the other extreme, have declared that it is nothing more than a natural manifestation of sexual life and should not be combated, are equally mistaken. We shall see, later on, that masturbation is, at the same time, capable of having psychological and physical consequences which are actually desirable.

In discussing the question whether masturbation is

natural or not, it is usual, and quite justifiable, to seek for equivalents in the animal world and among primitive peoples. In both domestic and wild animals examples may be found which appear to confirm the general and almost natural character of this substitute for sexual intercourse. In fact, animals always practice masturbation when normal sexual activity is impossible. Anyone who has a dog or a cat can verify this statement. During the period of rut, the dog shows unmistakable signs of activity so long as he is deprived of a female. A bitch masturbates by rubbing her back parts against whatever she uses as a bed, or calms her ardour by means of her tongue. The same habits may be observed in cats. It has also been noticed that horses, especially ponies, when deprived of normal sexual activity, stimulate their member in order to produce an ejaculation. Havelock Ellis supplies other examples of masturbation in goats, ferrets, stags, rams, camels, elephants, bears, hyenas, parrots, crested lapwings, monkeys, etc.

From the varied nature of this list, which is due to chance observation, it is clear that masturbation may be considered a common manifestation of sexual life in animals when normal expression is prevented. This remark naturally holds good for man's near relatives the monkeys. According to Tillier, masturbation among male monkeys is particularly common, the monkey using his hand to 'rub and shake the penis'.

We have had occasion to note that sexual forms of play are very frequently met with amongst certain peoples; in these games, masturbation naturally plays an important part. Ethnologists are unanimous in bearing witness to this phenomenon and in accounts of travels we find descriptions which leave no doubt about the public performance of these practices. Amongst the Namas, according to Fritch, masturbation is so common that it has become a part of popular custom and stories and legends give it a prominent place. Dr. Malinowski describes scenes of solitary and group masturbation in the Trobriand Islands. In girls this habit is observed from the age of four or five years and in boys a little later. Adults watch these scenes of group masturbation, which soon develop into real sexual intercourse, without finding anything in them at which to take exception.

In the history of European peoples examples proving that onanism is a common occurrence are equally numerous. The legend of Diogenes of Athens, who masturbated in a public street, is eloquent enough. Plutarch relates that the philosopher Chrysippus congratulated his colleague Diogenes on having carried his cynicism to such lengths as to masturbate in full view of the public. In fact, the cynics recommended masturbation as the wisest method of obtaining sexual satisfaction. The numerous attacks on masturbation found in Greek literature, and especially in Aristophanes, also bear witness to the fact that masturbation was a phenomenon of frequent occurrence.

Historical documents of all races offer further proof of the frequency of masturbation, and Mantegazza, it seems, was mistaken in attributing this practice to modern civilisation. We may conclude, with Havelock Ellis, that it is an extremely frequent manifestation, which may be considered as on the border line between the normal and the abnormal, according to the proportions it assumes.

It is interesting to study the way in which children are led for the first time to attempt masturbation. The first attempts are seldom conscious and the result of deliberate decision. In the majority of cases, some chance incident during gymnastic exercises, or a chance contact, produces agreeable sensations in the child. The Freudian school maintains that the attention given to a baby, which necessitates the handling of its genital parts, is sufficient to render the child aware of the peculiar sensitiveness of those regions and to induce it to reproduce, artificially, the sensation provoked in that way. However that may be, many statements dealing with the age of puberty reveal the accidental nature of the first impulse to masturbate.

Here are two accounts supplied by Dr. Liepmann:

' When I was ten years old I experienced my first voluptuous sensation while practising gymnastics and climbing a pole or a rope. I did not try to explain it and I did not consider it as in any way related to sexual matters. Moreover, a sense of personal modesty forbade me to speak about it to anyone. This sensation of voluptuousness was produced after a certain number of slow and long climbs, and was accompanied by the ejaculation of a liquid which, without having examined it, I took to be urine, although it flowed (without any erection) even after I had urinated.

' In after years, though I never made a habit of it, I frequently obtained this " agreeable sensation " by climbing in this manner when the occasion presented itself, masturbation being for me quite unconscious and involuntary. Then this tendency became less and less pronounced, finally disappeared altogether and was forgotten. After my fourteenth year, I do not remember ever having experienced or satisfied the same tendency. Up to the age of puberty, I never touched my sexual parts.'

And here is a story of a little girl:

' One fine day my mother said that, as I looked very ill, I must go with my father to see the doctor in order to find out what was wrong. Apparently I was supposed to have done all kinds of stupid things, for they would not believe me capable of doing anything good. I was very indignant about it.

' I was not aware of having done anything wrong, though I knew very well what my parents did every evening! Afterwards they wrapped my sexual parts in a bandage every night, in order, as my mother said, to prevent me from meddling with them. It was, however, in this way that I began to learn something new. My parents looked upon me with contempt, and I was always hearing it said that nothing could be done with me. The more depraved I felt myself, the greater was my tendency to isolate myself. I began to live in a world of my own. The worst of it was that I felt in myself an ardent longing for better and purer things, and the torments I went through every evening were fearful. This, however, came to an end. One evening I was able to go to bed without first hearing that " if I touched my sexual parts again the devil would come and sit at my bedside ". Then, out of spite, I was led to do what I had never done before; I wanted to have my revenge for the insult that had been inflicted on me: I masturbated. And that is why I have been more precocious than the others. However, shortly afterwards, I gave up masturbation, because I no longer found any pleasure in it. At that time I was, I suppose, about twelve years old.'

The confessions of masturbators contained in the work of Dr. Hirschfeld include two particularly characteristic accounts of the way in which onanist habits may be contracted. The first is given by a workman of about thirty years of age, sufficiently intelligent to be able to judge his own reactions impartially:

' I believe I began to practise masturbation at about the age of eleven or twelve. At least, it was then that I first did so consciously, and on considering the matter I realise that it was in quite a strange way that I came to begin it. For I made use of an egg-beater, holding a dish between my thighs and beating. This was always continued until the white of the egg became hard. And then to produce the desired result I used to hold the dish still closer to me and press it against my sexual parts. Then the peculiar feeling would immediately be produced and I would become, so to speak, intoxicated with it. Of course, I knew nothing of the consequences of all this, and therefore tried to bring about the same result again by pressing my thighs against each other. I succeeded in this so well that it became a passion with me, and I practised it perhaps from five to ten times every day. This was at a time when there was no question of erotic dreams, though later on it was no better. On the contrary, I began to read smutty things in a bad periodical which a friend of mine would quickly pull out of his pocket, and which could be devoured only at home. But it was not long before I began using the hand to masturbate, doing so in bed at night, and during the day in the w.c. The impulse was stronger than my will, and after a short time the most trivial object used to excite me. Pictures of half-naked women and even the words " *young girl* " were sufficient to rouse the desire in me. Even to-day I have not succeeded completely in mastering masturbation.'

The example of playmates seems to play a less important part in this respect. Many statements establish the fact that example, when it does not occur at an appropriate time in life, is mostly forgotten. Instead of encouraging imitation it may provoke aversion. Nevertheless, so soon as the sexual impulse makes itself felt, the reflex of masturbation appears, either spontaneously, or aided by memories conscious or unconscious, of a scene witnessed previously. The following example, also taken from Dr. Hirschfeld's work, shows how a young girl, though at first repelled by

the sight of a friend masturbating, finally came to imitate
her just before the beginning of the first menstrual period,
when she felt a strange excitement in her genital parts:

'I first of all saw it done by a little girl at school, and
although I turned my face away, being repelled by such an
ugly sight, I did it myself when I was at home, and lying
in bed. I do not remember whether I thought anything of
it when I did it. I only know that it was quite dark and
quiet. I was doubled up under the bed-clothes. When it
was over I often cried to myself. I went to bed frightened
and could not go to sleep without praying. My spiritual
condition went from bad to worse, and I kept on promising
myself never to do it again, until I finally comforted myself
and went to sleep. I never kept my promise. It happened
again; I do not know how long after, and I think not more
frequently than once a month. A year ago, I gave it up
as my mother caught me at it and gave me a lecture. So
out of love for my mother I gave it up until a little while
before menstruation. Then I felt such a tickling and
itching that I did it again with great passion. Next
morning I found that I was bleeding and had pains in the
knees and the thighs and could not get up. I told my mother
that I had done it again and that I was bleeding, for I
thought this was a consequence of it and cried bitterly.
Mother comforted me and gave me a second talk. I was then
thirteen years old.'

A variety of circumstances may provide the first impetus
to masturbate. Inflammation of the genital organs, or an
itching which induces the child to scratch, may give rise to
sensations of a sexual nature. In scratching itself the
child at first merely relieves the irritation, but this
procedure very soon leads to genuine masturbation. The
contact of rough underclothing, or of some object, may have
the same result. In such a case, the child is ignorant of

the fact that it is masturbating. In a child these repetitions are spontaneous. In adults they are half conscious and often combined with ignorance of the real nature of masturbation. Thus it is no rare thing to find persons who are masturbators without being aware of the fact. The classical example is that quoted by Havelock Ellis, about the lady who was a fanatical leader of a movement for social purity, and carried on propaganda in favour of chastity. One day, on reading a pamphlet on sexual enlightenment, she discovered, to her utter amazement, that for many years she had been indulging in masturbation without knowing it. This is a characteristic example of that combination of ignorance and blind fanaticism in sexual matters, which causes many to be led astray by the erroneous conceptions of contemporary sexual pedagogy. We may be sure that the lady in question belonged to that class of people who propagate absurd superstitions about the consequences of masturbation.

Unconscious masturbation is particularly frequent among women, because in them sexual excitement may be provoked more easily in an accidental way. Moll and other experts have remarked that bicycles, especially the old-fashioned kind with highly arched seats, were important mechanical aids to masturbation. The same thing applies to horse-riding with a man's saddle, and to that apparently innocent instrument the old-fashioned sewing machine, which obliged the user to lift the legs very high. Dr. Pouillet has stated that an orgasm is produced so frequently in women who use that kind of machine, that the supervisors have ceased to pay any attention to its occurrence.

In speaking of the technique of conscious masturbation, we may distinguish three chief methods: the use of the hand, the contraction of the thighs, and an imitation of the sexual act. It is curious to note that masturbators are generally attached to one or another of these methods, and rarely vary their procedure.

Masturbation with the hand is very widespread in all countries and among individuals of both sexes. It would be possible to make a further distinction between methods of masturbation with one hand and with two hands. It seems, however, that three-quarters of all masturbators prefer to use only one hand. A characteristic example is reported by Dr. Hirschfeld, to whom a prisoner of war confessed that formerly his wife was his right hand, and that since his captivity his right hand had become his wife.

Masturbation by means of pressing the thighs together is also very common, but especially among women. It appears that in Sweden this practice is extremely common, and that everyone in the country knows that it is the usual form of masturbation among women. Havelock Ellis observed a young peasant woman at a railway station, who even in public was able to indulge in this form of masturbation without attracting attention. She leaned back on her seat, with her legs crossed, and rocked her foot, making a vigorous rhythmical movement until suddenly her body seemed to stiffen as in a spasm. Her pallor, and the transformation of her whole being, were ample evidence to a well-informed observer of the meaning of that apparently innocent manœuvre. Townsend observed the same procedure in a little girl of eight months, Soutze in a girl of twelve. Adults very often prefer it because of its discreet character.

But a man also, by drawing his thighs together and exerting pressure on the member, may produce an erection and often even an emission. Here is the account of a masturbator who relates how he was led to adopt this method of masturbation:

'So far as I can remember, it began when I was about nine years old and in the third year of the primary school. It came first of all as a relief from the hard work involved in an arithmetical problem. I could not quite manage to find the solution, and became very worried on this account. I clapped my legs together, made an energetic movement and soon obtained by this means an indescribably pleasant sensation. To this day, a very hard piece of brain work calls up in me the strongest impulse to masturbate. Without this, I can hardly work. The more urgent and important the work is, and the shorter the periods allowed for recreation the more passionate is the impulse. During a written examination this impulse became most amazingly strong. I suppose I never masturbated more than at the time when I was sitting for my examination as a solicitor (the written test). At that time, I masturbated every day, fifteen times or more; perhaps a little less on some days (the competition lasted fourteen days). Whether the work was to be done at home, outside, or in the chancery office, the impulse to masturbate was always most urgent, and I could do nothing but give way to it without resistance.'

Another onanist was particularly sensitive to the sight of women sitting with their legs crossed, for this was connected, in his mind, with the idea of strong sexual excitement. He pressed his own thighs together and managed without much difficulty to obtain satisfaction.

Masturbation which consists in imitating the sexual act, may take the most varied forms. The man will try to execute the movements of coitus against an object which more or less evokes the image of the female sex organ. A well-known case is that of the prisoner who made an artificial vagina with his bread ration and declared that he gave himself the perfect illusion of normal copulation. Here is an account reported by Magnus Hirschfeld:

'In this matter, I am practical, perhaps even artistic. With a loaf of bread I make a realistic female abdomen with a vagina. In this way I get very near to the real thing. When the loaf of bread has hardened and been modelled, the whole mass acquires a certain firmness, while retaining its elasticity, so that the vaginal pocket does not give way to pressure except to such an extent as is necessary. I moisten the vagina with vaseline or grease and in this way I obtain what, in any case, is the most efficient substitute obtainable. This object, besides, possesses the great advantage that I am not obliged to hide it; I remodel it according to the needs of the moment, and nobody could have any idea that it is a sexual reproduction. With other substitutes one is always worried by the fear of their confiscation during the course of an inspection. Of course vaginal pockets made of meat are better, but they soon become spoiled and are also difficult to construct. The only disadvantage of my method is the sacrifice of the bread ration. As my member is of large dimensions, I use a considerable quantity of bread, and have to do without any for several days.'

The objects usually employed are those found within easy reach, as, for example, pillows. More dangerous was the invention of the masturbator who made use of the outlet in his bath, and who on one occasion, when his erection was particularly intense, could not liberate his member and had to call for help. Here is the account of a young student of twenty-one years who seeks in masturbation a compensation for the sexual act:

'During my fourteenth year, I simulated the sexual act by thrusting my abdomen against the bed, perhaps regularly once every week for a long period and then often not for a whole month. I am firmly of the opinion that I should not have lapsed into onanism if I had had intercourse (I am not referring to physical intercourse) with young girls from the time of my youth. For although, when I took dancing lessons, I was in love with a young girl, I felt no need to masturbate, despite the fact that I was in a state of excitement all through the week. When the dancing lessons came to an end I masturbated regularly once more. My most violent efforts to get rid of it have, as yet, been in vain.'

Objects used for masturbation by women are of great diversity. Women have at all times sought to provoke excitement by contact with a foreign body, and have made use, not only of objects similar in form to the penis, but to the most unlikely instruments as well. The industry dealing in intimate articles has for a long time been acquainted with the manufacture of the *godemiché*, a more or less cunningly devised reproduction of the male organ. This instrument was in every way similar to the penis.

' The only difference consisted in the presence, on its entire surface, from the tip to the root, of transverse undulations, the purpose of which was to permit of more energetic friction. It was made entirely of silver and covered with a kind of varnish, smooth, hard and flesh-coloured. For the rest, it was light, had thin walls and was hollow. Through the middle of the central cavity there passed a cylindrical tube of the same metal, about twice as thick as a goose's feather and containing a piston. At one end, the tube was closed by means of a screw. Around this little syringe, the inside of the external cylinder that imitated the penis, there was therefore an empty space. At the root of the instrument a piece of cork, in the form of a ring, closed the cylinder and allowed the stem of the little syringe to pass through the middle. Around the stem of the piston was a spiral spring which worked the piston by expanding.

'The hollow part of the godemiché—the word is from the Latin *gaude mihi*—was filled with water which had been heated to a temperature at which it would not burn the lips. The opening was then closed by means of the cork provided with a ring by which to pull on it. By pulling back the piston, the little pump was then filled with a solution of fishes' eggs, white in colour and prepared in advance. The heat of the water was communicated to the solution of fishes' eggs, a solution so similar to a man's seminal secretion that it could be mistaken for it.'

The objects which surgeons have been called upon to extract from the bladder or the vagina of women onanists present a most bewildering variety. Besides the traditional bananas, we find carrots and cucumbers, pencils, pieces of sealing wax, hooks, needles, candles and tooth-pick holders; tooth-brushes and hairpins seem to be most in favour. These last were so frequently used that, in 1860, a surgeon invented a special instrument to extract them.

Masturbation is not restricted exclusively to the genital organs. It may be practised on other erotogenic zones, especially the breasts and the buttocks, on the latter by means of flagellation. Rubbing the nipples is capable of provoking very intense sexual excitement and is therefore well adapted to the ' solitary vice '.

Works on sexology often quote the case of a fifty-year-old man, who for many years had masturbated in this way before a glass, without knowing that it was masturbation. Such ignorance is comprehensible if we remember that this form of onanism rarely culminates in the emission of semen, and that its effect is limited to voluptuous sensations.

Individuals with highly developed anal sensitiveness are prone to masturbate in that part of the body, and employ a large variety of objects as instruments of pleasure. The Sexological Institute of Berlin, recently destroyed by the

Nazis, contained a collection of objects found in the rectums of onanists, some of them of such dimensions that one could hardly believe that they had been used for that purpose. One of them was sixteen centimetres long and five centimetres wide.

It has been, and still is, a much discussed question as to which sex is more inclined to masturbate and more persistently addicted to it. Mere figures would be misleading because the differences between the two sexes must be taken into consideration. During the first period of puberty, it is not surprising to find that the figures are higher for girls, since sexual maturity is reached earlier in the female sex. At a later period young men establish social relationships more easily, and normal sexual activity renders onanist practices unnecessary. In married life, it is again women who more frequently have resource to masturbation, for, as we shall see in other parts of this work, it is more difficult for a woman to obtain sexual satisfaction than it is for a man, and thus wives with an exacting temperament are driven to seek satisfaction by artificial means.

Nevertheless, in spite of these factors which seem to make the woman rather than the man predisposed to masturbation, it is among young men at puberty that masturbation is most common. We may perhaps attribute this phenomenon to the more audacious and enterprising character of boys; the timidity and sensitiveness of girls causes them to be more prudent in these practices. It is just before the menstrual period that girls succumb most frequently to the temptation. At other times, their sexuality seeks an outlet in practices that could not be described as onanistic.

This brings us to what experts call psychological masturbation. Before broaching this delicate subject we must make it clear that masturbation, even in the strict sense of the word, is not an exclusively physiological phenomenon, since all sexual activity is accompanied by a psychological reaction. Research might well be devoted to what takes place in the brain of a masturbator, at the age, of course, when this manifestation is conscious, for, we repeat, spontaneous and unconscious masturbation in children is rather a reflex. The most typical and 'healthy' form of masturbation is that in which the subject imagines the presence of the desired person. But this is not by any means the case with all masturbators. Since inveterate onanists are sometimes found amongst psychopaths, the most morbid phantasies and the most improbable dreams are often the psychological accompaniment of masturbation.

This is Dr. Hesnard's pithy description of the psychological process of masturbation:

'The solitary pleasure is at first made up of a vague organic voluptuousness, a sort of sharp giddiness, hardly distinct from the satisfaction of a desire specifically localised in the sexual organs. It is not accompanied by any psychological factors, nor by any mental representation. It is purely a conscious reflex.

' But soon it gives rise to a reverie, first of all unconscious, and then vaguely directed towards normal erotic aims and objects, or less frequently, towards imaginary perverse complications.'

The psychological repercussions of this habit, remorse, a feeling of guilt or of moral defilement, and depression leading even to suicide, will be discussed in the chapter we propose to devote to the consequences of masturbation.

There are two chief forms of psychological onanism, the day dream and the night dream. Day dreams are indulged in by emotional persons with a highly developed imagination and an artistic disposition. In this case an insignificant detail may give rise to a reverie, not necessarily sexual, but one in which love is always the essential element.

An incident which on being read particularly strikes the imagination of the young man or the young woman, may be continued in dreams, which then become a new source of excitement. In fact, in hypersensitive persons thought in itself may suffice to give rise to voluptuous sensations. Hence the enormous importance of the pornographic industry. It is a fact, proved by the testimony of masturbators, that the impulse to masturbate is often aroused by reading a pornographic passage.

People who indulge in day dreams are for the most part too sensitive to indulge in masturbation in the strict sense of the word. Very often they are not even aware of the sexual character of their thoughts. The researches of Hamilton give some idea of the frequency of day dreams. Twenty-seven per cent. of men and 25 per cent. of women stated that they had had erotic day dreams before they were enlightened. Only 1 per cent. of men and 2 per cent. of women said that they had had no reverie of this kind after puberty. Fifty-seven per cent. of men and 51 per cent. of women confessed that between their eighteenth year and their marriage these day dreams played a big part in their lives. Among married men and women, 26 per cent. of the former and 19 per cent. of the latter were still subject to day dreams.

While it is only in exceptional cases that day dreams are accompanied by masturbation, in nocturnal dreams it is much more frequent. It is important to observe, however, that these practices take place during the dream and are consequently unconscious. The erotic dream is a phenomenon almost universal at the age of puberty. It culminates in an involuntary emission with young men, and in a sensation very near to orgasm in young women. It is curious to observe that on awaking one has usually no recollection of these dreams. It is the physiological reaction that interrupts sleep and only this final sensation remains in the memory.

The Freudian school attributes an enormous importance to the dream, which it regards as the expression of repressed desires. The dream is said to gratify the wish which could not be gratified in real life, owing to moral inhibitions. When looked upon in this light, involuntary emission may be considered a form of disguised masturbation. Like masturbation during adolescence, the erotic dream is a natural outlet for the sexual instinct, and all the superstitions to which this phenomenon has given rise have no more foundation than the imbecilities which masturbation has inspired in false moralists.

Involuntary emissions, which are normal in adolescent boys, persist in adults who live a life of enforced chastity, and they take place with a regularity that proves them to be the manifestation of a sexual instinct which has not been satisfied. According to the statements of experts, they occur naturally once a fortnight or once a month in a normal celibate. The Italian specialist Gualino, quoted by Havelock Ellis, who based his observations on an interrogation of a hundred normal men of the intellectual class, has made some curious statements. Erotic dreams with emission begin shortly before sexual maturity. Almost all the replies bear witness to erotic dreams at the age of 17 years. In 37 per cent. of the cases these dreams were not preceded by any sexual experience. In 23 per cent. of the cases, by masturbation only. The dreams are usually of a visual, rarely a tactile character. In 27 per cent. of the cases the desired person was an unknown woman, in 56 per cent. she was known only by sight. In 34 per cent. of the cases involuntary emission took place shortly after actual sexual intercourse, but it occurs most frequently when the young man is courting a person whom he loves and confines himself to contact of a kind that excites him.

It is curious to note that the object of one's love and desire rarely figures in erotic dreams. When the memory of these dreams persists, it may usually be noted that the imaginary partner is either an indefinite person who cannot be identified, or a person to whom one is more or less indifferent. Dreams about the person loved are very frequent, but they rarely take on a distinctly sexual character.

In women the erotic dream is much more diffuse. It is true that the sex instinct may evince itself regularly in this way in adult women, but the woman does not experience the orgasm in a dream after she has performed the sexual act. Moreover, the erotic dream in a woman does not always bring relief analogous to that obtained by the normal sexual act. Erotic dreams in a woman produce excitement rather than relief.

Psychological masturbation in the form of erotic dreams may be artificially induced by appropriate reading immediately before going to sleep; more than one masturbator has confessed to having in this way provoked the dream which relieved him. The rôle of masturbation has not been made sufficiently clear, since, as we have indicated, the manipulations are mostly unconscious. It is nevertheless certain that persons who emphatically deny that they have ever masturbated, have stimulated their sexual reveries by manœuvres calculated to increase voluptuous sensation.

*   *   *

From what has been said it will be seen that masturbation is a manifestation of sexuality, a stage in the evolution of the sexual instinct. It remains inoffensive only so long as it is practised provisionally and as a makeshift. Onanism tends to become a habit in individuals who have no perverse tendencies whatsoever, but who are unable to find a normal outlet for their sexual activity. It is important, therefore, not to let these tendencies run riot, and to see that they do not go beyond the limits of the normal. While denouncing the exaggerated attacks of which masturbation has been the object, we consider certain precautions and even treatment useful as a means of reducing this necessary evil to a minimum. By way of example, we quote a treatment proposed by Reinh-Gerling:

' The treatment of onanism must be carried out as follows: Absolute cleanliness of the whole body. A bath, at first in tepid (30° C.) and later in cool (25° C.) water is to be taken in the morning on rising. The sexual organs are to be washed with mild soap or with pure cool water.

' If any irritants, dirt, or hardened smegma are found under the foreskin, they must be removed for irritation makes the cure of onanism very difficult if not impossible.

' The presence of worms is one of the contributing causes of onanism, especially in girls, and their elimination is an urgent necessity.

' Constipation should be relieved by an enema at 30° C. A well-chosen diet with a daily ration of sour milk will also be helpful. All stimulants are to be rigidly avoided. Wine, beer, liqueurs, and even fermented fruit-wine are equally harmful to the onanist, as are also coffee and China or Russian tea. Meat should be eaten only sparingly, and pork, smoked meat, ripe cheese and caviar should never be taken. Spices such as cinnamon, pepper, and cayenne pepper are also to be avoided.

'Rice, maize, oats, barley, green vegetables and carrots (but not celery), green salads, fruit stewed and in every form may be recommended as most suitable and sufficiently nourishing. Water is the best drink, and even when a palate is spoilt, an apple, a pear, or a few strawberries will satisfy thirst much better than a cool glass of beer.

'The last meal should be taken two and a half or three hours before retiring, and should not contain anything that is difficult to digest. It is also inadvisable to take much liquid shortly before retiring.

'Daily exercises and games in the open air played to the point of fatigue, occasional sawing or wood-chopping, rowing, gymnastics, swimming, running, hard and tiring house-work are splendid diversions. The onanist should go to bed thoroughly tired, and rise as soon as he wakens. The patient (for so must we call him) should not be allowed to lie in bed awake.

'Before retiring it is desirable that the bowels should be emptied; in any case the bladder should be emptied. The hands should be placed outside the blankets before sleep begins.

'The bed should contain no soft lower portion. The mattress is quite sufficient in winter as in summer. Feather-beds should be replaced by horse-hair cushions and quilts or woollen blankets lined with linen.

'The patient should lie, if possible, on his side; he should avoid lying on his back, as this posture produces pressure on the seminal vesicles, due to the filling of the bladder, and brings about an erection.

'The bedroom should be cool, and at least one upper window may be left half open. Tight clothes are forbidden. Woollen underclothes should not be worn, as they irritate the skin. The trouser pockets should be at the back above the waist and not at the sides or in front.

'Girls should never wear corsets as they produce congestion in the lower abdomen and favour onanism or hinder its cure. For obvious reasons they should not use a sewing machine during adolescence. On the other hand, daily gymnastic exercises are essential if onanism is to be successfully combated.

'All reading matter should be carefully chosen. Humorous articles, sea stories, adventures which awaken enthusiasm, are not only strong incentives to activity, but also indispensable as a source of recreation and diversion. On the other hand, obscene literature, which stimulates the thoughts and the imagination in unhealthy ways, is to be rigorously avoided. As the patient should never take part in obscene conversations, his relations with comrades of his own age need to be carefully watched. Obscene thoughts are most difficult to combat.

'In difficult cases of onanism hypnotic suggestion may be employed in conjunction with the precepts given above and will be found to be a sovereign remedy. A popular introduction to the subject may be found in various well-known works.'*

* *Editor's Note.*—A little reflection concerning the treatment recommended in the foregoing paragraphs leaves me with the feeling that the cure (or rather the treatment, for I am not at all sure that it would bring about a cure) is worse than the disease. The unfortunate onanist who gives himself up to the treatment recommended above would have little time to think of anything else. Long and complicated directions of this sort only succeed in focussing the patient's attention on his condition, so that he spends his whole time thinking of masturbation, wanting to masturbate, fighting against the temptation, at last succumbing to it, and then suffering from remorse until the cycle is completed once more. I have found it much better to explain to the patient that masturbation will not do him any harm at all and that he can masturbate as often as he wants to. For a short period I get him to see me once a day, and, as soon as I have rid him of the fear of harmful consequences, I find that the frequency of the habit begins to diminish. When it reaches moderate proportions, I am satisfied. I find that the energy which used to be frittered away, in the conflict between the desire to masturbate and the endeavour to suppress the desire, is now available for the ordinary tasks and pleasures of life.—N. H.

The rational methods indicated by other physicians who specialise in this matter are not very different from the above. What is important is to eliminate, in the first place, and in all circumstances, the organic factors which induce individuals to scratch themselves, e.g. parasites or inflammation due to itching of the skin. Hygiene is therefore one of the first conditions to be observed in preventing and in combating masturbation. The physician in attendance, however, has at his disposal powerful psychological means, the efficiency of which is often superior to that of physical treatment. Obviously, these methods will vary according to the subject.

As for drugs, the doctor may sometimes recommend bromide and other sedatives. In recent times, certain practitioners have resorted to puncturing the skin in order to reduce the sensitiveness of the body.

At all events, the last thing a doctor should do when faced with a young masturbator is to frighten him, or to threaten castration or other similar punishments. We shall see, in the following chapter, that if the consequences of masturbation sometimes become really injurious, the reason may be found in interference of this kind, since it frequently produces serious nervous troubles in children.

CHAPTER VI

THE CONSEQUENCES OF MASTURBATION

Masturbation common during adolescence. Regarded as harmless by primitive peoples. Considered by Romans as unworthy of men but fit for women. Condemned by Christianity as a sin. Every kind of disorder attributed to masturbation. Widespread prejudice. Damage done by sense of guilt induced by condemnation of parents, teachers, clergy and doctors. Injurious only to those predisposed to psychological instability. In moderation preferable to strain of abstinence. Modern medical opinion. Warning against excesses.

IF we have judged it profitable to devote a special chapter to the consequences of masturbation, it is because there are few problems of sexual life which have given rise to so many false and mischievous conceptions. The consequences of masturbation are in reality due, as we shall see, rather to the campaign directed against these practices with a passion worthy of a better cause. To-day, in fact, it is well known that if so many masturbators have been driven to suicide, or other acts of desperation, the cause lies not so much in the practice of onanism itself as in the state of depression artificially induced by worry about the habit.

It is curious that, although human beings have at all times been prone to practise masturbation, especially at the age of puberty, condemnation has not always been aroused to the same degree. Basing our observations on historical data, we have had occasion to note that the Greeks were acquainted with onanism and that the Cynic school even ecommended it. In general, the attitude of the ancients may be represented as a shrug of the shoulders. Even those who showed signs of condemning masturbation in men appear to have been quite tolerant in the case of women. As we have observed elsewhere, the most rigorous judgment, that of Aristophanes, is not, properly speaking, an attack. It simply amounts to saying that masturbation is a practice unworthy of all save women, children, slaves and old men. The inhabitants of ancient Rome had a somewhat similar attitude, though they were perhaps a little less indulgent than the Greeks.

Our readers are already aware of the indifference shown by primitive peoples to precocious sexual manifestations. For them, masturbation in children is merely an innocent and rather amusing form of play, which does not call for more alarm than childish attempts at coitus.

After the advent of Christianity, we find a progressive modification in public opinion, which becomes more and more evident as we approach the middle ages. Certainly, it was not for hygienic reasons that the representatives of the clergy so violently condemned this practice, but because they disapproved in general of sexuality. During the same period, however, the practice of masturbation became more and more widespread. This is quite easy to understand if we bear in mind that sexual life during the middle ages was infinitely less free than in ancient times, and that young men frequently had no means of satisfying their sexual appetites in a normal way.

But it was the pioneers of sexology who, before the appearance of any literature on the subject, insisted on painting masturbation in horrible colours. While the theologians of the Middle Ages were content to regard the practice as a sin, which would meet with its due punishment in the life to come, the first specialists on the subject regarded masturbation as the cause of the most fearful physical evils.

There is hardly a morbid symptom, from the most innocuous to the most deadly, that was not attributed to masturbation by the infuriated enemies of the practice. Embarrassed looks, a tendency to blush, paleness, rings around the eyes, hollow cheeks, thinness, anxiety, depression, sensitiveness to cold, hesitating manners, an agitated appearance, shortness of breath, a tendency to solitude, were all said to be the result of onanism. Painful urination and retention of the urine, caused in reality by a congenital weakness of the sphincter, were also classed among the consequences of masturbation. This terrifying list could be prolonged *ad infinitum*. Other symptoms which were commonly attributed to masturbation make modern experts smile. Let us mention, by way of example, warts, perspiration of the genital parts, redness of the eyelids, the habit of biting the finger-nails, moodiness, pallor, moist hands, sweaty feet, and finally intestinal troubles and impotence. But the most serious evils for which onanism was held responsible, and which remained for a long time associated with the idea of that practice, were epilepsy and general paralysis. These opinions, which, to say the least, are extremely exaggerated, were continually dinned into masturbators, so that even those of them who did not indulge to excess, discovered non-existent maladies in themselves or attributed their slightest ailments to these sins. It is interesting to see the way masturbators anxiously observe the state of their health and make their own diagnosis, putting the blame on onanism. Here is an example:

' For months I have not been able to digest any warm food. I bring it all up. The only things that my stomach will tolerate are gruel, puddings, etc.; but they must always be cold. And I am always very thirsty. I can never go to sleep before one o'clock in the morning, yet when it is time to get up I am so dead tired that I want to go on sleeping, but my work calls me and I have to do it even though I have had no rest. I have to work hard all day, and in the evening I am so exhausted that *nothing* interests me. I cannot fight against onanism under these conditions, and I cannot give it up, although for me it is like the tortures of Hell. I practise it from one-half to three-quarters of an hour and produce a seminal emission, by which time I am trembling all over. Frightful headaches are the result, yet, although I am terrified by all this, I have to indulge in it every evening. I give myself a rub-down with cold water every morning and every evening, but it doesn't help me. I have to masturbate. I want to ask you most urgently to begin treating me for this. Every night I am terrified. Then some days it seems so foreign to me that I do not want to think about it. I want to tell you that, in spite of this passion of mine, I can *never* do harm to any man, and rather than use violent means to get something, I would do without it. It is now more than half-past two in the morning, but I can find no rest. To-day was the first day for many months that I did not do it—the first day that I did not follow the call of passion; but who knows how long I can hold out? I beg of you to help me.'

Dr. Garnier, who towards the end of last century studied the consequences of masturbation with all the zeal that the question demands, has collected a number of observations, some of which reveal the state of mind of these hypochondriacal masturbators. The first one we quote comes from a young man who, impressed by what he overheard about onanists being subject to impotence, fears to attempt normal intercourse:

'From the age of eleven (I am now eighteen), I have masturbated with my hand, on an average, twice a day.

This must be attributed to the fact that I am physically and mentally precocious and have led a somewhat lonely life since my childhood. And look at the results: unbearable physical and mental fatigue, a failing memory, and in particular, what I fear is incurable degeneration of the intellectual faculties. . . .

'I have tried several times to give up this vice, but all in vain. If I do not succeed in this last effort, *I shall know what remains for me to do.*

'You will tell me that normal intercourse is the remedy. Do you not think that, being of a timid character, depressed and very emotional, I shall be reduced to impotence if I attempt it and that the only result will be ridicule and shame? . . . .'

The following statement is also characteristic of the hypochondria of masturbation:

'A student, twenty-six years of age, in the faculty of arts at Bordeaux relates that in December 1886, as a result of having caught cold two years previously, he was attacked by violent erratic pains in the loins and arms, which afterwards became localised on the left side of the chest, and were so severe that he was unable to lie on that side. A year afterwards, the pains became more severe in the head and the legs, and were accompanied by involuntary trembling and contractions which the sulphur baths ordered by a doctor failed to relieve. These symptoms were sometimes so violent, especially in the legs and along the spinal cord, that he was unable to lie on his back.

'"The cause of this condition", he said, "is certainly masturbation, practised at college between the ages of fifteen and nineteen, very frequently and sometimes quite frantically. Intercourse with girls up to the age of twenty-two put an end to this fatal habit, but not completely, however, for I still often indulged in it, and it required unbelievable efforts on my part to stamp out this vice, which I consider a mental disease." '

Popular tracts, written for the most part by laymen, are chiefly responsible for this veritable mental malady, which was rampant among young people not long ago.

The following passage from the work of a Swedish poet, Augustus Strindberg, shows what consequences such publications may have:

' Johann opened the drawer and took out this deplorable piece of writing. His eyes perused the pages without daring to stop; his face became pale; his pulse ceased beating. So, at the age of 25, he was condemned to death or to insanity. His brain and his spinal cord would lose all their vitality and his face would look like that of a dead man; his hair would fall out and his hands would tremble. It was terrible. What remedy was there? Jesus. But Jesus could not cure the body but only the soul. At twenty-five, his body was irrevocably condemned to death and the only thing left for him to do was to save his soul from eternal damnation.'

Even such celebrated experts as Rousseau and Kraft-Ebing were unable to rid themselves of the century-old prejudices, and expressed the opinion that onanism might, in the long run, produce affections of most diverse kinds. Garnier, an authority on the matter, while possessing considerable understanding of the phenomenon of masturbation, often lapses into exaggeration when describing the effects of prolonged onanism. This is what he says:

' . . . Being often performed in a standing position, it (masturbation) is sure to bring about, by means of the solar plexus, an incessant series of reflex actions which, like so many electric discharges, pass backwards and forwards between the genital apparatus and the nervous system. Hence the unwonted flow of blood and its mechanical accumulation in the plexus of the pia mater. Congestion of the marrow is a consequence of this, as is seen in creeping paralysis of the lower limbs, several cases of which have been observed after coitus in an upright position. The mechanical action involved, friction, pressure and suction, repeated and prolonged, very soon reduces the sensitiveness of the penis and reacts in a short time upon the sympathetic organs, the testicles, the breasts, the throat and the nose. Deformity of the glans and dilatation of the cavernous bodies—produced by stagnation of the blood in the vesicles of the erectile tissues during these artificial and prolonged erections—make these tissues unstable and soft during sexual intercourse. Coitus exerts only a feeble local influence upon the dulled senses and the perverted sensibility of these masturbators. Timidity and shame, inspired by this vice, uncertainty, vagueness or absence of sexual desire, all contribute towards the making erection impossible apart from onanistic practice, and render normal intercourse difficult. Hence the zeal masturbators manifest for violent and immediate measures, such as the hand, the mouth and mechanical instruments.*

' Cold, dull, often effeminate, if not hermaphrodites or even pederasts without knowing it,† these unfortunate people usually fail to produce a sufficiently strong erection,

* *Editor's Note.*—In order to save the reader from any unnecessary apprehension as a result of reading these and some of the following paragraphs, it is necessary at this point to add a reminder that these descriptions of the supposedly catastrophic results of masturbation are quoted only because of their historical interest. They have no foundation in fact. The truth is that over 90 per cent. of people masturbate, and that very few of them experience any lasting evil effects. Where evil effects occur, they are due, in the vast majority of cases, to *worry* about masturbation, and not to the masturbation itself.—N. H.

† *Editor's Note.*—It is difficult to understand how anybody could write such nonsense as this. Since a pederast is a person who has anal intercourse, it is obviously quite impossible for anybody to be a pederast without knowing it.—N. H.

unless they meet with a woman who captivates, fascinates and seduces them. Otherwise there is nothing to guide them and they remain ineffective. Through force of habit, some of them obtain a semi-erection and arrive at a seminal emission by means of mutual masturbation. They are not, however, impotent, when they rub themselves or masturbate. A mere examination of their turgescent organ is sufficient to produce an erection. A skilful and subtle woman could therefore easily get the better of them. How can they be brought in contact with such a woman? Accustomed as they are to exciting themselves when alone, they do not understand how to abandon themselves to their companion, how to experience erotic sensations and how to communicate them. Like frigid women, *they feel nothing*. They fail to have an erection. Aphrodisiacs and nerve tonics are then the only resource. In this way, masturbation may sometimes engender loss of sexual desire and lead to prolonged celibacy.'*

We cannot be too insistent in denouncing the havoc played among young people by the propagation of extremist theories about the effects of masturbation. In the name of hygiene, parents and teachers have forced children to undergo third-degree examinations worthy of the instigators of the Inquisition, and they have literally tortured them by painting in the most lurid colours the consequences of their ' criminal ' acts, instead of helping them through the particularly painful period of puberty. They succeeded in giving children a deep sense of guilt, the consequences of which were often tragic. The following confession of a religious and very sensitive little girl is quoted by Dr. Liepmann:

* *Editor's Note.*—It is only in extremely rare cases, and in persons of highly neuropathic predisposition, that even excessive masturbation can lead to this result.—N. H.

'And now, I must make a sad confession: During my school years—what a gloom obscures them—I got into the habit of masturbating, but without putting my hands on my bare sexual parts. As a matter of fact it was only from my eighteenth year onwards that I began to know my body. I masturbated only rarely, for I was full of shame at the thought that God had seen me, and I felt that there was something wrong in it.

'I had been brought up in a thoroughly Christian way, and on Sundays I had to attend all the services. Every time that I masturbated, I promised God never to do it again.

'Later on, as a girl, I suffered severely from a sense of guilt, and I imagined that God would punish me by sending me a child, so that everybody would know of my wrong-doing.'

With some doctors, a mere glance at a young patient, who looked paler than usual, or the slightest abnormal sign revealed by an examination of his genital parts, would suffice to make them immediately accuse him of onanism and threaten him with the worst of evils. A child who was not guilty would be filled with anguish, a genuine masturbator would be overcome.

The following account, given by an officer, shows the reaction of a little boy who had never masturbated when confronted with the unexpected accusation of his doctor:

'I entered a cadets' preparatory school at Köslin at the age of ten. In this place, sexual indulgence was not by any means unknown. An elder classmate and a superior officer even wanted it with me, but I did not understand and turned away from it. I spent three years in Köslin without ever practising masturbation, either alone or with others. I never spoke about it to anyone. However, an event which

[105]

I can never forget drove me to it. I remained in the sixth class, and even in the second year I was not exactly a model pupil. One day I was sent to the hospital. The doctor who was there ordered me to take down my trousers, looked at my sexual parts and said, more or less word for word: " It is easy enough to see that you masturbate. If you don't give it up, you will have to come into the hospital, and I shall put your arms and legs in plaster of Paris." I could honestly say that I was truthful in this respect, that I had never practised masturbation and was perfectly innocent. This incident upset me very much.'

The numerous examples that we have considered it necessary to quote are sufficient evidence of the fact that it is precisely the excessive solicitude of parents and educators which is at the root of the evil effects attributed to masturbation. These pedagogues have no idea how much they themselves are to blame when the child entrusted to their care becomes melancholy and even goes so far as to attempt suicide. The most serious result of despair due to masturbation is, of course, suicide. After having solemnly sworn never to do it again, the child in many cases is unable to resist a new temptation; he then becomes thoroughly ashamed of himself, accuses himself of being weak-willed and unworthy, and finally comes to believe himself to be abnormal, insane, or a monster of wickedness. The idea of suicide often haunts him for a long time, and believing himself to be the victim of fate, he does not succeed, even on reaching adult years, in completely extricating himself from the habit acquired during childhood, and he finally succumbs. Stekel quotes the farewell letter of a female masturbator, which needs no comment:

' My dear Otto,

' When you read this letter, I shall no longer be alive; I am expiating my sin by death, because I can no longer endure a life in which I have become addicted to a terrible vice, while you consider me a pure person.

'Know, then, that since my childhood I have indulged in masturbation. I began in my earliest childhood, and continued it even after my marriage. I am too weak to give it up of my own accord, and since I notice signs in myself of its terrible effects, I cannot burden you with a sick wife. It is quite voluntarily but with a heavy heart that I am bidding goodbye to life. How can I look you in the face, how can I look into the faces of the children, feeling myself defiled and humiliated in such an unutterable manner?

'No, I cannot live any longer. Accept my thanks, my dear, for all the love that you have bestowed on me. I hope you will find a wife who will appreciate your confidence and your love. Seek a wife who will be worthy of you. Kiss our two little ones; this parting is most painful to me.

'Forgive me, I cannot help it.

'It is you I bless with my last breath.'

Even when neurasthenia, so frequent among those who practise masturbation*, does not lead to this fatal conclusion, it helps to make the victim a person set apart, one removed from society, seeking in vain a remedy for his solitude. Dr. Kapffs, in a pamphlet devoted to this question, describes in vivid terms the story of the inner life of a masturbator:

'Thus, the internal world of the man becomes a desert, ever more and more desolate, in which no green plant grows, and no water of life flows, where there blows only the dry wind of the tempest, burying the last green oases.

'Ever more desert-like, overwhelmed by images more and more extravagant, his soul becomes the prey of fixed

* *Editor's Note.*—It is again necessary to emphasise the fact that the neurasthenia is due, not to the masturbation itself, but to the guilty feelings which become associated with it, owing to faulty teaching on the subject.—N. H.

morbid ideas, while the noblest faculties of the mind, the power of thought and of judgment, sentiment, will and memory vanish more and more every day. Soon, there comes a dreadful melancholy, a feeling of disgust with life, that no joy can overcome, and of indifference to society, conversation, the arts, science, religion, and all that is fine. It is an internal death that leads to insanity or to suicide.'

Such effects are to be found only in particularly emotional individuals, for otherwise, judging by the enormous percentage of girls and young men who have attempted to satisfy themselves by means of masturbation, the greater part of the human race would be neurasthenic and inclined to commit suicide. Fortunately, these feelings of remorse and these struggles against one's own instinct are phenomena of short duration, though rather frequent. Over-zealous educators forget that they themselves, at the age of about fourteen or fifteen, considered themselves abject creatures, and experienced the same terrible anguish; if only they still remembered the torments of former days, they would certainly not inflict them on their pupils. But as disagreeable things and things one does not like to remember are easily forgotten, they are all the more ardent in their sermons on purity, which in turn make new victims. The description given by Wilhelm Stekel, without any false modesty, of the calvary of his own youth, is therefore of special value in this connection:

' Will you permit me to tell to you the story of my struggles and my sufferings? I was of the same age as your son, when one of my comrades passed me a book entitled *How to Keep Healthy*, innumerable copies of which were circulated among young people.

' The consequences of masturbation and of the loss of semen were described in it in a light that was more than terrifying. What horrible sufferings lay in store for the poor wretches who fell victims to this terrible crime. (Naturally, I did not know, at that time, how common this " crime " was among young people.)

' The reading of this book caused me to pass through a serious psychological crisis. Thanks to my robust constitution and my healthy mind, I was, in the end, none the worse for it.

' Nevertheless, I repeat that the reading of that book had a most devastating effect on me. I was at that time passing through an important period of psychological development. The few verses that I had written gave me the illusion of being a great poet. I loved nature, and enjoyed looking at it. A sunrise would make me weep with emotion. But my health was, as I thought, ruined for ever, and, although I was of a rather happy disposition, such horrible ideas completely upset me.

' Soon, I experienced my first wet dreams, and the anxiety occasioned by this catastrophic event, with its loss of semen, haunted me irresistibly and caused me to develop real hypochondria.

' I rushed off to doctors to get examined, I read numbers of books, but all that merely added to my anxiety, especially since none of the practitioners I consulted seemed to understand me.

' The spectre of masturbation and its after-effects haunted me up to the time I entered the university. I never ceased to consult the great scientific authorities of the time, but they only treated me with probings, and electricity, with water and with bromide.'

The author afterwards states that he was cured, as if by magic, through consulting one of his professors, who said that one emission per week might be considered perfectly normal.   *   *   *

When we try to discover the causes of these erroneous ideas, broadcast for centuries, and shared by those who were otherwise among the most enlightened, we can only make a statement which, despite its simplicity, explains a great deal. Thanks to sincere confessions and to statistics which were not available in former times, we now know that 95 per cent., if not 100 per cent., of young men indulge in masturbation during puberty. Hence, the slightest disorder, the origin of which medical science had not yet sufficiently explained, was often attributed to onanism. A few questions put by the doctor or the parents, or merely a deduction drawn from their observations, revealed masturbatory practices on the part of the patient, and immediately relations of cause and effect were erroneously established between onanism and various disturbances. According to this line of reasoning, one would be justified in explaining tuberculosis or venereal diseases by attributing them to masturbation, since it is fairly certain that every consumptive and every syphilitic person has practised onanism, at least occasionally.

This error, which consists in confusing cause and effect, is characteristic of the question of onanism, especially as regards the incidence of epilepsy, hysteria and other nervous diseases. It used to be customary to say: ' He is epileptic because he masturbates ', when it would have been truer to follow the contrary course of reasoning and say: ' He is epileptic, his nervous system is unbalanced, and this brings about anomalies of the sexual instinct which lead him to masturbate '. Timidity is another case in point. The experts of former times, when they saw a timid young man embarrassed, taciturn and unsociable, came to the conclusion that he masturbated. But in a great many cases it was precisely his timidity and his lack of enterprising spirit that caused the young man to avoid female society, so that when the sex instinct made itself felt, he was forced to lapse into masturbation.

In addition to the large numbers of less serious symptoms observed by the enemies of masturbation and classified as consequences of that practice, are phenomena associated with the transformations of the organism which take place at puberty and have no connection whatever with masturbation.* We repeat that it is ignorance of the real causes of the diseases met with in masturbators that is responsible for the erroneous theory which made masturbation the bugbear of youth.

It is only during the last two or three decades that medical science has revised its opinion on the subject of masturbation. Physicians and psychiatrists began to examine this problem in quite a new light. They soon discovered the fact on which we have already insisted, namely, that the commonly accepted theories concerning masturbation could not stand the light of a scientific examination, and that if the consequences were sometimes serious, they were due less to the practice itself than to the vogue of the erroneous opinions which had been propagated in such a way as to play havoc with the soul of youth. This devastating influence has continued up to the present day, for the veil of hypocrisy has not yet been completely torn from all that has to do with sexual matters. The adolescent, terrified by the prophecies and threats of his well-meaning elders, sincerely believes that he will soon end his days in a mad-house, or perhaps in prison or on the guillotine (scaffold).

*   *   *

* *Editor's Note.*—Owing to the profound changes in the balance of the glands of internal secretion which take place at puberty, boys and girls at this age are subject to such symptoms as blushing, pimples on the face, etc. In the past these have been regularly, though quite erroneously, attributed to masturbation.—N. H.

What are the actual effects of masturbation, in the light of modern science? After having refuted the old theories, it is important not to leave that question unanswered. An exaggerated and precocious loss of semen, say some. But that loss is not greater than in the course of normal coitus; it is on an average three grammes, and when repeated it becomes considerably less. The small amount of albumen thus wasted by the organism is amply compensated for by food.*

With regard to the lassitude which follows masturbation, we may recall the old Latin adage, *post coitum omne animal triste* (every animal is sad after coitus), and we may add in this connection: *post masturbationem omne animal triste.* Coming back to earth after the ecstasy of orgasm always entails a certain sadness, but whereas, after normal coitus, this sadness is moderated by the presence of the partner and by amorous affection, after masturbation all consolation is lacking and the subject realises more clearly that the manœuvre he has indulged in is only a makeshift.

It is true that the nerve-wracking tension provoked by sensual desire has disappeared, but it is replaced by spiritual tension and the desire to escape from that solitude is merely increased. This condition is very characteristic of puberty. Besides, the lassitude following masturbation is often greater than that which follows coitus; this is quite comprehensible, because the practice of masturbation implies a stronger effort of the imagination.

Dr. Hirschfeld, in a study of post-masturbatory exhaustion, has made an interesting observation on this subject. It is in the following way that he explains the fact that the lassitude observed in a man after the emission provoked by

---

* *Editor's Note.*—The amount of semen lost at an emission is small in quantity, and the loss of it has no more importance for the bodily health than the loss of saliva from the mouth or tears from the eye.—N. H.

masturbation is more pronounced than after coitus: The orgasm itself is not more exhausting in the one case than in the other; it is only after the emission that the difference begins. To the loneliness produced by the absence of a partner, there is added a physiological need, for whereas in the presence of a woman a certain amount of excitement still continues, stimulating the activity of the glands and immediately provoking genital secretions and reducing to a minimum the state of vacuity of the glands, the masturbator, once his act is accomplished, lacks all excitement and the vacuity is prolonged; hence, lack of energy, lassitude and disgust.

What appears to be really serious is interruption of masturbation before emission occurs. The effects of this are more harmful than those of *coitus interruptus*. While in this latter practice emission is produced, though in an abnormal way, in the case of interrupted masturbation emission is entirely lacking. It is fear of the supposed effects of masturbation that incite many young men to interrupt this act at the psychological moment. They little suspect that, while wishing to do well, while seeking to avoid the illusory consequences, they expose themselves to a real danger. The psychological troubles which may be brought about by this outrage to nature are not questioned by anyone. It is as a result of this practice that neurasthenia is to be feared, and, in the long run, disturbances of erection and emission. An incomplete masturbator, who prolongs indefinitely the duration of the excitement, runs much more risk of lapsing into impotence than does a masturbator who for some time practises complete masturbation to the exclusion of normal sexual intercourse.

Excessive and regular masturbation may produce the habit, in a man just as well as in a woman, of mechanical excitement, and necessitate a well-defined position, without which the orgasm cannot afterwards be brought about. It is in this way that the practice of masturbation, when carried too far in the case of a man, may so deaden his sensitiveness that the elastic and humid contact of the vagina can no longer provoke an orgasm.

Here is an example of that anomaly, mentioned by Garnier:

' A young and handsome officer, thirty-two years of age, blonde and somewhat effeminate, belonging to a family of importance, came on 5th February, 1883, after eighteen months of married life, and confessed his inability to have an erection and to render his young wife pregnant, in spite of their mutual love. An erection was certainly produced during the amorous embraces of his wife and the contacts which she effected, as he had accustomed her to these manœuvres in order to produce it; but it failed so soon as he attempted intromission, in spite of the stratagems employed. This was caused neither by the volume of the penis, which was rather small, nor by the narrowness of the vagina; the habit of masturbation, practised up to the age of twenty-two, was the only possible cause, for he proved impotent even before his marriage, during a few rare attempts with prostitutes. With him, intercourse consisted in a kind of mutual masturbation leading to emission, for intromission, being impossible at the beginning of the act, always remained incomplete.'

In addition to the impossibility of having an emission during coitus, mention must be made of premature ejaculation, that is to say, ejaculation before the intromission of the penis. Here again, it is practically certain that we are not concerned with a direct consequence of masturbation, but rather with an effect of the hypochondria of masturbation. It is chiefly the morbid state produced by anxiety that brings about this disturbance. Individuals predisposed to this form of anxiety fall victims to this indirect consequence of masturbation; a healthy person whose nervous system is normal hardly ever shows such symptoms.

All kinds of troubles have been attributed to masturbation in women. Its effects are summarised by Garnier as follows:

'Whether practised alone or by two people, this masturbation—apart from the troubles it causes during menstruation, i.e. pains, neuralgia and hæmorrhage—is at the same time prejudicial to normal intercourse. The use of the hand during such a practice brings about wasting or atrophy of the breasts. Rubbing, suction or sapphism produce the same danger; if extended to the whole vulva, they bring about congestion and deformities which are serious and obvious stigmata, which are evidence of this vice and which make it easily discoverable by examination of the genital organs.

Some even went so far as to state that masturbation in young girls was responsible for their sterility in after years. To-day, few still believe this, but it is none the less true that masturbation has specific effects on a woman. Since the existence of the hymen in a girl does not allow of an imitation of coition, the manipulations are limited to the other genital organs, and in the long run they modify sexual sensibility. The clitoris, having become accustomed to regular excitement, may become the centre of sensitivity, at the expense of the vagina. The woman cannot then find satisfaction in coitus except by the aid of local contacts. The fixation of enjoyment in the region of the clitoris may, later on, prevent a transference of sensibility from the clitoris to the vagina. But, even in cases where masturbatory habits have left their traces in the form of minor troubles of genital sensibility in the woman, the case is not a desperate one. The mutual understanding and affection of the partners will easily overcome these inconveniences, especially since they are chiefly in evidence at the beginning of normal sexual life, and tend gradually to disappear.

Somewhat more serious cases caused by masturbation have, however, been recorded. They are due to so-called mechanical masturbation, which is particularly dangerous for women. In the preceding chapter we have enumerated the objects which are used by young girls, and especially by women who are impelled to interrupt normal sexual life in order to satisfy their sex instinct. It will be readily understood that these instruments, which vary according to circumstances, are not without danger to the sexual organs, the mucous membrane of which is particularly sensitive. Lesions and infections of all kinds have been known to result from the use of these objects, which are quite unfit to be placed in contact with the genital organs. But, here again, it is obviously not masturbation itself which is the real source of the evil, but rather a particularly unhygienic and imprudent method.

It would, however, be dangerous to draw too general a conclusion from this chapter and to say that, since masturbation is a normal and practically harmless phenomenon, it would be wrong to put any obstructions in the way of it. It has not been our intention to lay down the principle which consists in giving full play to the caprices of the sexual instinct. In this case, as in others, moderation is the general rule to be observed. In fact, if the ' masturbation of compensation ', as certain experts have called the crude attempts observed during puberty, is not the horrible and dangerous vice which some would have had us believe, it is a sexual perversion, and therefore an abnormal phenomenon when it becomes a regular practice in an adult. In analysing the consequences of masturbation, it is important to establish a clear distinction of a quantitative nature. It would naturally be impossible to reply in a categorical manner to those who ask how many times per day or per week one may masturbate without lapsing into excess, but it is evident that excess may be harmful. What constitutes the limit is an individual question, as it is in coitus. We shall see from what follows that the rules governing the frequency of sexual intercourse in marriage are very variable. They may run from once per day to once per month—and it is the same with masturbation.

In the same way the duration of the onanist's act must not be exaggerated if it is to remain harmless. Finally, the period during which this habit is continued is, as we have seen, of the greatest importance. A young man and a young woman of healthy constitution will not be tempted to continue these practices so soon as they have the opportunity of a normal sexual life, and if this opportunity is delayed for too long, the fault lies in the social system and not in the vicious character of the persons in question.

In short, if medical science knows of masturbators who have paid dearly for their habits, let us look for the cause of these deplorable consequences in deficient sexual enlightenment, in a morbid predisposition, or, finally, in the constraint imposed by economic and social conditions. We cannot terminate this chapter better than by quoting the conclusion given in a work of Hirschfeld and Bohm on sexual enlightenment, which has the merit of having destroyed more than one prejudice:

' The lies with which the phenomenon of masturbation has been surrounded must be destroyed, and youth must be liberated from the psychical burden which is so hard to bear. Man is not born a sinner, any more than a tree, a bird or a fish. To describe as bestial the sexual instinct of an adolescent and its manifestations, is an injustice to mankind and to the whole animal kingdom.

' When one sees individuals of both sexes tormented by sexual troubles, one is tempted to exclaim: " Man, what hast thou done with thy brothers? ".'*

---

* *Editor's Note.*—Once more it is necessary to warn the reader against the fantastic catastrophes which are popularly supposed to follow the practice of masturbation. Masturbation is a normal phenomenon which appears in the vast majority of healthy children, as well as in young adults who are, for one reason or another, unable to obtain the normal satisfaction of their sexual appetite for a long time after they have become sexually mature, and ripe for mating. In adult life masturbation offers such poor satisfaction, in comparison with normal sexual intercourse, that no normal healthy adult would practise it, except *faute de mieux*. —N. H.

CHAPTER VII

PUBERTY

Period decisive for whole of future life. Initiation rites among savages and primitive peoples. Effect of race and climate. Changes in voice, manners and deportment. Importance of interstitial glands. Secondary sexual characters. Difference between puberty and maturity. Homosexual phase. Awkwardness in presence of opposite sex. Revolt against parental authority.

PUBERTY, the period when we notice the first appearance of the procreative faculty, is characterised by profound physical and psychological changes. The body and mind of the individual are subjected to a radical development which evinces itself in disturbing phenomena of a mysterious character. Those with whom he is in contact do not understand the extraordinary transformation of the adolescent youth, who himself cannot clearly discern the complex changes to which his ego is subject. This period is decisive for the future development of the human being, and a knowledge of the processes connected with puberty is essential for educators and parents conscious of their duties. Inadequate attention to children during puberty may, in fact, change the whole course of their development, and give rise to difficulties which will afflict them for the rest of their lives. For that reason, we have deemed it useful to study in greater detail the various aspects of the period of puberty.

The mystery of sexual development has always interested

people, and even primitive races attach special importance to this decisive period. In many tribes the onset of puberty is associated with mysterious rites, incantations, and operations in the case of boys and girls. Not infrequently, these ceremonies include painful tests, such as the extraction of the teeth, tattooing, and even mutilation of the genital organs. In order to test their powers of resistance, certain races impose various privations on their adolescents, evidently with the object of producing warlike men.

The American Indians, according to Swanton, attribute considerable importance to the experiences acquired during this critical period. They believe that every sensation and every thought of the boy or girl during puberty will leave its mark on the life of the adult. That is the origin of the precautions taken to prevent evil, the magic incantations and the tests of endurance.

Among civilised peoples we find traces of these customs. The origin of certain religious customs can be traced to the rites of primitive races in connection with puberty. The first communion in the case of Catholics, and the admission of the adolescent into the Jewish community, for example, are nothing more than a refined form of the practices of savage peoples.

There is no fixed time for the onset of puberty in the human species. The age at which the first signs appear varies according to race and climate, as also does their duration. Everybody knows that in southern countries puberty is reached very early, and that this gives rise to marriages at an age when the adolescents of other regions are only on the threshold of puberty. While in Scandinavian countries the first signs of sexual development rarely make their appearance before the fifteenth year, in the tropics a woman is ready for marriage at the age of fifteen and often already a mother. We shall have occasion to return to these questions once more in the chapters devoted to sexual development in men and women.

Let us now pass on to a study of the phenomena of puberty. We have indicated above the double nature of the transformation which takes place in a young person at this period. It is both psychological and physical, and corresponds to the development of the two elements inherent in sexuality, the ideal and the material. Let us first note that the auto-erotic sexuality that we have observed in children tends to be transformed into allo-erotic sexuality, that is to say the sexual impulse, instead of remaining concentrated in the ego, seeks an object in the external world.

Everybody is familiar with the ungraceful figure of the girl or the boy who, having lost the charm of childhood, has not yet acquired the manly character or the womanly charm of the adult. Before reaching the state of a marriage-able woman, whose body is ready for maternity, the graceful, sexless girl passes through a period during which her body has an ungraceful appearance, her limbs seem too long, her gestures are awkward and her attitude one of embarrassment. The same lack of proportion is observed in the adolescent boy, whose body lengthens rapidly and whose voice breaks, the deep tones alternating with the more strident ones and producing a comical effect. The secondary sexual characters, such as the growth of hair on the body in both sexes, and the development of the breasts in the girl, do not make their appearance all at once. Their development is slow, and before assuming their final form they have the effect of creating a certain lack of harmony in the external appearance.

The external signs of puberty reflect the internal trans-formation of the organism and the complete development of the genital apparatus. We have already explained the anatomy of the male and female genital organs, and have called attention to the extremely important part played by the principal sex glands: the ovaries in the woman and the testicles in the man. In addition to these organs, the activity of which is evinced by ovulation and the production of spermatozoa—two internal processes manifesting themselves externally by the menstrual flow and by seminal emissions—the human organism includes a number of other glands of internal secretion, the influence of which on sexual activity is certainly very great. By pouring their products, known as *hormones,* into the blood, these glands help to determine the whole sexual life of the human being. Among the glands of internal secretion which are important from the point of view of sex, we may mention the thyroid, the parathyroids, the pituitary, and the suprarenal capsules. But the glands with which we are chiefly concerned, when considering puberty, are those which have been discovered comparatively recently, and the real function of which has yet to be explained. They are the *interstitial glands,* so called by two French experts, Ancel and Bouin, who made a study of them. Steinach has also described them under the name of puberty glands. For a long time nobody was aware of their presence, and the general action exerted by them on the organism was attributed to the ovaries in women and to the testicles in men. They are, however, independent organs, situated adjacent to those more important glands which reach their full development at puberty, function throughout the whole of the sexual life, and become atrophied with the appearance of senility. The time of life at which they develop is proof of their importance from the point of view of sex, and it is for this reason that they have been called the puberty glands. The study of castrated animals confirms the hypotheses of experts with regard to the special part played by these glandular bodies in the development of sexuality. It is practically certain that these small glands determine genital activity and sexual character, by means of the hormones they produce.

It is worth while devoting a few words to another gland, the thymus, which is situated near the sternum and which seems to play a negative part in the phenomenon of puberty. During childhood the function of the thymus is to compensate for the action of the genital glands and to maintain the organism in an infantile state. It is at about the fifteenth year that its action begins to wane: the secretion of hormones first of all slows down and then ceases completely. The absence of the hormones of the thymus permits of the appearance of the secondary sexual characters. If, however, the function of the thymus is interfered with and comes to an end sooner than it should, the result is sexual precocity, with all the organic troubles that this phenomenon brings in its train, including, among others, rickets and the arrest of growth seen in dwarfs. It is therefore important to prevent, by all possible means, the cessation of thymus function before the normal time. Mention may be made here of a glandular body, peculiar to the woman, the *corpus luteum*, which appears at the same time as ovulation, and the rôle of which is also insufficiently explained at present. It is to be hoped that later researches in this domain will succeed in explaining the mystery of puberty, on the basis of a more precise knowledge of the glands of internal secretion.

We have said that puberty is characterised by the appearance of the procreative faculty. It is, however, important to distinguish between puberty and maturity. The latter term is applied to the capacity of procreation, i.e. of giving life to normal beings, in such a way that the organism of the generator is none the worse for it, while puberty merely indicates the first manifestations of the activity of the sexual organs. Puberty very rarely coincides with the adult form of exercise of the sexual faculties. The latter, as we shall see, takes place much later, for while a girl reaches puberty, in temperate climates, at the age of thirteen or fourteen, the average age at which she enters on her sexual life, that is to say, sexual intercourse and the functions of maternity, is between eighteen and twenty-two. The transition from auto-eroticism to allo-eroticism is not effected by leaps and bounds, and normal sexual activity is incompatible with puberty. Many experts are of the opinion that before turning towards the opposite sex, the individual during puberty goes through a homo-sexual phase. It is true that there exists a vague and unconscious need of a partner, and the adolescent youth is not yet attracted by girls of his own age. He first of all chooses, from amongst those in his immediate environment, an object whom he can endow with his ideals, these ideals being coloured by eroticism, though he himself is unaware of the fact. He has a consuming desire to give vent to the desires which arise within him, and to bestow upon another the wealth of affection of which he knows he is capable, so he takes a schoolmate or a teacher, for whom he professes unbounded admiration. It is only little by little, through education and the influence of the life he sees around him, that he becomes sensible to the grace of young girls. It is a much debated question whether ideal love for a member of the opposite sex arises prior to the appearance of sexual desire, simultaneously with it, or later on. Apparently there is no hard and fast rule in this matter, and the development depends on individual character. It is, in fact, no uncommon thing for an adolescent, even before having any suspicion of his sexual needs, to profess passionate though platonic love for a woman. On the other hand, cases have been known of young boys who through their precocious sexual activities had developed the appetites of adult men, although their psychological development had not yet reached the stage where the individual is capable of spiritual love. All this applies equally to girls, but with the difference, perhaps, that in their case sexual activity seldom takes place until later, that is, before the appearance of amorous affection.

In our opinion, the danger of this homosexual phase, observed in boys and girls during puberty, has been greatly exaggerated. Confronted with these excessive manifestations of affection for an individual of the same sex, over-zealous parents and educators have explained it as evidence of vice, and imposed various kinds of restraint upon the adolescent youth. But to give a boy or girl passing through this phase of homosexual love an idea of the aberration involved in such a tendency, is perhaps more dangerous than to allow full play to this first amorous flight. The phenomenon, moreover, is of short duration, and it is only when it is prolonged beyond the usual time that anxiety is justified.

The manner in which the sexuality of girls and boys manifests itself in the presence of members of the opposite sex varies according to the sex and the individual in question. What characterises a young man in his earliest relations with a young woman is manly pride. But before becoming conscious of his manhood, the boy experiences, usually in secret, boundless timidity with regard to the girl whom he loves. He feels his position is ridiculous and shameful, and rarely declares his love. But he is soon acquainted with the pleasure of normal sexual relationships and becomes conscious of his real sexuality. Normally, the memory of his earlier attempts at masturbation calls up nothing but disgust in him. But it frequently happens that his timidity towards the woman he loves persists, and that his sexual needs are satisfied only by mercenary women. In such a regrettable case, psychological sexuality and physical sexuality are dissociated.

In a woman, coquetry and the craving to be seduced correspond to virile pride in a man. Long before she becomes aware that her organism craves for complete sexual connection, the young girl during puberty experiences emotions of the most varied kind in the company of young men. She wants to be destructive, she wants to please and to inspire desire. But even when she finds, amongst those who surround her, a young man to whom her thoughts continually return, and with whom she believes herself to be in love, she is not ready for a sexual union, with the sacrifice that it entails. Usually an unconscious need to preserve her physical integrity prevents her sacrificing her virginity. Only girls whose sexual development is abnormal are unaffected by this instinct and prostitute themselves at an early age, as we shall see in the chapter devoted to prostitution.

In addition, however, to the manly pride and the feminine seductiveness which accompany the first manifestations of sexual activity, we must mention also aggressiveness, the instinct of domination which characterises the male in love matters, and submission coupled with the desire for protection which is found in the female. In normal persons these characteristics are in evidence at an early period, and become more pronounced in the course of physical and psychological sexual development.

On the psychological plane, puberty is characterised by the development of a social sense. The period of childhood is marked by profound attachment to the family. The life of the child is in a sense vegetative; he is incapable of objective or personal judgment and sees everything through the eyes of his parents. Escape from the guardianship of the family often takes the form of a violent reaction. Although until quite recently content to obey his parents, the adolescent now manifests his independence by revolting against paternal authority. He always 'knows better' than anyone else, and the slightest remark wounds his pride. He begins to consider his parents' views old-fashioned and reactionary, and thinks himself grown up and able to manage his own affairs. Family bonds weigh upon him like shackles. In the girl, this need of independence, though manifesting itself in a less violent way, is equally imperative. Though she may not dare to defy the will of her parents, she pouts and is subject to attacks of bad temper; she shows signs of nervousness, and only grudgingly carries out the orders that she is given. But the lack of pugnacity which characterises her as a girl makes her adolescence more tolerable to her parents. Coquetry prevents her revolt becoming very annoying and she makes use of her feminine charm to obtain from her friends the liberty to which she aspires.

At the time that adolescents, of both sexes, break away from parental care and become conscious of their part in social life, they are consumed by ambition and aspire towards infinity. They are dissatisfied with the circles in which they mix, and their curiosity about all and sundry is directed towards all manifestations of human life. They want to undertake all kinds of enterprises, and the means at their disposal seem unlimited. They dream of great accomplishments and feel that glory and immortality are in store for them, and they are filled with an ardent desire to begin living an independent life so that they may make their dreams come true.

After centuries of ignorance on all matters connected

with the body in general and the sexual organs and their functions in particular, science has rehabilitated that part of the human being. When first this was accomplished, the leaders of the ' materialist ' movement showed a strong tendency to go to the other extreme and explain all human reactions in terms of physical mechanism. Thus the disturbing manifestations of boys and girls during puberty, their restlessness, their anxiety, their strange flights and their ardour, were considered as external signs masking the desire for copulation. This, however, would mean the negation of those spiritual factors which at puberty reach their full development, parallel with that of the body. In order to understand the mysteries of puberty, it is essential not to subordinate one of these factors to the other, but to study them simultaneously, to examine their correlation and their reciprocal influence, while giving to each one its proper place.

Puberty is a time of sexual development, psychological as well as physical.

CHAPTER VIII

FROM GIRLHOOD TO PUBERTY

Menstruation and the need to prepare a young girl for its onset. Explanation of phenomena of menstruation. Duration and periodicity. Complex physical process which gives rise to flow. Fate of the ovum. Individual reactions at time of periods. Physical and psychological crisis. Hygiene of menstruation. War-time amenorrhœa. Virginity and its value among different races.

THE first menstrual period is nature's warning to the young girl that she has reached puberty. We have noted in previous chapters the dangers which confront the young girl left in sexual ignorance by her parents and teachers, when menstruation first makes its appearance. We shall therefore not refer to the matter in the present chapter nor broach again the question of the first appearance of the menstrual flow.

Menstruation, by which is understood an external hæmorrhage from the sexual organs, is only the outward and visible sign of a highly complex process. Menstruation occurs at intervals of four weeks and ceases after a varying number of days. The other and more important part of the menstrual cycle is not outwardly perceptible, and consists in the release of an ovum from the ovary.

Temporary interruption of menstruation occurs during pregnancy and nursing; it may also be brought about by illness, nervous disorders or malnutrition.

Normally, menstruation occurs regularly throughout the

[129]

period during which a woman is sexually mature, that is usually from about the fourteenth to the forty-ninth year. But exceptions may be observed every day. The periods often begin much earlier, at twelve or even at ten years of age, or as late as the twentieth year. Sometimes they cease with the fortieth year, in rare instances with the thirtieth. There have been cases where they continued with perfect regularity until the sixtieth year.

On an average one can reckon with a span of from thirty to thirty-five years. Usually, the earlier the appearance of menstruation the longer the capacity for child-bearing, and vice versa.

Climate strongly influences the date of the first menstruation. As a rule puberty is reached earlier in southern countries than in northern ones, as is also the menopause. The standard of living also exerts an influence. On the whole, girls brought up in better circumstances menstruate earlier than those of the poorer classes. Well-nourished and well-developed girls also mature sooner.

The recurrence of menstruation varies with almost each individual. One usually reckons twenty-six to thirty-one days betwen the periods, sometimes less, sometimes a little more. The standard interval is every four weeks, but not all women enjoy such regularity that the day and the hour can be foretold. It must also be borne in mind that many women neglect to note the date of their periods. They are 'sure' they are regular and do not give them another thought. It is therefore easy to understand how difficult it is to estimate exactly the time of the last period, especially during pregnancy, when a few months have passed without menstruation taking place. For that reason I emphasise the importance of keeping a record of every menstrual period and of marking each date in the calendar. By this means women will be spared much anxious uncertainty and also save their physician much valuable time.

The duration of the period also varies with every individual. Normally, it lasts from four to six days, yet there are very short periods of only two days, and very long ones of from eight to ten days, without its being due to any physiological disturbance. The one thing certain is that the periodicity and duration of menstruation is peculiar to each individual.

The flow varies in quantity from 30 oz. to 80 oz. An exact calculation is difficult and one can only make a rough estimate. Strong and healthy individuals generally lose less blood than weaker ones. Women living in cities and under good conditions have a more copious flow than do those in the country. Slight contractions of the uterus and pain in the loins usually accompany the flow.

Under normal conditions menstrual blood is dark red in colour, and fluid. One or two days before the actual arrival of the period, and frequently for some time after the flow proper has begun, a mucous secretion is discharged from the uterus and the vagina. This secretion, which combines with the menstrual blood, produces an acid reaction when secreted from the vagina, and prevents coagulation of the blood, interruption of the flow, and clotting. The scarcely noticeable odour of the flow (which, however, is quite *sui generis*) is due to this secretion.

To understand the more intimate facts of menstruation one must realise that the flow itself is of small importance. The changes which take place in the uterus, in the form of a monthly cycle culminating in the menstrual flow, are due to the internal secretions of the ovary. There are at least two of these internal secretions, possibly more. One of them is secreted by the tissues around the site of an ovum, after the ovum itself has ripened and been shed from the ovary.

The exact date of this shedding of an ovum, known as ovulation, is not known, but all the evidence we have at present suggests that it occurs about mid-way between two menstrual periods. The ovum, on being released, finds its way into the open end of the fallopian tube, and then passes down the tube towards the uterus.

As a result of the internal secretion of the ovary circulating in the blood, certain changes take place in the uterine wall. The mucous membrane becomes thick and spongy, and the glands hypertrophy, so as to form a suitable ' nest ' for the ovum if it should happen to be fertilised. If the ovum is not fertilised, the internal secretory activity of the ovary changes, so that the thickened mucous membrane breaks down and is cast off, together with a certain amount of blood, and it is the discharge of these substances that constitutes the menstrual flow. After a few days of this process, the ovarian activity changes again, the uterine lining enters a resting stage, menstruation stops, and the whole cycle begins all over again.

If the ovum is fertilised, the usual cycle in the activity of the ovary is upset. The particular internal secretion which gives rise to menstruation is not produced, and menstruation does not occur until after the fertilised ovum has been expelled from the uterus, normally at the end of pregnancy nine months later, unless it is expelled earlier, if miscarriage takes place.

If the ovum is fertilised it fixes itself on the inner wall of the uterus, and the congestion of the organs no longer has the effect of destroying the membrane but serves to develop it. The blood is diffused and menstruation is stopped. With impregnation the period of pregnancy begins.

In some cases the general health is subject to disturbance a few days before the beginning of the period. The woman may have no aptitude for work, be easily exhausted, have palpitation of the heart, feel weak and cold, have little appetite, and turn with disgust from certain articles of diet.

There may also be local disturbances due to congestion in the genital organs, e.g. a sense of contraction in the loins, a feeling of oppression and heaviness, constipation; the breasts, too, may be painful and swollen, and the nipples very sensitive.

Finally, there may be nervous symptoms, headaches, and more or less irritability. In short, women at that time feel themselves ' unwell '. This feeling is usually relieved when the flow begins. Often, however, it remains throughout menstruation.

Nevertheless, all these complaints are part and parcel of the normal process and there are few women who menstruate without some discomfort and pain.

But it is quite another matter if these typical symptoms become intensified; if, for example, instead of an insignificant hardening of the abdomen there appear violent spasmodic cramps; if the pains in the loins become intolerable; if a simple aversion to food turns to nausea; if slight nervousness becomes a real psychosis, then it is no longer a matter of natural functions but a morbid disturbance of menstruation which must be diagnosed, defined and treated*.

*Editor's Note.—Menstrual pain can be very intense and quite disabling. Many girls and women have to give up their occupation and even go to bed for a day or two every month; or, even more frequently, though they do not give up their occupation, they spend two or three days in misery owing to menstrual pain. In all such cases a competent doctor should be consulted. It is first of all necessary to find out the reason for the pain, in each individual case, for only after the cause has been accurately diagnosed is it possible to make a successful attempt to cure

This applies also to the periodicity and duration of the flow itself. Here, too, we take the healthy woman as standard. If menstruation occurs irregularly or if it fails to occur at all, disturbance of the genital system may be presumed.

We have already seen that a few days before the appearance of their first period, and even later at the time of the flow, some girls find themselves in an abnormal condition characterised by lowered resistance and a decrease of physical capacity; they also tend to manifest various nervous and mental anomalies, loss of self-control and emotional intensity being the cause of many of the offences committed during that time.

This tendency to prostration, which easily degenerates into melancholy, is strikingly illustrated by statistics which show that out of 40 suicides 35 were committed during menstruation. Also, since sexual feelings are greatly intensified at that period, it is easy to understand that the young girl at the time of her first menses needs especially affectionate care, for in addition to the biological factor, a psychological crisis accompanies this important event. It is not without reason that Havelock Ellis and several other scientists have demanded that a young girl should

it. In many cases the pain is due to incomplete development of the uterus associated with the presence of a 'kink' in the organ. Instead of the blood flowing out freely, it is dammed back at the point where the 'kink' is, and the uterus has to make spasmodic contractions in order to force it past the obstruction. It is these contractions which cause the pain. There are a great many drugs which have been prescribed at one time or another for the relief of menstrual pain. Some are successful in some cases, others in other cases. It has been found, in the last few years, that the insertion of an intra-uterine ring for the purpose of contraception results, in a great many cases, in the relief of menstrual pain. This was so striking in my own series of cases, that I began to try the effect of the ring (quite apart from its contraceptive effect) in certain cases of menstrual pain, and in a considerable proportion the results were strikingly good. Painful menstruation is also treated sometimes by dilatation of the neck of the womb.—N. H.

be excused at that time from her studies and saved all other exertion. There is a movement in America which demands twelve months' complete holiday at this critical period. The young girl is to spend the year in the country and receive special tuition, so that her studies are not completely interrupted. Obviously all these demands are more or less illusory so long as present-day conditions persist, which scarcely permit the realisation of such ideals. There are few parents who could afford the expense of the year's holiday that is required.

We must nevertheless strongly advise parents to be particularly heedful of their daughter's physical health when she reaches puberty, especially if menstruation is accompanied by any disturbance. Menstrual irregularities will take a cruel revenge if their importance is unrecognised and ignored.

An interruption of menstruation occurs in normally sexed women and in normal circumstances only during pregnancy. It may also occur as a result of a serious psychological disturbance, but that is extremely rare. Such a disturbance sometimes takes the form of a spurious pregnancy, the origin of which is a great hope or a deep fear. After a physical examination has convinced the woman of her mistake, menstruation soon resumes its normal course. In cases where the flow is said to have failed to appear for one period only, the trouble may often be ascribed to carelessness in keeping a record of the date.

Interruption of menstruation (amenorrhœa) without pregnancy was common during the world war. It was called war amenorrhœa, and both married and unmarried women fell victims to it. In recent years it has formed the subject of medical research. It appeared without definite symptoms, lasted for months, in some cases for years, and passed over without any special disturbances. It was a question of neither spurious nor actual pregnancy. The menstrual process was simply stopped by unsuitable food and various other influences. At first it was supposed to be due to the strain of war time, mental upheaval and sexual abstinence. It soon became obvious, however, that the disturbance in the genital organs was the consequence of under-nourishment. The ovaries suffered a certain degree of degeneration, which caused atrophy of the graafian follicles, followed later by a morbid shrinking of the uterus. Hence the arrest of function of the internal genital organs, and amenorrhœa. As soon as conditions permitted a better supply of proteins and fats, as well as a change of general diet, the organs resumed their normal functions and menstruation reappeared. It is interesting to note that ' war bread ' was particularly injurious; the poorly prepared and badly baked flour* contained a large amount of ergot which, after being absorbed for some time, caused actual poisoning of the female system.

Menstrual hygiene, as we have seen, is of great importance to a woman's health. Menstruation affects not only the genital organs but the entire body. Women are therefore strongly urged to rest. All unnecessary strain, physical and mental, even tiring social engagements, should be avoided during that time. It would be beter if women were to remain ' at home ' during that period, so that they could wear loose-fitting clothes and dispense with a corset or belt†.

Later on we shall deal with the question of those garments. Here we shall merely say that old-fashioned stays should be

* *Editor's Note.*—This refers to rye bread, which is largely used in Germany and certain other Continental countries.—N. H.

† *Editor's Note.*—This seems to me to be quite unnecessary in the case of normal women who wear ordinary clothing.—N. H.

entirely discarded, because during menstruation, when the breasts are sensitive and breathing is less easy, all constriction must be avoided. They were as dangerous as many another fashion which served less as a support to the back than as a means of ensuring a ' good ' figure.

During menstruation the abdomen as well as the breasts must be free from all pressure, or injury may result not only to the external but also to the internal organs. Constriction of the then clogged intestines and of the congested genital region hinders the normal course of menstruation. It is also advisable to clean the intestines one or two days before the flow with a mild laxative. This will also have the advantage of stimulating the frequently sluggish bowels. Finally, one should micturate frequently.

As regards nourishment, starchy and strongly spiced foods should be avoided, as well as liquids which tend to increase blood-pressure, like red wine and strong coffee.

The most important hygienic rule is scrupulous personal cleanliness. The old superstition that underclothes must not be changed during menstruation and that the vulva and vagina must not be washed is a hygienic heresy. One should, however, take care to avoid catching cold; sudden change of temperature may have an adverse effect on menstruation.

The best means for ensuring cleanliness and guarding against chills is the popular diaper or sanitary napkin which is held by a belt around the waist and kept directly in contact with the vulva, thereby absorbing the menstrual blood. The best kind is made of a gauze bag filled with cotton-wool or cellulose, which is burned after use.

Unfortunately this type of diaper has the disadvantage of frequently chafing the sensitive skin of the upper thigh, so that many women cannot wear it and have to substitute a home-made washable pad of rough texture. But this is by no means such a good absorbent even when filled with cotton-wool.

In olden times, women were considered unclean during the menstrual period. This is a point of view which no one to-day would uphold. And yet, when one considers the careless habits of some women during menstruation, there would seem to be a certain justification for the old belief. Scarcely anything is so repulsive as a woman who, during menstruation, is not absolutely clean. It is essential at that time that the genital parts should be washed two or three times daily with lukewarm water and soap, then dried and powdered, the latter as a protection against chafing.

Underclothes may be changed as often as desired. Clean clothes need to be well aired before being worn and dressing and undressing should be done in a warm room. The vagina may occasionally be douched with lukewarm water, and baths may be taken, but very hot or very cold baths should be avoided until after the flow has ceased.

Menstruation is the most obvious and definite sign of puberty in women, and is evidence of physical and psychological development. It is characterised by intensified activity of the genital glands, development of the breasts and of the pelvis, growth of hair in the armpits, change of voice, and sometimes even an alteration in the colour of the hair, etc. The body has the ill-proportioned appearance of which we spoke in a previous chapter, but finally develops into the marvellous harmony of the female figure. We have already had occasion to analyse the psychological crisis which characterises this period. In the girl this phenomenon is even more pronounced than in the boy.

' With the appearance of menstruation, and even before, the normal girl begins to take an interest in everything concerning love. But restraint, arbitrarily exercised over the sexual instinct, can induce pathological indifference. The normal girl falls in love at this time with anyone and everyone, and makes frequent changes in the object of her affection; now it is the teacher, man or woman, now the young or middle-aged man next door. Love letters are exchanged and they arrange their first meeting. At this time even friendship assumes a tempestuous and exalted character.' (Stekel: *Letters to a Mother*.)

It would be a mistake, however, to believe that this romantic and exalted attitude is the only manifestation on the part of the girl. Simultaneously appear inclinations less sublime. In the boy, the desire for independence is manifested by a rebellious attitude towards paternal authority. In the girl this revolt may find expression in jealousy of her mother or her older sisters. The girl is conscious of her sexual personality and begins to see rivals in her mother and sisters. She insists on being considered a woman and no longer a child.

If the mother adopts a reasonable attitude and is willing to yield her place in society without insisting on the precedence due to her age, she will succeed in mitigating the conflict and avoid inflicting pain on her daughter.

Let us devote a few words to the anatomical character of virginity, which is made the subject of so many heated disputes. The presence of the hymen or maidenhead is reputed to be the guarantee of virginity, but we wish here and now to stress the falsity of this belief.

What exactly is this membrane which has caused so many prejudices, the existence, or rather the non-existence, of which has ruined so many homes, destroyed so many lives, and which is glorified as the young woman's supreme treasure? It is a membrane situated at the entrance to the vagina, partially (and in abnormal cases completely) closing it, and is present in most girls who have not had sexual intercourse. This definition confirms what we have stated in the chapter on anatomy, i.e. that the shape of the hymen varies. The hymen may be so under-developed as to constitute no real obstacle whatever to the penetration of the vagina; on the other hand, it may completely close the orifice and cause serious disturbances such as suppression of the menses, etc. In the majority of cases the maidenhead forms a ring or semi-circle which makes the orifice smaller, the result being that the male member cannot penetrate into the vagina without tearing it. Neither for scientific nor for medico-legal examination should absence of the hymen be taken as proof of previous sexual intimacy. And there are medical and criminal records of numerous cases where, after repeated sexual intercourse, the hymen had remained intact. The relative size of the orifice and the elasticity of the membrane sometimes permit coitus without rupture, especially if the male organ is small. It sometimes happens that pregnant women have an intact hymen; this can be explained in two ways: first, that emission took place at the entrance of the vagina, and that fertilisation was effected by spermatozoa which penetrated the aperture of the hymen; secondly, that the hymen was merely distended by a normal sexual act. On the 7th of March, 1912, a German medical weekly reported a case in which the hymen was still intact after two confinements. The criminologist Wachholtz states that out of 102 cases of rape that he had been called on to examine, 70 had suffered no rupture of the hymen. The intact hymen is, therefore, no guarantee of virginity.

To this must be added the fact that mistakes are liable to be made at the examination. Even after the membrane has been ruptured, fragments remain, which, in view of the multiplicity of forms taken by the hymen, might lead one to conclude that it was intact. In some countries girls try to compensate for the ruptured hymen. For instance, in one province of France it is not unusual for women to conceal their lost virginity by placing in the vagina fish bladder filled with pigeon's blood. Nowadays, modern surgery can repair a mutilated maidenhead.

If an apparently intact hymen is not necessarily a guarantee of virginity, the absence of the membrane is no proof that a woman is not a virgin. There are cases where the hymen is defective from birth, or is so rudimentary—this is of frequent occurrence—that it does not in any way obstruct the entrance to the vagina, and the wedding night is passed without pain or loss of blood. Gymnastics, a fall with the legs apart, or carelessness in douching the genital organs can also rupture the membrane. It is, therefore, obvious that the presence or absence of the hymen is no criterion where virginity is concerned. A woman can go from one affair to another, and even indulge in debauchery, without injuring the maidenhead—as Prévost has shown in his description of the *demi-vierges*. It would be absurd to limit the definition of virginity to the actual existence of the hymen.

This opinion was expressed by Saint Cyprien. When a nun, accused of having lost her chastity, attempted to justify herself with these words: ' But one may examine me and verify the fact that I am indeed a virgin ', he replied: ' The hand and the eye of the midwife cannot give us that certainty. Even if one finds intact that part of the body where she can be dishonoured, a woman may have sinned with another part of the body which, although dishonoured, defies examination '. (From Ivan Bloch's *Prostitution*.)

The Fathers of the Church have generally recognised the fact—too often forgotten in our time—that virginity is not merely an anatomical contingency but also a psychological one. Saint Jerome has said: 'There are virgins in the flesh who are not in the spirit, whose body remains untouched but whose soul is corrupt. Only a virginity which has never been soiled by a desire, either of flesh or of the spirit, is a worthy offering to Christ'.

We see, then, what an examination for virginity amounts to. If not only the act itself but the mere thought of it is unchaste, how many virgins remain? This looks like a sophism, and it would be if one took the words literally. It would be tantamount to saying that a man who, in a fit of rage, expressed the desire to murder someone was guilty of actual murder. We must therefore distinguish between the impulse and the act itself. What we set out to show is that virginity, contrary to general belief, is not clearly marked, but that it allows room to numerous intermediate stages.

It would be equally erroneous to believe that virginity is venerated everywhere by all peoples, or was at all times. On the contrary, among some primitive peoples, virginity is an object of contempt.

'The South Sea Islanders, the Malayans and the Northern Asiatics, the natives of Madagascar and of South Africa, etc., are completely indifferent to virginity. To the Vatiacs and the Chibchas of Colombia, extinct to-day, the hymen was a mark of disgrace, for it proved in the eyes of those natives that the girl was unfit for intimacy. The Sakaval (Madagascar) girls deflorate themselves, and in Central Australia it is customary to perform a surgical operation to destroy the membrane. With the majority of primitive peoples, the girls live a free sexual life up to the time of their marriage, and are sometimes even compelled by their customs to submit to sexual intercourse. This is not considered ignominious and their sacrifice earns the respect of the tribe. From these facts it is evident that primitive peoples attach no importance whatever to virginity.

'Among more civilised people, chastity in woman is considered a primary virtue, and a man has the right to demand that his fiancée be pure. This was the case with the Egyptians, the Hebrews, the Arabs and the Greeks. Moses enforced it most rigorously. The man had the right to send the young woman back to her parents if he discovered that she was not a virgin. She was then publicly tortured to death. " She has dishonoured thee, Israel, by sinning under the roof of her father, and thou must extirpate the sin of her blood." In Egypt, it was customary among the Arabs and Copts for a matron, or even the fiancé himself, before the marriage and in the presence of witnesses, to introduce his forefinger wrapped in linen into the girl's vagina in order to obtain proof of her virginity by the appearance of blood.' (Bonn.)

The prestige of virginity, therefore, does not correspond to anything in nature but is merely a social phenomenon consequent on the development of civilisation. If we were to discuss the problem of pre-nuptial continence, to question whether or not sexual intercourse is desirable before the legal union, we should be departing from the purely scientific standpoint which guides us in this work, and taking our stand on the uncertain ground of social controversy. However, that is not our intention. While taking up a purely biological point of view, we must nevertheless stress the fact that, according to the statistics of several specialists, psychological and physiological disorders of various kinds may be induced by prolonged continence. If, therefore, our social system prohibits sexual intercourse without the sanction of marriage, and at the same time places economic difficulties in the way of marriage, the conclusion is clear. We stumble here on to one of the failures of our social system.

The remedy is not to be found in such arbitrary phrases as 'free love at any price' or 'abstinence until marriage'. These ready-made slogans are much too superficial. So long as contradictions exist between biological exigencies and the demands of present-day civilisation, the solution of the problem will rest with the conscience of the individual, and depend on her sense of responsibility towards herself, her partner, and her children.

CHAPTER IX

FROM ADOLESCENCE TO MANHOOD

Changes in behaviour and appearance of boy at time of puberty.
Psychological difficulties. Hero-worship. First experience of erection.
The physiological explanation of erection. Erotic dreams and involun-
tary emissions. The problem of abstinence. Sexual freedom allowed
the young man but denied the young woman. Resort to prostitutes.
Effect of disgust. Separation of sexual and spiritual love.

' DEAR FRIEND,

' You will be astonished to notice the great change which
has taken place in your son. Every day he seems different,
sometimes full of exaggerated hopes and eccentric ideas
and projects, at other times gloomy, sulky and taciturn,
doubtful of his own capacities and of his own self. He
refuses to enter the room if you have guests; sometimes he
is cynical, at other times he blushes when the conversation
has some connection with the question of love. In short,
he is passing through an age of awkwardness.

' I have already told you that puberty represents a
revolution in the life of a human being, for it marks the
passage from childhood to adult life. Great things are
taking place on the physical and psychological planes. Up
to the time of puberty the child has been indifferent to
sexual matters. Now, the secondary sexual characters
begin to appear. The development of the larynx causes the
voice to break and acquire a new intonation. In man, the
voice becomes deeper, the first hairs make their appearance

on the upper lip, parts of the body become covered with hair, and, the sexual organs having reached maturity, seminal fluid is secreted.

' This great change is due to the increased activity of the genital and other important glands, the internal secretions of which are responsible for the intensification of the sexual instinct, a phenomenon observed in the physical as well as in the psychological domain.

' The attitude of the adolescent towards the female sex is ambivalent. He feels himself to be already partly a man, but by reason of his age, he is still only a child. He is therefore like the fox who said the grapes were too sour. He pretends to despise girls and the female sex in general. He shows enthusiasm only for men who accomplish great things, for the heroes of sport, and for his comrades who are further advanced in school than he is. He seems to be interested in nothing but athletic feats, and he has a smile of compassion for girls who want to behave like boys.

' But, internally, he is on fire. Despite his apparent contempt for girls, he is likely to fall in love with one, or even with a grown-up woman, whom he deifies in his first —strictly secret—poetic efforts. Usually, the love affair is unsuccessful and provides a source of inspiration for further artistic productions.

' Puberty, the time when the creative instinct awakens, is a wonderful period in the life of the adolescent, being made up of the continual ebb and flow of the inferiority complex and the mania for great things. Everything is seen from two standpoints at this time. Everything has two faces and two colours. Heaven and Hell seek to join themselves by a bridge where the mind in distress can find unity.'

This passage, taken from the work of Stekel, *Letters to a Mother*, sums up in a striking manner the state of mind of the adolescent that we have sketched in the chapter devoted to that critical phase in sexual life. Let us now examine briefly the physiological phenomena which, in the life of the young man, mark the passage from childhood to sexual maturity: erection, and seminal emissions.

Long before experiencing the torments of the budding sexual appetite, the adolescent has been acquainted with the miracle which has dominated humanity from time immemorial, and which has given rise to mystical beliefs— the palpable manifestation of virility, the male organ in erection. All through the ages the phallus has been the subject of plastic and pictorial art. From the Aztecs to the Chinese, from the magic wand found at Laugerie-Basse and dating from the oldest Magdalenian period, to the phallic reliefs of the Middle Ages, the male organ in erection has given rise to compositions of every description, and as a symbol of fertility has played a part in religious ceremonies and pagan rites. In Greece, at the time of the rural Dionysian festivities, processions were organised, in which the bearers of the phallus marched solemnly while the crowd sang phallic songs. In Rome, the emblem of virility played an equally important part in the bacchanalia and at the feasts of Venus and of Priapus. In addition, the phallus was worn as an amulet, and house fronts were often adorned with it, as a protection against evil.

It is no exaggeration to apply the word miracle to this physiological phenomenon, the nature of which remained for a long time hidden from human understanding. Let us try to explain the mechanism of that function which so often sets man's will at defiance, appearing when he does not desire it, and failing to appear when he does, thus showing itself to be independent of his reason.

In order to understand the complex process which results in erection, it is necessary to consider several factors. Let us begin with the part played by the internal secretions, the importance of which we have mentioned in the chapter on puberty.

As a result of recent scientific discoveries, it is now known that the whole sexual life of a man is dominated by the hormones that the glands of internal secretion pour into the blood. The properties of these products are still shrouded in mystery, though their power has been appreciated. Through the medium of the circulation of the blood, they carry to all parts of the body certain stimulants of a sexual nature. Their action upon the brain determines reactions in the nervous system. Borrowing a term from electricity, one may say that the genital hormones ' charge ' the brain erotically, that is to say, they make it more receptive to amorous impressions.

The sexually stimulating impressions are registered by the cerebral nerves. The brain then discharges. This phenomenon may be compared to that which takes place when the button of an electric bell is pressed: the electric current is set in motion in the one case as in the other. This stimulating current is conducted to the centre of distribution, which is probably situated in the mid-brain, and is there transformed. It then descends through the spinal cord to the region called the centre of erection, which is situated in the lumbar region. In this centre of erection, the *nervi erigentes* come into play. These lead to the cavernous bodies of the penis and provoke an influx of blood. At the same time, muscles are put into action which, following on the influx of blood, raise the member, which has become stiff.

In reality, the process is much more complicated than would appear from this schematic description. But it will not be difficult to realise that many factors play a part in this phenomenon and that psychological and glandular disturbances may impede it.

In the chapter dealing with impotence we shall see that erection is subject to disturbance by various disorders and abnormalities which may render fertilisation impossible.

It is important not to overlook the psychological factor in the mechanism of erection. External stimuli contribute to the process we have just described and intensify the activity of the glands. In the adult male, erection normally accompanies healthy amorous impressions. The sight of the beloved woman, and especially contact with her, naturally gives rise to the phenomenon. But in the adolescent youth, whose sexual energy is being accumulated but cannot be spent, erection is often produced by incidents which are only vaguely connected with sexuality. It would be wrong merely on this account to credit the young man with vice or morbid phantasy. His apparent perversion is merely the effect of gland function which is normal at that age. The following account, given by a student, of an adventure that he had at the age of sixteen, clearly shows what slight things may suffice to disturb the newly awakened senses of an adolescent boy:

'When coming home after an autumn review I suddenly caught sight of a fairly young woman, stooping down quite close to me in the grounds of the training camp, and urinating noisily. I had no other thought than to get out of sight by running as fast as I could, and then the storm broke out in the form of a seminal emission in convulsive jets. I was surprised by the colour of the secretion, which was white and strangely milky, but I soon read something on the subject and I gathered that the colour was quite normal. I was satisfied with this. I had been enriched by a new experience. I had now felt in myself a state of tension the existence of which I had never before suspected. Despite that fact, it never occurred to me to have promiscuous sexual relations.'

The first erections are soon followed by spontaneous emissions, which take place usually in the night rather than in the day. This phenomenon, which is known as pollution, is explained by the need to eliminate the accumulated secretions which would normally be ejaculated during the course of sexual intercourse. Such an involuntary emission is a kind of safety-valve for the ungratified sex urge. These involuntary emissions are repeated with astonishing regularity in young men during puberty, in some cases every two or three weeks, in others every week. In most cases they are accompanied by erotic dreams and a sudden sensation of voluptuous satisfaction. Occasionally they are preceded by masturbation, as we have had occasion to point out in the chapter dealing with that subject.

Experts have attempted to explain the connection between the physiological phenomenon of involuntary emission and these erotic dreams. Is there a relation of cause and effect, and if so, is the emission necessarily the effect of the erotic dream? As a matter of fact, the reverse may be the case. The tension of the glands may react on the seminal vesicles, and thereby set up the reflexes of erection and emission, which in their turn provoke the erotic dream. In other words, it is perhaps the physiological phenomenon that determines the psychological reaction. This question, however, has not been studied much and it is difficult to obtain precise information on the matter. In any case, the phenomenon of involuntary emission is the simplest and at the same time the most convincing proof of the need which exists in every adolescent youth of giving his genital apparatus the opportunity for activity that it demands.

The young student whom we have already quoted describes the impression made upon him by his first involuntary emissions. This is a typical case which, with slight differences, might apply to all young men:

'They were nocturnal emissions which took place first at long intervals, afterwards at shorter intervals. When the first one occurred, I was not at all afraid as I knew what to expect. But, naturally, the incident did not add to my sense of pride. On the contrary, I tried as well as I could to wash out those annoying starchy-looking stains on the bed-clothes, because I considered the whole thing disagreeable and unclean. But none of the preventive measures I took had any success.'

Female sexuality is distinguished by regular periods—demonstrated by the menstrual flow. Experts asked whether the law of periodicity does not also operate in the sexual life of the man. Observation of the animal kingdom seems to favour this hypothesis. It is true that in the human species no distinct periods of rut have been noted, but there are indications of an intensification of the sexual impulse during certain seasons, especially in spring. Certain morbid cases, it is true, have shown a recrudescence of sexual appetite at regular intervals, but for the moment this much discussed question has not been solved and the law of sexual periodicity in man is not confirmed except in special cases.

We now come to the most important problem raised during the period when the adolescent youth becomes changed into a fully grown man: the problem of continence. From the onset of puberty, which, as with women, varies with different races and in different climates, the young man is physically capable of normal sexual activity. Does this mean that from the moment the first erections appear he is to indulge in sexual intercourse? Among many primitive peoples with whom the social problem is reduced to a minimum, the question does not arise. Young men have sexual intercourse as soon as they are capable of it and as soon as they desire it, choosing as partners young girls of their own age and their own *milieu*. But this very simple solution could not be applied without modification in our society. In the eyes of our society, love represents something more than a physiological act and it would not be practical to advise an adolescent boy, whose psychological faculties are insufficiently developed, to respond freely to his impulses. Neither erections, nocturnal emissions, nor even the desire to masturbate, can be regarded as an indication of full maturity. We are not unaware of the fact that a prolonged repression of the sexual urge, which finds no opportunity of expression, in other words a long period of continence, may result in an excessive excitability which will threaten the equilibrium of the organism, both physically and morally. And it is not our intention to preach continence. We merely wish to point out the importance of adequate preparation before launching out on a normal sexual life. Now that we are aware of the harmless nature of provisional masturbation, there is no reason why the adolescent who begins to feel the need of sexual relief should be pushed into the arms of the first woman who offers herself to him.

The question of the first normal sexual relationship appears to be quite a different matter for women, as compared with men. Whereas society is pleased to decree continence until marriage in the case of a girl, young men are given considerable liberty—a liberty which seems to be implied by the laws of nature. The institution of prostitution exists chiefly for the purpose of giving sexual initiation to young men. That is a statement which, as will readily be understood, gives rise to disputes. Without wishing to moralise, we cannot refrain from indicating the risks, both physical and psychological, which a young man takes when he goes to these mercenary creatures for his sexual initiation. When he resolves to copy his more daring comrades, his action may be inspired by genuine desire, but is often based rather on vanity and curiosity. At bottom, he despises street women, considers them a kind of merchandise and his adventure a form of commerce.

Lyttleton in his remarkable work sums up in the following words the attitude of the young man who frequents brothels to the women whose services he purchases:

‘ The average young man, who likes the spicy things of immorality, finds them in town and thinks that there is little chance of their coming to the ears of his mother and his sisters. He neither suppresses nor moderates his arrogance. He takes it with him, in a more or less disguised form, to the brothel, where it colours all his thoughts and acts the whole time he is with the prostitutes, embracing and caressing them, as he would a horse, in order to get from them all he can for his money.’

Amorous debaucheries with venal women usually leave an after-effect of depression, and this is especially marked in the case of women of the lowest category. Physical disgust is mingled with the fear of contagion, for young men very soon learn to appreciate this danger and to be particularly afraid of it. Dr. Liepmann, in a work on the sexuality of adolescence, quotes from the confessions of a young student, whose first experience had no other result than to disgust him profoundly:

‘ I was not always able to control myself sufficiently and one evening I followed a prostitute. . . . It was in the Elsass-strasse. At that time I was sixteen and a half years old. It was the first and the last time that I went after a woman on the street. In fact, the woman was so dirty that finally she inspired me with disgust. It was enough to make me sick. I went home and washed myself with some sublimate that my brother had given me. Nevertheless, for four weeks I trembled with fear of contagion.'

The dangers of prostitution for adolescents are twofold, physical and psychological. To the first category belong venereal diseases, for which we are reserving a special part of this work. But the danger is not entirely limited to this. Association with prostitutes sometimes leads to alcoholism, to an irregular life, and even to the use of drugs. Obviously this is not always the case, but it is the duty of adults, when they are concerned with education, to put young men on their guard against these dangers.

The dangers which threaten psychological health are those psychological wounds which venal love so often causes in those who have resource to it. Society despises prostitution, and the young man who has a tendency to identify love and prostitution, this being the only form of sexual love that he can experience, is led to despise love in general. The first experience makes an indelible impression upon him. The repulsion felt in the arms of the woman, once the ecstasy has come to an end, produces in him a form of dual sexuality: physical love and spiritual love will remain in his case for ever separated, the former appearing bestial and the latter sublime and far above sexual defilement. This is why many men cannot love a woman whom they have possessed and cannot possess a woman they love. Psychological inhibition renders them impotent before the woman they really love.

These Don Juans are unfortunate men whose insatiable desires urge them on from one woman to another; their adventures never bring them real satisfaction—that happiness which comes from the union of body and soul, and realises the full harmony of life.

Stimulating contact with girls, when prolonged without

arriving at a normal conclusion, may have injurious effects on the nervous system of a young man:

The following case of a student is quoted by Dr. Liepmann:

' I was seventeen when in May 1914 a comrade from the zoological gardens, a fellow student, renewed my acquaintance with a young girl from the Tauenzien quarter. That girl used first of all to excite me terribly and then let me down and make fun of me. She would let me kiss her on the breasts and feel all her charms with my hands, but when I wished to possess her completely, she used to laugh and tell me that my brain was upset. In a rage, I broke off all relations with her.'

It is perfectly obvious that to avoid such dangers it would be necessary to bring about a sweeping sexual reform, one which would consist in a radical revision of present-day sexual ethics, based as they are on the cult of outward appearances. It is with the hope of such a reform that we conclude this first book, in which we have followed the human being from birth to sexual maturity.

Our final words shall be the searching question formulated by Montaigne more than three centuries ago:

' Are they not themselves beasts, those who designate as bestial the act which caused them first to see the light? '

BOOK II

SEXUAL INTERCOURSE

BOOK II

CHAPTER X

LOVE

*The sexual instinct and the instinct of procreation. Procreation
frequently the result of sexual intercourse but not its aim. Independence
of the sexual instinct. Sexual gratification among primitive peoples.
Physical love and platonic love. Origin of the mistake. Platonic love
and the tendency to masturbate. Is sexual desire a sin?*

WE stated in our introduction that love is a compound of
physical and psychological elements, the harmonious co-
existence of which is alone worthy of the name of love.
Before beginning the actual study of sexual relations, we
want to clear up certain misunderstandings concerning the
aim of such relations.

There exists a very widespread misconception, according
to which the sole object of love is procreation; so that the
sexual instinct is regarded as being equivalent to the procreative one. This error is supported by the fact that the
crown of love between two human beings is the birth of a
child.

To conclude that this possible consequence is the *aim* of
love is just as mistaken as to uphold that, because life
invariably ends in death, death is the aim of life. Nietzsche
made very clear the distinction between the sexual
instinct and the wish to procreate when he wrote: ' Childbirth is a frequent result of the satisfaction of the sexual
instinct, but it is neither the aim nor even the necessary

outcome of the latter '. He goes even further and denies the existence of a primitive instinct of procreation: ' The procreative instinct is a pure myth '. Nietzsche thus expresses in a more striking way an opinion formulated before him by philosophers and naturalists, that sexual instinct serves procreation but is not its slave; it has an existence of its own and its individual aims, and seeks only its own satisfaction. Sexual union is sometimes associated with the desire for offspring, but more frequently intercourse is accompanied by a definite wish that offspring shall *not* result. Granted that the desire to procreate is innate in human beings, particularly in women and to a lesser degree in men, it generally becomes manifest later than does the sexual instinct; this alone proves the independent existence of that same instinct. Moreover, the desire to procreate is not only totally lacking in many women, and in even more men, but a child can be definitely unwanted without sexual desire being in any way decreased.

If sexual instinct were synonymous with procreative urge, the former would disappear as soon as its aim, fecundation, were reached. But we know that on the contrary sexual desire is not extinguished, and is sometimes even increased, in a pregnant woman. This contradiction is so patent that a well-known sexologist has expressed it rather crudely: ' How can you lump love and procreation together, when the question that bothers humanity is how to have intercourse without pregnancy resulting? '

There have been voices raised to say that such a differentiation between love and procreation is a regrettable sign of the degeneration of our civilisation; that in primitive times man had intercourse for the sole purpose of procreating, and that lustful desire independent of procreation is a perversion of natural instincts.

This is an obviously false conception because the very

difference between human and animal sexuality resides, not only in the selection of the mate, but above all in the fact that whereas in the animal sexual desire is only manifest during the periods of heat, in the human being desire is ever present.

'Scientists have observed that the period of rut is definitely related to that of the birth of the new generation, inasmuch as nature has so arranged it that offspring will be born at a time which is favourable to its support and development. Experiments have indeed proved that the period of rut in animals changes if they are transferred to other climes or from freedom into captivity.'

Whereas sexual instinct in animals seems to be intimately bound up with procreation, in human beings it has become independent of it. Let us remember that, as soon as they are fecundated, female animals exhibit no further sexual urge until the following period of heat. The fact that in man this instinct is not ruled by 'mating seasons' shows clearly that its significance cannot be identified with procreation. Therefore, to consider this independence of sexuality a sign of degeneracy entails considering man's emancipation from the laws of the animal world also as a sign of degeneracy. The moralists who condemn the joys of love when they are indulged in for pleasure's sake solely, and who argue that sexual relations must be limited to procreative purposes, do nothing but advocate animalism. This conscious voluptuousness derived from the conquest of love is peculiar to man, whilst instinctive and unselective coupling is a shameful beastliness and a flagrant misuse of man's wonderful gifts.

A study of primitive-peoples shows that sexual enjoyment, as an end in itself, is one of man's inborn needs. Primitive man not only performs coitus without intent to propagate, but does not even connect the two things. This ignorance is not restricted to races whose mental evolution has not yet reached the stage of logical reasoning; it has been found among certain semi-civilised people too. Originally, man no more associated coitus and childbirth than does an infant who finds that he obtains pleasure by touching his genital organs. Even comparatively advanced primitive tribes do not clearly link the two phenomena. The natives of British New Guinea believe that conception takes place through the breasts and that later the child moves down into the abdomen; the Australian aborigines believe that the fecundating spirit ' Ratapa ' introduces itself into the woman's body, and that impregnation follows the eating of certain fruits; the Queenslanders imagine that the children are inserted ready-made into the mother's entrails in the form of a snake or a bird; the Eskimos believe that children are of supernatural origin and that the man's ejaculation is only intended to feed the fœtus. There is a certain analogy between these beliefs and those of children concerning childbirth. In children, as in primitive man, the beginning of sexual evolution manifests itself exclusively in a search for pleasure; the knowledge of the relation between sexual acts and procreation comes later, and later still the desire to apply that knowledge. It is therefore proved that human love is not the slave of procreation; according to Magnus Hirschfeld, this love serves to intensify and ennoble human life in three ways:

' The more intense voluptuous emotions make man more attached to life and make the latter more worth living; love links human beings one to the other and achieves between " thee " and " me " a union which enables human society to grow into a higher organism; finally, love enables man and woman to perfect themselves morally and physically.

' In short, it can be said that sexual and love instincts are not procreative instincts, but instincts of sensual enjoyment.

The aim of love, or rather its meaning, is to intensify this enjoyment and that of life. The process of procreation follows an invisible course for a long time after coitus, and is determined by the meeting of the two germinal cells in the woman's body; these two cells are the only two which survive among the millions of similar ones which, after a brief life, disappear without having achieved their end. If love's sole goal were procreation, we might rightly wonder as to the purpose of those innumerable life-germs and of the vital and amorous energy with which man, like the whole of nature, has been endowed.'

* * *

Another frequent misconception is that which distinguishes between two kinds of love: ' base ' or ' carnal ' love and 'ideal' or 'platonic' love. In the introduction we have shown how this distinction is several centuries out of date, and that the fusion of physical and spiritual love is the hall-mark of true love, humanity's great conquest.

We have also stressed the fact that the acceptation of the expression ' platonic love ' rests on a misunderstanding; the Greek philosopher had in mind an abstract idea and not the relation between two human beings.

What exactly is understood to-day by the term platonic love? An ideal of love between a man and a woman free from all carnal desire. As we have seen, the relations, between persons of opposite sex, which do not tend toward a complete union, cannot rightly be called love. If, then, it becomes a question of friendship, it remains to be seen whether friendship between the two sexes is possible without being ' troubled ' by desire.

We do not altogether deny the existence of asexual friendship between man and woman, but in that case real friendship can easily be differentiated from one in which the lack of sexuality is only apparent; the latter form of

friendship is only a makeshift for love, deprived of its carnal elements, either unconsciously or through false modesty.

This aberration of the feelings is found mostly in young girls and women. We may say that in general every young girl goes through a period of self-deception, when she uses platonic love to prevent herself recognising her growing sexual urge, which she cannot indulge under pain of social ostracism.

In his book *Woman**, Dr. Bernhard Bauer gives an excellent analysis of this process, which may be called the genesis of self-deception:

'A sensually developed girl knows love only through books and her own feelings. She has been brought up according to the standards of her class, and her modesty compels her to repress her feeling as a matter of course This " straight " girl of irreproachable repute meets a young man whom she likes so much that her heart beats faster at sight of him. She is, however, so closely chaperoned that her conversations with him must remain strictly impersonal, while a look or a handshake are enough to stir her emotions. She is in love or very nearly so, but for the sake of convention she must look indifferent and repress her sentiments.

'But in the privacy of the night, she can give rein to her feelings and she dreams of passionate embraces; on awakening, her mind is full of love and she goes on day-dreaming.

'However deeply roused physically, however willing to surrender to her temperamental urge, and to throw down her defences, she is held back by the fear of pregnancy and disgrace; this same fear is the only curb of millions of girls and the origin of so-called platonic love.

'These unfortunate girls try desperately to find an outlet for their repressed feelings, then one day they think they

* Published by Jonathan Cape, London.

have found it: platonic love shall be the sublimation of their
desires and in its name all passion discarded; it will be their
*ersatz** for love.   But beneath this pretence the sexual
factor persists.   For the sexual factor is present whenever
men and women speak of sentiment, and particularly when
a man and a woman deliberately deny its existence and
do their utmost to ignore it.'

Platonic love is therefore a mere expedient designed to
replace, as well as it can, the real thing; and as such it is
comparable to masturbation.   Both may be conscious or
unconscious, both are outlets for emotional adolescents, and
serve, so to speak, as lightning conductors, finally degenerating into abnormalities and perversions if continued in
adult life, in preference to normal relations.

The exalted platonic love of adolescence must no more be
condemned as an unnatural tendency than its twin, masturbation; indeed, the two usually exist side by side.   But to
glorify platonic love is just as absurd as to encourage
onanism in an adult.

Spiritual love without its physical complement, or physical
love without its spiritual counterpart, is incompatible with
maturity, since the primitive instinct is no less sublime
than the spiritual element.   'Through some ineffable
mystery, the mucous membranes contain within their
obscure folds all the wealth of the infinite', Rémy de
Gourmont wrote in his *Physiology of Love.*

If sex enjoyment without spirituality is to be deplored,
the perfect harmony of both has been justly glorified by
Mantegazza: 'Voluptuousness in union with love is a virtue,
and the theologians' subtle casuistry is far more impure
than the most ardent kisses'.

The pall of hypocrisy which was threatening to blot out
love's wonderful flowers is beginning to lift; more and more,

* Substitute.

sensual love is becoming acknowledged as one of the noble manifestations of human life, instead of being branded as a bestial sin. It is encouraging to hear even clergymen like the Rev. Gustav Frenssen declare:

'Carnal love is not a sin, but, on the contrary, one of the most beautiful things in life, a gift from God, just like spring or summer breezes. Enjoy it in all happiness and peace, wish it with all your heart to those who desire it, as you would wish them the sight of the sea or the caress of an autumn wind.'

CHAPTER XI

LOVE IS NO LONGER A MYSTERY

Choice of a partner. ' Why just that one and not someone else? ' Love at first sight. The secret of the unconscious. The girl in the brown hat. The surge of love. Specific conditions.

WE have seen that the main difference between human love and animal rut is the conscious selection of a mate.

The more individualised love is, the more it has for its object a definite person instead of sex in general, the worthier it is of its name. The degrading character of prostitution does not reside so much in its venality—since our whole sexual life, whether in or out of wedlock, is inseparable from economic factors—as in its exclusively carnal character which excludes the spiritual factor altogether; it is solely a matter of sex irrespective of person.

What is now the process of selection entailed by ' falling in love ' with someone? For a long time, it was believed that this process could not be explained by reasoning, and that it belonged to metaphysics, because reason does not seem to play a primordial rôle in love, and is even sometimes very much opposed to it; even supernatural influences were supposed to be at work, particularly where love-at-first-sight is concerned. This is no poetical fiction, but actual reality; it may happen that on first meeting someone, a sort of inner voice is heard saying: ' This is the One '. Such a phenomenon seems inexplicable logically, just as it is impossible to define what exactly one loves in the loved one. That is why it was deemed impossible to give a scientific explanation of love.

Modern psychology has nevertheless succeeded in solving the enigma of this age-old mystery. ' Love's mechanism ' has not yet been illuminated in all its details, but its chief components have been isolated by science. The explanation of love-at-first-sight, the most extreme and striking example, is particularly typical and we shall therefore give it here.

Every sexually developed human being is ready for love; that is to say that he is impelled by a strong sexual instinct which may at any moment drive him irrevocably on to a definite person as the love-object, provided that this person answers his specific love-ideal. The crux of the problem lies precisely in this ideal. It rarely coincides with that which imagination pictured; as far as reason goes, it is often but a makeshift. How often a woman who has always maintained that her ideal was tall and fair has fallen in love with a short, dark man; how frequently young men who were wont to grow quite lyrical over pure maidens have become passionately attached to a cocotte! Indeed, specific love ideals are not a product of reason; their source is in the innermost depths of the human heart, where the light of consciousness never reaches. There is the seat of unconscious impulses and instincts, therein are buried long-forgotten impressions and memories which remain undisturbed until the day when they suddenly emerge. It is in those deep layers which modern psychology calls, with Freud, ' the unconscious ', that this specific love-ideal is unknowingly formed out of impressions received from the outer world; some of these, although apparently forgotten, etch on the unconscious the main features of that ideal. We shall illustrate this process by an example.

A junior clerk, let us say, happens to be sitting in the Tube beside a girl who is obviously well above his station in life, and feels for her a sudden violent longing. She is wearing a most becoming brown hat. The boy knows that she is beyond his reach and he suffers at the thought. Yet, in the scuffle of the exit, he practically forgets her—we easily forget all that is disagreeable—but that girl in the brown hat remains engraved in his unconscious, and his specific ideal henceforth will wear a brown hat.

A few years later, that same young man meets at a tea-party a number of girls, one of whom is wearing a brown hat similar to the forgotten one in the Tube; automatically he singles her out, although he does not know her any better than he does the others; he feels spontaneously drawn towards her and definitely uninterested in the others; while he cannot explain the reason of his partiality, he is conscious of a latent sympathy between them, of an invisible link—briefly, he is in love.

Thus the brown hat has started in that young man a train of thoughts and associations; it has closed the circuit of the cells in his unconscious on which the first image has remained impressed.

The foregoing shows a characteristic of love's inception in so far as its object need not be an exact replica of the unconscious ideal; in most cases, a specific likeness or attribute, ' a partial attraction ' as Magnus Hirschfeld calls it, will suffice to start the process. This partial attraction may consist in a physical quality, of laughter or voice, for instance, or in a mental idiosyncrasy; a certain outlook, disposition or humour, an oddly shaped ear, a peculiarly clipped moustache, may be instrumental in establishing the contact with the unconscious ideal, just as well as a detail of clothing, or a personal perfume or odour. All this may sound a little odd, but it has nevertheless been scientifically proved. One rarely hears a lover explain, when asked what attracted him to his beloved: ' her ear ', ' the perfume of her frock ', ' the

way she holds her cup ', or ' the way her upper lip curls
when she laughs '. Absurd as these reasons may appear,
they are actually the first link in an association of ideas
which brings forth the image hidden in the unconscious.
Our mental life is indeed ruled partly by reasoning and
partly by seemingly insignificant impressions, the meaning of
which becomes clear only in the light of forgotten memories.

We have said that when man reaches sexual maturity he
is ready for love and that this state is bound up with specific
love-ideals. It is therefore clear that potential love becomes actual as soon as an impression or partial attraction
bridges the gap between the unconscious ideal and reality.
In fact, it would be more accurate to speak of a spark rather
than of a bridge, because, as in wireless, a definite wave-
length has to be emitted to induce the corresponding reaction in a particular psychological ' aerial '.

In a later chapter we shall show how the specific ideal
plays an important part in the sexual life of frigid women,
because not only the inception of love but sexual pleasure
itself depends on it; a woman cannot reach her climax unless
her particular specific conditions are fulfilled. As regards
this, it has been observed that impressions of childhood and
parental influence are essential factors of this love-ideal.

Love-at-first-sight is, as we have said, the most striking
instance in which the unconscious intervenes to the exclusion
of all reasoning. The opposite extreme is the case of two
individuals falling in love with each other after years of
friendship; here, the sexual urge has its roots in a conscious,
deliberate selection based on common tastes and interests
and on a mutual recognition of character. The manifestations of unconscious phenomena being of an almost volcanic
nature, violent, eruptive and uncontrolled, love-at-first-
sight is practically always stormy, while ' rational love ' is
generally more dependable. (But it must be emphasised

that ' rational love ' is not to be confused with marriages of convenience; the former is actuated by the partners' human value, the latter by their bank balance.)

Between those two extreme kinds of love, there is a whole series of intermediate stages into which both enter in varying proportions. The miraculous spark between conscious and unconscious does not generally flame up until after a period of ordinary acquaintance; it is then elicited by some gesture, some vocal inflection, or perhaps by a new frock, which creates the required impression and establishes the connection with the specific ideal. One may therefore, without being paradoxical, speak of love-at-first-sight after several months of mutual acquaintance.

CHAPTER XII

SEX-APPEAL

The part played by sight. Beauty not always desired. The sex appeal of the ugly. Erotic effect of certain objects. When the eyes make love. Erotic effect of music. The tenor always a favourite among women. Love and the sense of smell. The alchemy of love. Contact and caress.

IN the preceding chapter we have studied the psychological mechanism of love's inception. We are now going to analyse briefly the impressions which direct the selection of one's mate, that is, erotogenic impressions as they reach us through our five senses; we shall classify them accordingly and review the relative sexual importance of sight, hearing, smell, taste and touch.

The text for this chapter may thus be Stendhal's definition: ' To love is to find pleasure in seeing, touching and smelling, with all the senses and as closely as possible, a lovable and loving object '.

*   *   *

Since man is a visual animal, it is natural that his sexual orientation and love selection are also determined mainly by sight. Then, as he nears the object of his desire, sight becomes less important and touch and smell more.

As regards the actual constituents of visual sexual pleasure, it would be hasty and superficial to limit their definition to that of beauty in the absolute, because the ideal of sexual beauty varies widely with time, country and individual taste. The opulent charms in which sex-appeal

[172]

lay for Rembrandt and Rubens must be reduced at least by half to satisfy sex-appeal as our modern civilisation conceives it. We are even further from sharing the æsthetic taste of the Kaffirs, whose criterion of beauty is pendulous breasts and pierced nostrils and lips ornamented with rings. Individual taste also shows certain preferences in such matters as the colour of hair and eyes, height, etc.

Even supposing that in a specified environment beauty and ugliness have absolute values, *beautiful* will not always be synonymous with *desirable,* so much so that to identify the ideal of beauty of a period with its notion of sex-appeal requires a systematic synthesis. Indeed, there are many people whose taste does not accord with accepted standards, and just as numerous are those for whom outward features do not constitute a specific amorous requirement, or who are rather attracted by ugliness, or at any rate by a type of beauty which is not to everyone's taste. There are women who only like men who wear spectacles; there are men who have a passion for drooping breasts; and hunchbacks are highly rated on the love mart. In other words, each individual has his own particular sexual ideal, which means that beauty is a matter of consciousness (inasmuch as the latter accepts the conventional notion of beauty), whereas the other erotic influences affect the individual more through his unconscious.

The relation between the impressions received through the five senses, and sexual excitation, varies therefore with individual needs. But even in cases where there is a distinct departure from the average, one should not speak of abnormal taste, because non-conformity to average is not necessarily pathological.

What now are the elements of sex-appeal most favourable to creating erotic impressions? It is noteworthy that nowadays indirect objects are often found more exciting erotically than immediate ones; thus a man is more interested in looking at a woman's breasts than at her genital organs; a lightly veiled feminine body is considered more exciting sexually than stark nakedness. Is this a sign of the decadence of our time? We cannot say. A body is always more exciting in motion than at rest, provided both harmony and rhythm be preserved. A striking example of this is the Eastern *danse du ventre,* in which the dancer's exposed body is no more stimulating erotically than the actual rhythm of the dance. All primitive dances have a definitely sexual character and seem to support the theory that every dance has an erotic origin.

It would be superfluous to stress the sexual importance of clothing. To emphasise female sexual characters and alternately to reveal and hide parts of the female body by various combinations of dress is the constant although changing aim of fashion. At one time even the male sexual organs were emphasised by the dictates of fashion—as, for instances, when close-fitting breeches were worn in which the male genitalia were contained in a kind of purse called the cod-piece. Knightly armour also included a special arrangement which drew the ladies' attention to the male sexual organs.

Besides its cut, the purpose of clothing (bride's and widow's dress, or the headgear of maidens among certain tribes) can create, through an association of ideas, sexual excitation. Also certain articles of apparel, like garters, shoes, brassières, may play an important rôle for fetichists, whose desire they may not only arouse but even satisfy. This last point will be examined more fully in the chapter on sexual aberrations.

Inanimate objects also can exercise sex-appeal by creating a strong visual impression on individuals who are particularly susceptible to such; a portrait, a photograph, a piece of statuary, can inspire love in some people. Literature has recorded more than one instance of fetichistic infatuation which cannot be considered pathological. Letters and drawings in the beloved one's hand have a distinct erotic value and can definitely reinforce the ties of love.

The part played by secondary excitants is responsible for the popularity of pornography, which we shall mention from that point of view when dealing with prostitution.

The eyes are capable not only of receiving erotic impressions, they can also provoke them. A Viennese scientist has rightly said that seductive glances are love-making with the eyes. Certain looks from a certain type of woman, with half-closed lids and a peculiar glint, can strongly excite a man sexually; conversely, women are often heard to say that a certain man has a fascinating look which drives them crazy. In medical records, we find cases in which a glance was sufficient to induce an orgasm.

Here again individual taste and specific love-ideals are the determining factors. We know, for instance, that Descartes had a passion for cross-eyed women, while more generally short-sightedness has a peculiar attraction for many men.

*   *   *

As regards hearing, we must distinguish between the sex-appeal of the human voice and the erotic influence of music. The timbre and volume of a voice, its purity or roughness, a particular accent, or even a slight defect of speech, like lisping, may influence the evolution of love, favourably or otherwise. Alexandre Dumas, the younger, relates that an actress who had come to see him heard the voice of one of his friends in the next room; she immediately stopped talking and sat listening to that voice with obvious delight, then asked Dumas to introduce his friend, with whom she fell in love at first sight—or, rather, she had already done so. This is a case of love-at-first-sight through hearing!

The erotic power of a beautiful voice is amply illustrated by the number of women who fall in love with large-bellied singers who are not particularly handsome, and are at the same time vain and egotistical. Caruso was by no means the prototype of masculine beauty, and yet his 'fan-mail' was even more bulky than that of the handsome Valentino.

Just as powerful is the influence of music, which Shakespeare called 'the food of love'; Van de Velde in his *Ideal Marriage* states that no one who is in any way susceptible to music can listen to the stormy orchestration of the second act of *Tristan and Isolde* without being deeply stirred sexually.

Besides melody, rhythm has equal if not greater importance. In all its forms, it is acknowledged by the psycho-analysts to have great sexual importance.

Everybody must have read Tolstoy's novel in which he describes Beethoven's Kreutzer Sonata. Stekel relates the following experience of one of his patients:

'When I was a student, I used to play the Kreutzer Sonata with a very passionate woman; she always became very excited any time we played, but this sonata had a particularly strong effect on her. After reading Tolstoy's novel, we again played the Kreutzer Sonata, and after the third movement she was like a Bacchante.'

*　　　*　　　*

The part of taste in sexual life is directly connected with kissing; the 'sweetness' of the lips, the sucking of the partner's lips and tongue, and the flavour of his or her saliva have a definite erotic action. The same applies to kissing the other parts of the body, but here it is difficult to separate taste from smell; the latter is much more important and we shall examine it more closely.

In the animal world, sex is dominated by smell; dogs illustrate this very well; their mutual sniffing is the counterpart of the human exchange of glances. Scientists assert that sight replaced smell when man ' got up on his hind legs ', and thus extended his field of vision; the sense of smell in man has been degenerating ever since, but in love it has nevertheless remained an important although underrated factor. There is every reason to believe that the Eastern practice of nose-rubbing corresponds to the sniffing of animals.

An odour can be either attractive or repellent, but what is repellent to one may be attractive to another; the shades are numerous and subtle, and we must limit ourselves to accepted averages.

Among repellent odours, that of a diseased stomach or of decayed teeth (halitosis) is particularly unpleasant; it is actually set down in the Koran as a valid cause for divorce. A nicotine-laden breath is offensive to some women and attractive to others ('he has such a mannish smell'); men more rarely appreciate the smell of tobacco in a woman, which is explained by the fact that originally the use of tobacco was an exclusively male habit. As an instance of love's capriciousness in this connection, we may recall Stekel's woman patient who enjoyed intercourse with her husband only when he smelt strongly of beer; yet an alcoholic breath is usually obnoxious.

The odour, taste, and degree of acridity of perspiration may exert a great influence in love relations. Mediæval and even contemporary beliefs attribute aphrodisiac properties to handkerchiefs and articles of apparel saturated with perspiration (*vide The Alchemy of Love*). Tyrolean peasants are in the habit of holding a handkerchief under their armpit while dancing and of giving it afterwards to an unyielding sweetheart; popular superstition asserts that this is an infallible way of conquering a girl.

And there is a legend which tells how, during the wedding festivities of the King of Navarre and Marguerite of Valois, the Prince of Anjou (the future Henry III) fell desperately in love with Marie of Cleves. He went to one of the palace rooms for a few moments' rest after dancing; in that same room the lovely Marie of Cleves, then engaged to the Prince de Condé, had just taken off her sweat-soaked chemise and put on a fresh one; the Prince of Anjou happened to mop his brow with the cast-off garment, and there and then fell in love with the wearer. Love-at-first-sight became this time ' love-at-first-smell '!

Binet has recorded the case of one of his students who was one day sitting in a public garden engrossed in a book; he suddenly found himself so stirred sexually that he actually had an erection; looking up, he saw sitting next to him on the same bench a red-haired woman with a strong but attractive body-odour which he realised was the cause of his emotional disturbance. Apparently this lady's odour corresponded to a specific susceptibility in the young man. This shows the unconscious character of erotic reactions.

The specific odour of menstrual blood repels practically everyone, although there are a number of exceptions to this rule. There are also persons who are sexually attracted by the smell of urine or fæces.

The special odour of the genital organs, which is the most powerful sexual stimulant for animals, has its effect on man also, but to a lesser degree. This odour is quite specific in both sexes and definitely individual as regards quality and pungency.

Provided it is not too strong, it has a stimulating influence on a normally susceptible member of the opposite sex. As a consequence of our customs, this influence cannot be exercised unless the two parties have reached an already advanced stage of intimacy. If mixed in any way with other odours due to lack of cleanliness or abnormal secretions, sexual emanations become most repulsive.*

The genital odour is more marked in women than in men, and becomes intensified with desire, which causes secretion from the vestibular glands; in some women, all the bodily secretions are activated by sexual stimulation and the resulting body-odour constitutes their strongest attraction for some men. The same remarks apply to man's semen, the effect of which on woman is variable but always connected with sexual excitement.

Besides natural odours there are also vegetable and animal scents which man has used since time immemorial for erotic purposes and which have given rise to the perfume industry. In our chapter on ' The Alchemy of Love ' we shall discuss in greater detail the aphrodisiac use of scents and unguents, but we may remark here that their use is twofold: they conceal unpleasant odours, and arouse desire by their action on the olfactory nerves. To conclude this outline of the part played in love by smell, we shall quote the words of the greatest love expert; Giacomo Casanova thus expressed himself in regard to kissing: ' Is it not every lover's ardent desire to inhale part of the beloved? '

*   *   *

We now come to the fifth sense, touch. It is the last move in the game of love and the most important one. Van de Velde distinguishes two kinds of sexual touch, the active and the passive (caressing and being caressed) ; active touch resides in the tips of the fingers and the tongue, and in the

* See *Man and Woman in Marriage*, by Dr. Evans. London: The Bodley Head.

hands and feet; passive touch spreads all over the body. The lips take part in both active and passive touch.

Active touch is merely a sort of reconnoitring of the loved one's body and is important where the selection of a partner is concerned, when it is limited to harmless contacts like shaking or kissing hands, walking arm-in-arm, etc. As we know, those ' innocent contacts ' are enough to rouse sexual desire and have an essentially sensual character. A soft or hard, smooth or rough, cold or warm hand is as important to the touch as the colour of the hair or the shape of the mouth is to the sight, perfume to the smell, and voice to the hearing. If, as we read in innumerable novels, ' a stranger's handshake sent a soft shiver all through her ', we may speak of ' love-at-first-touch '.

As regards touching the other parts of the body, the passive sensations thus created are no longer a matter of sex-appeal; they belong to actual sexual relations or, more exactly, to the prelude to intercourse. They will be dealt with in the next chapter.

CHAPTER XIII

KISSING AND OTHER LOVE-PLAY

The four stages of sexual intercourse. Flirtation and coquetry as pre-ludes to love. The three senses which are involved in kissing. The sexual kiss and the asexual kiss. The biological function of love-making. Difference in the sexual sensations of a man and those of a woman. The danger of routine. The special rôle of the female breasts. The classical advice given by Maria Theresa's doctor. The 'genital kiss'.

BEFORE going any further it may be useful to recapitulate what we have said so far.

We have seen that sexual instinct is active from birth and manifests itself in a number of varied ways within the boundaries of normality, remaining at first limited to the individual's own body (auto-erotic phase). We have followed the genesis of this phenomenon, from its more harmless manifestations in suckling babes through early childhood on to the upheaval of puberty when both sexes begin to become sexually mature. We have observed how, to the instinct of pleasure and relaxation, a new instinctive element is added, the longing for a love-object, that is for a partner of the opposite sex instead of oneself. We have described how the selection of this object from the immediate environment is made with the assistance of both physiological and psychological factors, how a sexually developed human being seeks a mate answering to his physical and mental ideal and how he falls in love. We thus come to the concrete

[181]

manifestation of that love, in other words to sexual relations.

Dr. Van de Velde mentions four stages of sexual relations: the prelude, love-play, sexual connection, and postlude. In this chapter we shall study the first two; the following chapter will deal with actual coitus and its sequel, and we shall devote a special chapter to the wedding-night. Were we to follow a chronological order, the wedding-night should come before the sexual act and its variants; but as the first coitus is a specific and complex case, we have deemed it more advisable to study first the 'everyday' procedure.

*　　*　　*

The preludes of love have been partly analysed in the previous chapter; here we shall merely complete our observations. The first symptoms of love already constitute a kind of prelude; by this we mean the more or less discreet contacts of early acquaintance and the various grades of flirtation. By flirtation we do not, however, mean the camouflaged sexual relations practised by American youth of the *demi-vierge* and ' the edge-of-the-bed seducer ' types. The boundary between prelude and love-play, always rather difficult to define, has become considerably hazier of latter years; yet instinct ought to differentiate between two such very distinct degrees of intimacy, and we shall therefore not even attempt to establish a theoretical boundary; enough to say that it is crossed from the moment when touch begins to play a predominant rôle. From a purely tentative function limited to furtive touches, hand-clasps and other such contacts, it becomes supreme as soon as lips meet for the first time. That is why we shall begin our analysis of love-play with kissing.

Many theories have been evolved by scientists concerning the possible origins of kissing. It may be a refined outcome of prehistoric sadism and anthropophagy; passing through the stage of amorous biting it may thus have become sublimated in the form of the kiss. Havelock Ellis sees in kissing a development of the sucking of the maternal breast by the baby, while other authorities associate it with the nose-rubbing of the Mongols, itself an evolution of the animal sniffing. In fact, certain mountain tribes, like the Chittagongs, do not say ' Kiss me ' but ' Smell me '; on this evidence, some scientists assert that the essential element of kissing is the inhaling of the partner's odour, and this makes of it a compound of two primary instincts, hunger and love.

However that may be, we can draw two conclusions from these various theories; first, three senses participate in a kiss, viz., touch, smell and taste; the former is the dominant element among white races; in the second place, asexual kisses have the same origin as sexual ones, the quest for pleasure. Of course, a mother's kiss on her baby's mouth causes a totally different emotion than does that of two lovers, but the fundamental motive is the same; it has indeed been proved that even a baby's sucking comes under the same head. As far as the actual lovers' kiss goes, there is no definite distinction between an affectionate and a passionate kiss; here again the dividing line is most elusive. But there is no platonic kissing, any more than there is platonic love; as Bauer has said, ' A loving kiss can never be chaste; the two things are incompatible. To love platonically and to kiss is as absurd as a hunger-striker who would carry out his purpose by becoming a vegetarian '.

Ovid in his *Art of Love* thus stressed the sexual character of kissing: ' He who has stolen a kiss and knows not how to steal the rest deserves to forfeit his advantage '. However innocent it may appear, a kiss is never asexual and always constitutes a stage between desire and possession;

even when it does not lead to actual intercourse, it is nevertheless an intermediate step between desire and its fulfilment.

The forms and the intensity of excitation of the kiss can be infinitely varied. The *Kama-Sutra* and other Eastern love-books give endless descriptions, of an almost grotesque accuracy, of osculatory variants, each with its particular name. In fact few caresses are as rich in shades and subtleties as the kiss. From the fleeting contact of closed lips to the sucking of the upper or lower lip of the partner, from the timid meeting of tongues to the deep penetration of the 'wet-kiss', there are innumerable degrees of excitation, beginning at a slight shiver and ending at an actual orgasm.

The variants multiply still more when kissing is extended from the mouth to the whole body. The transition is easy from the lips to the neck, and thence on to more intimate parts, until the last resistance is overcome. That an innocent kiss can thus develop into amorous intimacy of the most daring order, proves our contention that there is no such thing as an asexual kiss. Kisses are only more or less sensual; as the Italian proverb puts it, if somewhat crudely: *Donna baciata, mezza chiavata.*

This continuity in the scale of kisses leads us from the prelude to the love-play that immediately precedes the sexual act. Any attempt at limiting amorous manifestations is, as Dr. Hirschfeld says, like trying to prevent a stone from falling, light from dispelling darkness, clouds from changing into rain.

Let us remember that it is not sensuality that is sinful, but rather the contempt of the gifts of nature; we should therefore keep in mind Balzac's dictum:

' To grasp quickly the subtleties of pleasure, to develop them, to give them a new style and an original expression, therein lies a husband's genius.

' Between two beings who are not in love, this genius is lasciviousness, but caresses over which love presides are never lascivious.'

*　　*　　*

A fact which should be taken into consideration more than it usually is, is that love-play, i.e. caressing of all the erotogenic zones, including the genitalia, is no less important an element of the sexual life than is the sexual act itself. To do full justice to love-play, outside of the pleasure which it affords, its physiological import must not be neglected. Its function is twofold; first of all it helps to diminish the inequalities between the sexual sensations of the man and the woman, which hampers their simultaneous orgasm and often precludes it. It is a well-known fact that a woman usually needs more time to reach her climax; if this is ignored, she remains unsatisfied after the man has had his orgasm. It is not only a question of time, but also of the woman's unpreparedness at the beginning of connection.

To make the foregoing clearer, we may compare it to the joint ascent by a man and a woman of a mountain, the top of which corresponds to her orgasm and his emission. In the one case the man and the woman start on their ascent from the same level, but the woman walks more slowly, so that by the time she reaches the top, the man has already been descending for some time; in the other case, they both go at the same pace, but the woman starts from a lower level and therefore again reaches the top after the man.

In both cases, the matter can be arranged if the man, before starting the ascent, gives his partner a suitable start by means of appropriate love-play; she will then start ahead of him and they may thus reach the top simultaneously.

This is the first purpose of love-play. If however the woman reaches the top first, there is no harm done, as the man can always follow her, whereas the opposite is disastrous because the man may not then be able to help the woman to reach her climax.

The second function of love-play is perhaps even more important. It proves not only that such fore-play is not sinful or depraved, but also that nature itself requires it to facilitate reproduction. Every layman knows that the sexual act is practically impossible if both partners are not sufficiently roused. To bring them to the proper pitch is the aim of love-play. In the woman it stimulates the glandular secretions which lubricate the vulva and the vagina, thus facilitating intromission. In the man love-play provokes erection and urethral secretions which also act as a lubricant.

Without erection coition is not possible, and without the aforesaid secretions in both partners, there is a definite danger of damaging the female organs at the time of penetration.

Love-play is therefore not an invention of vicious or degenerate people, but a physiological necessity, and we must no more hesitate to discuss it than we do other manifestations of the sexual life. If there are any readers who seek sexual excitement, instead of useful information, in this book, they will be disappointed. Most physicians have met patients who come to the consulting-room rather in the search for new sensations than for medical advice, but the risk of this cannot make us hesitate to fulfill our task of enlightening sensible men and women who need guidance on sexual matters, and who feel somewhat at a loss in a world which still is too much under the sway of hypocrisy.

*   *   *

It is well known that there are certain parts of the body, called erotogenic zones, which are particularly sensitive to caresses and kisses, but the degree of sensitivity varies greatly in each individual; some people are generally more susceptible to caresses than others, and in everyone some parts are more particularly sensitive than others. The erotogenic zones are found principally around the natural openings, the mouth, the ears, the eyes, to which must be added the nape of the neck, the arm-pits and the breasts (particularly in women), the thighs, the hips and the lumbar region of the spine (especially in men), together with the hollow of the knees, the navel, the genital parts and the anal region.

It is the existence of individual differences which makes the greatest tact and discrimination necessary.

Once a man knows his partner, he can arouse her by caresses as non-committal as a kiss behind the ear or passing his hand through her hair. But, however effective, caresses must never become a matter of routine, as their psychological effect may then take the form of some such mental reservation as ' Now he is beginning his repertoire again '. It may also happen that the erotogenic zones lie in hitherto untouched parts, so that caresses call up a re-action the opposite to that desired; the partner may then become exasperated to such an extent that even if the true erotogenic zones are found they fail to react. This applies particularly to the genital parts during the first hours of intimacy of a newly married couple; extreme delicacy is then needed, as well as great self-control, although the indulgence and understanding of the other partner is equally indispensable.

Some men, for instance, do not like their face touched but dare not say so for fear of hurting their wife's feelings; they would prefer to have caresses on the nape of their neck, where the hair grows, their armpits or the palms of their hands. Kisses and caresses on the eyes and the surrounding parts are appreciated by some and not by others. Sensitiveness varies not only according to the part of the body but also according to the nature of the caress; a light touch is preferred by most people, although some enjoy hard pressure. Caresses can be performed in different rhythms, while kisses on the body can be shaded from mere contact of the lips to suction or actual biting, always according to the taste of the individual. Oriental manuals of love give long descriptions of erotic biting, but making allowance for individual differences such arbitrary classification is out of place, if not absurd.

The one principle applicable to all amorous practices is ' do only that which pleases your partner '; any caress that results in one-sided pleasure savours of rape and renders the partner incapable of abandonment. It may happen that one of the partners finds a caress unpleasant or even painful but does not mention it because of false modesty; it is necessary therefore to be very gentle, particularly in touching certain regions, like the genital organs of both sexes and, to a lesser degree, the breasts, where violent pressure frequently produces a pleasurable sensation.

The feminine breasts, especially the nipples and the surrounding parts, have a special rôle in love-play. The relation existing between the nipples and the uterus is well known. Every mother has experienced the uterine contractions that for a few days after birth are caused by the sucking of her baby. Gynæcologists usually advise women to avoid any friction of the nipples during the last months of pregnancy, lest it induce premature labour.

This correlation, which has always struck observers, led the mediæval anatomists, who did not know the function of the spinal cord, to suppose that there was a direct connection between the nipples and the genital organs; Leonardo da Vinci was particularly interested in this phenomenon and a pen-drawing of his, which represents a couple in the act of copulating, shows the connection clearly.

Here again sensitiveness varies with each individual.

Not every woman likes having her nipples touched, some even find it painful. Sensitiveness in the nipple and areola also varies at the monthly period.

The ultimate object of all love-play is the genital parts. The man's testes are extremely sensitive and any rough contact is painful. Although some men are greatly excited by a comparatively violent caress on the scrotum, in the majority of cases even a slight touch may cause lasting discomfort. The most voluptuous caress for a man is a light touch of the fingers beginning at the posterior part of the scrotum, proceeding around the testes and along the penis to the glans.

Caresses on the genital parts themselves are very effective if accompanied by touches on other erotogenic zones, more particularly on a certain region of the spine; progressive pressure on that region has a stimulating action on the genitalia and if skilfully applied is said to give enormous pleasure to a man. The area surrounding the glans is also very excitable.

The matter is much more complicated in a woman, for in her the erotogenic zones vary even in the genital parts. Feminine taste, especially if masturbation has been practised, can be so diverse that any generalisation would inevitably miss the mark. It remains with the man to find those centres by an intuitive and tactful exploration. It can, however, be taken for granted that in the great majority of women the most sensitive part during the first stage of excitation is the clitoris. In this connection, we may quote the classical advice given to Maria Theresa of Austria by her physician: *Praeterea sentio vulvam Sacratissimae Majestatis ante coitum diutius esse titillandam* (I would further advise that Your Most Sacred Majesty's vulva be titillated for a considerable time before coitus).

This piece of advice reminds me of the necessity of lubricating the female genital organs in order to assist penetration. The caress known as ' the genital kiss ' has undoubtedly the same purpose.

It would be wrong to consider this caress as an unnatural perversion. Animals and primitives practise it, and as regards the civilised world we again refer to Balzac's aphorism that ' caresses over which love presides can never be vicious '. This opinion is supported by Van de Velde, who maintains that a kiss on the most intimate parts of the beloved is in no way reprehensible either from an ethical, æsthetic or hygienic point of view, provided the partners are healthy and clean.*

The genital kiss is, however, subject to one essential condition: the man must proceed with the utmost delicacy and tact.

This caress is particularly indicated to rouse women whose sexual reactions are sluggish through lack of experience.

It is a different matter where conjugal life of long standing has established harmony and mutual co-operation in love-play.

At such an advanced stage of sexual relations, it is the tendencies, temperament, capacity and psychological make-up of the two partners that decide the limits of love-play and of the kisses (one-sided, alternate, or simultaneous).

In every game, the expert is forever trying to vary and perfect it and never misses an opportunity of doing so. It must not be otherwise in the most sublime and subtle of all games.

*   *   *

This chapter may be found a little too short by some of our readers, especially by those who, faced with their wife's

* Van de Velde: *Ideal Marriage*, Covici-Friede, N. Y.

frigidity, expected a choice of *modus operandi*. This will be dealt with in a special chapter.

Besides, one can learn technique, but never feeling, and feeling is the main factor, for the art of giving pleasure is the art of love and of devotion; without love the most perfect technique is worthless and becomes merely a soulless artifice; lovers can do no wrong because they are not on earth, but in Heaven, and in Heaven nothing is wrong.

CHAPTER XIV

THE SEXUAL ACT

Appeal to the goodwill of the reader. Attitude of the Church. What is permitted and what is forbidden. The protection of marital happiness. Love, an unknown territory. Eugenic considerations; the hygienic point of view. How the sexual act begins. Specific conditions. Ejaculation and orgasm in the man and in the woman. The woman's difficulty in having an orgasm. Three factors decisive for a woman. How to overcome the difficulties. The relation between the orgasm and impregnation. Courageous work of Dr. Van de Velde. The perfect marriage. Positions and attitudes during coitus. The 'Carezza'. So-called love of the 'Crimean Tartars'. Frequency of sexual relations. The man falls asleep immediately after the sexual act. Epilogue.

In the preceding chapters we have studied the more delicate shades of 'love-play', and have duly emphasised their physiological importance as a prelude to the sexual act.

Now that we are about to discuss the sexual act itself, we frankly admit to feeling a certain amount of embarrassment. It is not so much a question of constraint, because we know that in writing this chapter we are fulfilling a mission, even a threefold mission, as we shall presently see; but in spite of a clear conscience, in spite of the inner prompting to do our duty by our readers, we find it hard to overcome our uneasiness at the anticipated outcry from all those to whom anything concerning sex means lasciviousness and filth.

As we have no wish to cast doubts on the good faith of those people, we shall spare no pains to make our position

[192]

clear. We are thinking here chiefly of those men of good-will whose disparaging attitude towards sex is due to certain religious inhibitions. There is no doubt that they are victims of a misinterpretation of religious teaching.

If they and their insufficiently enlightened theologians would only study the writings of the Fathers of the Church and their commentators, as well as those of the Christian moralists, they would learn:

1. That whereas all sexual contact between unmarried men and women, even though they be betrothed, is a sin,

2. No sexual intercourse, however daring, between wedded couples is sinful,

3. Nor is any form of sexual activity, whether procreative or contraceptive.

The Church apparently has no wish to concern itself with the *modus operandi* of conjugal love or to prohibit the enjoyment of that which has been found to be such an important physiological factor. For this reason, we do not think that the description and analysis of this phenomenon should be condemned, or that anybody wishing to educate himself should be blamed for reading suitable literature.

The truly religious man will realise that honest sexuality is a wonderful gift from the Creator; to look upon that gift as impure instead of accepting it gratefully is, to say the least, impious, and makes of religion a mere cloak for spiritual deficiency.

*   *   *

We also wish clearly to define our standpoint for the benefit of those who, being afflicted by prudishness as a result of a false sexual education, are so hypersensitive that the mere mention of sex makes them self-conscious. Those people are unfortunately more numerous than might be imagined.

Provided they are honest with themselves, we shall easily

come to an understanding which will help them to overcome their inhibitions. It should be sufficient to explain to them the three considerations which have impelled us to devote this chapter to the sexual act, namely (1) the desire to increase married happiness, (2) eugenic ideals, and (3) personal hygiene.

With regard to married happiness, statistics show that in every civilised country divorce has never been so frequent or general as it is to-day. Marriage being the mainstay of modern society, its widespread disruption involves not only individual happiness but also the security of our social order.

Why has modern marriage become such a frail institution, contrary to what it was twenty-five or thirty years ago? One is struck by the fact that, whereas until the beginning of this century marriages, particularly on the Continent, were mainly based on social and financial considerations, modern youth tends more and more to overlook material factors in favour of love and sexual harmony. We are glad to record this, although it inevitably follows that the stability of such unions is gravely compromised if the wife does not find in wedlock the happiness which she expects.

We must not forget that during the first quarter of this century, and still more since the war, woman has evolved more fundamentally than during all the previous centuries. The feminine type which still prevailed as late as 1900 is now fast disappearing. We are all aware of the outward signs of this radical change; women are becoming 'masculinised': cropped hair, smoking, thinning cures, hectic flirting, sports and the resulting angularity of hitherto rounded contours, are so many symptoms which cannot pass unnoticed. But this outer change is only a reflection of a deeper transformation. The fierce and often bloody fight, which man carried on for centuries past in order to secure his individual liberty, woman is waging now, and just as intensely, although with more peaceful means; her weapons are a better education, financial independence through professional work, and freedom of action. Social independence has also taught woman that marriage does not imply duties only, but also privileges, one of which is the right to full sexual expression.

Contemporary literature is a true mirror of social evolution when it shows how acute is the problem of wives whose husbands, either through lack of experience or through clumsiness, disappoint their expectations.

In recent years, and principally in France, a number of novels have been published which deal with the problem of marriage. As an instance, we shall mention two which have justly met with universal success: *Belle-de-Jour* by Kessel, and *Amour, Terre Inconnue* by Martin Maurice. The latter especially goes to the roots of the problems. It is the story of a young couple who are sincerely in love with each other and whose sexual relations are what is conventionally called 'normal'. But in spite of, or perhaps because of that, the young husband is an imperfect guide in the maze of conjugal joys; he is inexperienced, and clumsy, and the refinements of physical love are to him an uncharted land.

If, therefore, we succeed through practical advice in increasing marital happiness, if we can make it secure even for those wives who are not fortunate enough to have a sufficiently experienced husband, we shall feel that we have fulfilled our mission, namely, to tighten dangerously relaxed conjugal ties.

It was with this aim in mind that we made it a point of devoting a chapter to the sexual act. Our second reason was eugenic considerations, for since part of this book deals with procreation, it would not be complete were we to omit the advice necessary to married couples who wish to exercise conscious control of conception.

From a hygienic point of view, it is equally important that a woman should know how to adapt intercourse to the various phases of her genital life (pregnancy, confinement, mild genital infections).

Such are the reasons which have inspired us to write this chapter. If we can rescue one tottering home, if we can help to the joys of maternity one woman who has been vainly longing for them, or save one woman from the harrowing worries of unwanted or undesirable childbirth, if we can teach one expectant mother how to satisfy her husband without jeopardising her own health or that of her baby, we shall have justified ourselves and proved the error of those who contend that the art of love is innate in every human being.

To those whose misguided modesty makes them avoid sexual questions, we repeat that our purpose is a righteous one and that we cannot therefore be expected to spare their susceptibilities at the expense of human happiness.

* * *

As for those who are the slaves of appearances, the pharisees and hypocrites whose cries of protest are always loudest, they are not worthy adversaries and it would be a waste of time to attempt to convince them. They are not to be persuaded by logical arguments because their mind is closed to logic; let us say it, they are to a great extent psychopaths.

The world-famous Viennese psychiatrist Freud has revealed the psychological mechanism of such people. They are usually individuals who either were formerly addicted to excessive masturbation accompanied by guilt-feelings, or have at some time indulged in real sexual crimes, or have not found sexual happiness in life and want to revenge themselves on humanity by preventing others from experiencing the joys of love. They are the people whose indignation is roused by a work of art representing a nude body, however beautiful it may be, and who are the first to cry 'pornography'; they besiege government offices with requests that nude statues and paintings be veiled or removed. It is on their account that such writers as Baudelaire and D. H. Lawrence have been branded 'improper' and their works temporarily banned.

It is characteristic of such psychopaths that the more vicious their sexual past has been, the more virulent are their protests, probably in order to smother their remorse!

Thanks to Sigmund Freud's discovery, we now understand the psychological mechanism of these poor people, and to understand is to forgive.

* * *

We have purposely defined at some length our attitude towards those who systematically object to any work dealing with sex initiation, because we hope to convince at least those among them who are of good faith. Our readers will surely approve our motives and we ask them to look upon the following essay in the same spirit; it is an honest attempt to serve an honest cause.

* * *

Properly speaking, the sexual act begins when the erect penis is introduced into the vagina. It would, however, be a mistake to think that the preliminaries which had come to an end were merely irrelevant play and that only with penetration does actual coitus begin. Nothing is more erroneous or more injurious in its consequences than this misconception and the practices which it engenders. The change from 'love-play' to connection must not be abrupt and sudden, but must be brought about by an ever-increasing tension leading to complete physical and

[197]

spiritual union. Coitus is the ultimate and most intimate love-phase and does not entail discontinuing love caresses, which on the contrary ought to be pursued more actively than ever. All the erotogenic zones of both partners participate in that union, which it would therefore be a mistake to limit solely to the genital parts. The sensorial reactions of intercourse should be felt not only in the genital organs but in every nerve and sinew of the body.

Those details are important because a sexual act without tenderness is a brutal action, primitive and unworthy of the refined sensitiveness of human beings, and also because a great many women cannot derive any satisfaction from intercourse unless it is accompanied by caresses of their erotogenic zones, which are often situated outside the vagina, e.g. in the clitoris, the hips, the breasts, etc. If therefore in the course of his caresses the man has noticed that certain of these regions give particular pleasure to his partner, he must continue to caress them in order to help her reach her climax, or even, in some cases, to make the latter possible.

In this chapter, as well as in that concerning frigidity in woman, we shall examine in detail the various aspects of feminine sensitiveness. In the meantime, since so many couples, otherwise perfectly united, end in parting through lack of physical harmony, we repeat once more that to most women coitus does not suffice unless it is accompanied by caresses on certain definite parts of the body, in other words, unless their specific amorous requirements are fulfilled.

After these generalities, we come to the description of the sexual act. It begins with the slow introduction of the penis into the vagina. When the woman is sufficiently 'ready', the latter is lubricated by secretions from the genital glands, so that penetration and friction are not painful, but on the contrary very pleasant. This is the initial phase, during which both partners have full control of their reactions. Their respective pelvic motions tend to centralise the general tension in the genital organs until it reaches a certain intensity. In normal circumstances the partners then realise that their reactions are getting beyond control; the man feels the approach of his emission and the woman yearns for deeper penetration; the climax is reached with the woman's orgasm and the man's emission.

Most laymen think that at the time of her orgasm some substance is emitted or should be emitted by the woman. Although this is not generally true, it undoubtedly occurs in a number of women. The only substance emitted, however, is the mucus which at the time of the climax is in the vestibular glands. We have seen that these glands become active under the stimulus of sexual emotion, and have also noticed the presence of mucus, which is not only very useful but even indispensable to the lubrication of the vagina and the painless introduction of the penis. This mucous secretion increases with the excitation incident to coitus, so that a certain accumulation of it in the gland ducts becomes possible. The spasmodic muscular contractions compress the distended glands and their accumulated secretions can be ejected under pressure through the excretory ducts.

Any other emission of secretion at the moment of the orgasm is possible only through the uterus. It is not improbable that the bulky mucous " plug " which some women expel after coitus is due to such spasmodic contractions. What must be remembered for practical purposes is that during the orgasm the uterus plays an active part and sucks in the seminal fluid by alternately contracting and relaxing. This supports the belief of the ancients that *uterus est animal sperma desiderans*, the uterus is an animal which desires the sperm.

These uterine contractions and the process of the feminine orgasm still require an explanation. Many men do not know for certain when their partner reaches her climax. In fact, although the orgasm manifests itself by rhythmic and spasmodic vaginal contractions, the male member does not always feel them; neither is the increase of the vaginal secretions a sure sign because the vagina is plentifully moistened from the start. It is not therefore by these physiological manifestations that the man can be informed of the woman's orgasm, but rather by her excitement, which then reaches its climax. The symptoms of this excitement have been scientifically defined: accelerated heart-beats and pulse, rise in temperature and arterial tension, dilatation of the pupils, deeper breathing, panting and moaning, sometimes little cries and spasmodic trembling. The general signs of the orgasm in a man are similar.

After satisfaction, which is perfect only when the two partners reach their climax simultaneously, or with a very short interval, comes relaxation, then drowsiness. Both are calm, tired, satisfied and replete; each feels a sweet tenderness for the other. The man relaxes more quickly than the woman; and provided that both have derived satisfaction from the act, both experience a sense of well-being and happiness, of pleasant tiredness, but not exhaustion. The much abused proverb *Post coitum omne animal triste est* (all animals feel sad after coition) applies solely to animals and to physical satisfaction derived from sheer animal lust.

Where love comes into play, that is to say, where physical and mental elements mingle harmoniously, there is no post-coital depression or exhaustion. On the contrary, it is after physical desire has been satisfied that there arises a sense of spiritual love, which is considered by all sensitive natures as the happiest state of all. But the primary condition for this is a successful sexual act. This is why we shall say a few more words on how to reach the climax after suitable preparations.

*   *   *

For the man, the process is simple. Normally, the excitation of the penis, chiefly in its forepart, is sufficient. The matter is more complex where woman is concerned. We have already mentioned her erotogenic zones, and we shall here supplement what we have said by detailing the function of the three female parts, the excitation of which can induce the orgasm. They are: the vagina, the clitoris and the uterus.

Without in any way excluding other erotogenic zones, those three organs play a predominant part in the sexual act. Some women require a simultaneous co-operation of all three in order to reach their climax, others need only that of one or two.

It is commonly believed that the vagina is the most easily excited of the feminine organs. It would be quite natural were this a fact, since it is the vagina which, during intercourse, comes into direct contact with the male member. Experience proves, however, that the vagina is not so excitable as logic would lead us to believe. This can be explained by the fact that the majority of young girls masturbate and, the entrance to the vagina being closed by the hymen, manipulations are confined mainly to the clitoris; sensation thus becomes centred there, and when later on normal sexual relations are entered on, the centre of excitability is already fixed and the vagina takes second place.

The clitoris is situated above the vaginal opening, sometimes so far above that it does not come into contact with the penis during coitus, if the latter is performed without

[201]

taking into account the woman's anatomical peculiarity. The combination of an insensitive vagina and an abnormally situated clitoris makes it difficult for a great many women to reach their climax.

Not infrequently, the most sensitive part of a woman's sexual system is the vaginal part of the uterus, but it requires extremely deep penetration during coitus to insure contact of the penis with the cervix. If the vagina is too long or the penis too short, a suitable attitude must be selected in which direct contact is replaced by seminal percussion. In this connection, we recall that, however appropriate the attitude may be, most women take a great deal longer than a man to obtain an orgasm. Once he has understood this, a husband will prolong the fore-play and pay particular attention to his wife's more susceptible parts—the clitoris and the cervix, the latter being easily detected with a little exploring.

A man ought never to proceed with connection proper before having brought his partner to the verge of her climax; simultaneous orgasms are thus rendered practically certain, a contingency which is of primary importance to conjugal happiness.

The relation between orgasm and fecundation has been discussed elsewhere, and we have described the sucking movements of the uterus, which draws in the seminal fluid and thereby facilitates the impregnation of the ovum by the spermatozoon. Owing, however, to the extreme motility of the latter, pregnancy may quite readily follow a connection during which the female has not reached an orgasm.

* * *

We have insistently dwelt on the excitability of certain parts of the female organism (vagina, clitoris, vaginal portion of the uterus), because it is closely connected with the question of attitudes during sexual intercourse.

*   *   *

Old Oriental love-manuals give variants of the sexual act by the hundred. We shall limit ourselves to those which are of a purely medical interest from the standpoint of conception and the production of the orgasm.

We can distinguish four principal positions in which the sexual act can be performed: (*a*) The woman lies on her back, (*b*) she sits astride the man, (*c*) the couple lie on their side, (*d*) the woman is arched and connection is effected from behind.

*   *   *

A. Dorsal position of the woman.—The woman lies on her back as indicated, and the man's body covers her. This attitude is the most natural one for a couple who really love each other and permits all manner of accessory stimulation; kissing, embracing, and the whole gamut of mutual caresses render it the most suitable for a close mental and physical union. The two primitive instincts, the woman's desire to surrender herself and the man's desire to possess her, are completely satisfied. This attitude shows a marked advance on the animal form of coitus, in that spiritual love here takes its place beside the physical.

We find four variations of this attitude according to the position of the woman's legs.

1. Normal.—The woman is flat on her back (cushions under her head if desired), her legs are apart and slightly bent, so as to facilitate the introduction of the penis into the vagina. Penetration cannot be very deep unless the woman's pelvis is raised by cushions placed under the loins. Excitation of the clitoris is not very great. So far as procreation is concerned, this position is neither good nor bad,

although the raising of the pelvis would favour it. Penetration not being deep, the vaginal region of the uterus remains untouched and does not receive the impact of the seminal ejection. This position is particularly suitable for women who reach their climax easily, and when the genital organs are sound it is not contra-indicated.

2. Flexed.—The woman's knees are drawn up almost to her breasts and to the man's shoulders; the lumbar region is markedly curved. The vagina is shortened by a half to three-quarters of an inch, thus allowing deep penetration. The consequent constriction of certain muscles raises the clitoris toward the penis and favours its excitation. The vaginal portion of the uterus is also reached. This position is capable of providing the woman with the maximum of enjoyment, while the deep penetration satisfies the man's virile instinct. The chances of impregnation are great, semination taking place exactly at the opening of the cervix. Contra-indications: the deep penetration with its violent repercussions may cause pain in the case of a sensitive uterus and thus interfere with the woman's climax. Lesions, ruptures and hæmorrhages may even result. To a pregnant woman this position presents risks of miscarriage, and it is distinctly dangerous after confinement.

3. Extended position.—When it is desirable to avoid deep penetration, for reasons of health (pregnancy, confinement, congestion of the vagina or of the uterus), this position is indicated. After the penis has been carefully introduced, the woman closes and straightens her legs, which are then clasped between the man's. Besides the aforementioned considerations of health, this position affords the woman great pleasure since the clitoris comes into easy contact with the penis; and the thighs being held together produce stimulation of the labia majora. Tired or half-impotent men are also helped by this attitude, for there is no risk of

the half-erected penis slipping out of the vagina. As the lower part of the penis does not come into contact with the vagina, the man's enjoyment is impaired.

4. Superextended position.—The woman sits on the edge of the bed and leans backward, propping herself on her elbows and forearms; her feet rest on the floor. The man takes his position between her legs and performs the act standing. If the bed is too low for a convenient connection, a few cushions will overcome the difficulty. This way is particularly suitable for obese people. If the woman does not recline too much, penetration is not deep and the same considerations as in No. 3 apply. The woman must be careful not to lie on her back, nor to raise her legs, as connection would then be effected as in No. 2 with the same consequences.

B. *Straddling positions.*—The characteristic feature of these attitudes is that the man is either lying or sitting down, while the woman, after connection has been established, is astride him.

5. Anterior.—The man being on his back, with his legs slightly bent, the woman sits on him and leans backward against his thighs. She can also bend over him in a kneeling attitude and rest the upper part of her body on her hands. This way is particularly advisable in cases where the man is physically exhausted, as it enables him to remain passive and allows the woman to take the active part; a partially erected penis is not apt to slip out, especially if the woman leans slightly forward. Penetration will be deepest if the woman's body makes an angle of 45 degrees with the man's. Excitation of the cervix is facilitated. Since she takes the active part, the woman can move freely to induce her climax. The position is very practical for obese couples, but has psychological disadvantages, for not only are the two bodies not in contact, but kissing and caressing are rendered

impossible. The chances of impregnation are somewhat diminished because the spermatic fluid gravitates out of the vagina.

6. Posterior.—This position differs from the previous one in so far as the woman has her back toward the man. She can either sit on her thighs or rest on her hands and knees. The latter variation is advantageous only when the man is very corpulent. Some women derive satisfaction from this position because of its visual possibilities. Penetration is very superficial, a fact which makes this attitude suitable for pregnant or recently confined women, since they can regulate penetration to suit their requirements. The clitoris and the vaginal portion of the uterus do not come into play.

7. Posterior seated position.—This is similar to the straddling anterior position, the difference being that the man sits instead of lying down. This is better done on a chair to ease the position of the legs; the woman's toes touch the ground. A close contact of both bodies is thus secured, but the attitude is somewhat tiring. The clitoris and the cervix are both excluded from contact.

8. Anterior seated position.—The same as above, only that the woman's face is turned to the man. Unless she leans far forward, penetration is very deep. This way has the advantage of leaving the man's hands free to caress the breasts and titillate the clitoris. If the woman's pelvis or the man's abdomen is very developed, penetration cannot be so deep.

9. The 'tree' position.—Certain Oriental erotic books highly recommend it. If when in position 7 the man rises to his feet, so that his hips are clasped between the woman's thighs while she holds on to his neck, we have the 'tree' position. It has the advantage of considerably increasing voluptuous sensation and of providing a contact that is

both physical and psychological. It is, however, a tiring attitude.

C. Side positions.—The couple lie on their side during intercourse.

10. Posterior.—In this the woman's back is turned toward the man—an advantage in cases of pregnancy because deep penetration is not possible. Here too the man's hands are free for the required love-play.

11. Anterior.—This position differs from the previous one in that the couple face each other. The woman opens her thighs slightly and once the penis is introduced into the vagina she squeezes it hard. The same remarks apply as in No. 3.

D. Arched positions.—The woman bends over and connection is effected from behind.

12. Standing.—The woman stands on the floor and bends over a bed or a chair. Penetration is deep and the erotogenic zones can be easily excited. The drawbacks are chiefly psychological.

13. Kneeling.—The woman kneels on the bed and rests on her elbows, or she may bend low enough to put her head on a pillow. This position is open to a number of variations and allows very deep penetration.

Two other versions of the attitudes which we have described above are called respectively the *Carezza* and *Crimean Tartar's Love*; they have found favour with a number of couples.

The *Carezza* was particularly advocated by Alice Stockham, of Chicago. From a physiological point of view, it has the drawback of eliminating the relaxation required after sexual excitement. Forgotten for a time, it is now being revived and its practice recommended; we quote below a description of it.

'Manifestations of tenderness are indulged in without

physical or mental fatigue; the caresses lead up to connection and the sexes unite quietly and closely. Once the necessary control has been acquired, the two beings are fused and reach sublime spiritual joy. This union can be accompanied by slow controlled motions, so that voluptuous thrills do not overbalance the desire for soft sensations. If there is no wish to procreate, the stormy violence of the orgasm will thus be avoided.

'If love is mutual, and if the *Carezza* is sufficiently prolonged, it affords complete satisfaction without emission or orgasm. After an hour the bodies relax, spiritual delight is increased and new horizons are revealed with the renewal of strength.'

This will show that the *Carezza* is beyond the reach of average people. Such sexual intercourse suggests a reversion to misunderstood religious ideals and would seem to entail serious repressions.*

* * *

The *Crimean Tartar's* method bears a certain resemblance to the *Carezza*, but does not exact the same extreme control, although it too consists in prolonging intercourse beyond its usual duration. 'There is', declare the adepts, 'a harmless method of attaining full voluptuous satisfaction for both parties which is devoid of the inconveniences of repeated intercourse, or of those of the esoteric *Carezza* or of the jarring strain of interrupted coitus.' This method, which the Crimean Tartars have known and practised for centuries, increases the voluptuous sensations and sense of virile power. All movements are repeated rhythmically but without haste until the man feels ejaculation to be near; he then stops, and despite the fact that emission does not occur, he experiences a sensation of inward flow. After a few minutes, he can resume his movements until he is

* *Editor's Note.*—Carezza is definitely *not* to be recommended.—N. H.

again on the verge of ejaculation, which he delays by a
new pause before repeating the process. The voluptuous
sensations of both parties are very intense and their
orgasms occur simultaneously after two or three repetitions.
The emission is particularly abundant, so that copulation
comes to a normal conclusion from both the physical and
psychological standpoint.*

*　　*　　*

A question frequently asked of physicians, and one which
we must not fail to take up briefly here, is that of the
frequency of sexual intercourse. The differences between
individuals, augmented by those of race, climate, profession,
environment and physical stamina, not to mention a great
many other factors, do not permit us to lay down any
definite rule. Extreme continence may be just as harmful as
excess, and the best plan is to follow the dictates of personal
need and desire. The difference between the requirements
of each partner must also be taken into account, but if the
couple are in harmony, spiritually as well as physically,
they will have no difficulty in adjusting themselves. When
it is the woman whose needs are greater, suitable love-play
will fill in the gaps and the quality of the relations will make
up for their infrequency.

As a reference rather than as advice, we mention below
the classic prescriptions formulated in the past. Mohammed
fixed eight days as the interval between sexual acts,
Zarathustra nine days, Solon and Socrates ten days.
Luther was more generous and allowed intercourse twice
a week. Moses did not stipulate any set interval and
merely forbade intercourse during menstruation and the
week following menstruation.

In general, however, it may be said that coitus on two

* *Editor's Note.*—If this prolongation of coitus is practised to excess,
it can have harmful results.—N. H.

successive occasions twice a week seems to be a normal
ration for a healthy couple and that the hygienic value of
this practice has been proved.

*   *   *

Up to now we have considered solely the physical aspect
of sexual relations, but we know that the first essential of
love is physical and psychological equilibrium. Although
we shall study this in detail in later chapters, we cannot
omit to mention here an all-important element of mutual
sexual satisfaction, which is generally underrated; we mean
the complete concentration of the individual during intercourse, a sort of collaboration of the mind with the body to
bring about the orgasm.

The part which worry or psychic disorder may play in
sexual life is too little known. Inhibitions, such as fear
or modesty, can prevent the complete enjoyment of sexual
intimacy; an inopportune thought, either of material
cares on the part of the man or of domestic troubles on the
part of the woman, is capable of destroying the train of
voluptuous sensations, thereby causing the man to relax
and rendering ejaculation impossible, while the woman,
though less visibly affected, experiences unpleasant and
slightly painful sensations.

But the partners must not only prevent their thoughts
from wandering; they must concentrate all their emotional
faculties, and *will* the arrival of their orgasm. External
circumstances, it is true, can exert an influence either
favourable or unfavourable, but if the psychological attraction is sufficient it will triumph over all passing troubles.
Each partner is influenced strongly by the other one. Concentration of thought, moreover, manifests itself in physical
reactions, and when it leads to a simultaneous orgasm it
creates the only truly complete union of two human beings.

*   *   *

We thus come to the fourth and last stage of sexual intercourse, which we shall call the postlude. It is fraught with dangers, not only physical, but also psychological, as for instance that of one partner falling asleep too soon after coitus is over.

Men are more prone to do this, and many women have found it difficult to accustom themselves to it. They regard it as an inexcusable lack of respect and as an animal form of satisfaction when a man, two minutes after the orgasm, turns on his back, falls asleep without even troubling to say good-night and is soon emitting resounding snores. In love manuals, the fact is usually emphasised that in the woman excitement increases more slowly and voluptuous sensations die out less quickly, so that she has not reached the state of complete physical and mental relaxation by the time the man, now quite calm, has gone to sleep. This is, of course, not an absolute rule, but a woman sometimes remains awake for some time after intercourse, and has leisure in which to brood over the small amount of satisfaction which she derived from the sexual act. Sexual excitement is often powerless to overcome sleeplessness when the latter is due to worries, mental or otherwise, such as the fear of pregnancy or of menstruation.

If, however, intercourse has been as satisfactory for the woman as for the man, her relaxation is still more marked than his, because she has made a much more strenuous effort. She wants to stretch her limbs, to rest her whole body and avoid all excitement. In short, a thoroughly satisfied woman goes to sleep as quickly and as deeply as a man.

The complaints of women who reproach the man with turning over and dozing off too quickly are, as a psychological observer has remarked, explained by the desire to pose as victims. Every other grievance against their husband is translated into ' Look at him there, asleep; all he wanted was to relieve himself. *I* can't sleep, but a lot he cares '. This is the explanation of the widespread belief that the woman needs not only fore-play but also after-play in her love-life. But a woman who reaches her climax either simultaneously with or shortly after the man, needs no more after-play than he does. She may even fall asleep immediately after her orgasm, while the man is assailed by worries. On such occasions he feels the need, after their complete union, to share his thoughts with her ... but there she is, asleep. This case occurs as frequently as the former one, but the man rarely holds it up as a grievance.

After intercourse, loving couples have a tendency to exchange a few light caresses, as a sign of their inner contentment. Let us point out in this connection that after intimacy some men and women cannot bear the slightest touch on the genital parts, however gentle it may be; the man feels only an unpleasant tickling, while the woman finds it distinctly painful; in any case, such caresses cannot revive desire. The reactions vary with individuals and even in the one individual. No rule applies here.

When two people are in the habit of going to sleep in close embrace, neither of them will think of complaining because the other falls asleep first. What is more, to have the beloved sleeping in one's arms is a wonderful feeling, only to be compared with that of clasping a contented baby.

CHAPTER XV

THE WEDDING-NIGHT

Marriage should not begin with rape. Traumas of the wedding-night. The consequences of false modesty. The rôle played by clothes on the wedding-night. Fear of revealing physical imperfections. Hypochondria and fixed ideas. Size of the male organ. The inferiority complex. Technique of defloration. Oriental recommendations. Position recommended by Van de Velde for defloration. Gradual defloration. Difficulties of defloration. Disappointments of the wedding-night and how to avoid them. The art of love requires patience.

To most men, the physical symbol of 'purity', the hymen, is the only peculiarity which distinguishes a virgin from a woman of sexual experience. To this prejudice we oppose, however paradoxical it may appear, the following postulate:

'Of all the obstacles which a virgin presents on the occasion of her first sexual intercourse, the hymen is the least important.'

In fact, the perforation of the maidenhead—which, as we have previously pointed out, is not even always necessary—is merely the tangible sign of an elaborate process, of the beginning of a decisive stage in a woman's life. In a bride's instinctive recoil from her first sexual act, the fear of physical pain (which is usually very slight) is only a secondary consideration. In most cases, the young woman is herself not clear as to the real reasons of that combination of fear and shame which has its roots in her innermost soul.

[213]

This fear is more than the anticipation of the slight physical hurt the young woman might suffer. Its importance is bound up with the deeper sources of the woman's unconscious resistance to her defloration.

Vital and fundamental changes follow when a woman enters a full sexual life. This involves a fear of consequences, responsibilities, dangers. This fear must be dealt with whether it is conscious or unconscious. And it is here that the considerate lover has the opportunity to apply the art, skill and consideration which may well shape the entire pattern of the future happiness, spiritual and sexual, of himself and his bride. The uninformed lover is apt to bungle the whole affair through misunderstanding or underestimating the woman's problem. The informed lover will understand and use tenderness and delicacy and tact. It cannot be too strongly emphasized that the most critical period of marriage is the bridal night.

' Do not begin your marriage with a rape ', Balzac wrote, and we might add ' not only should defloration not be a rape, but it ought to be the result of seduction. The husband should use his marital rights to seduce his bride, not to treat her body as he pleases '.

Advice to a young husband could be condensed into the following sentence: ' On your wedding-night, seduce your wife by all means, but do it with delicacy and consideration, keeping in mind that the least false step will make in her heart wounds that will never heal '. Such spiritual wounds due to a psychological or physical shock are called 'traumata'. Modern psychology teaches us that trauma may give rise to all sorts of morbid disorders, which are all the more difficult to cure because their origin is generally forgotten. The most frequent pathological manifestation due to a bridegroom's clumsiness is what is known as ' frigidity '. Many women who believe themselves to have been frigid from birth (though such a thing is not possible) do not realise that their inability to enjoy sexual pleasure is due to a painful impression received on their wedding-night and now buried in the unconscious. This subject will be studied in detail in the chapter on frigidity in women.

In addition to frigidity, a number of morbid symptoms and a great deal of neurotic anxiety can be attributed to some incident of the bridal night and may become so serious that only a psychologist after a long and painstaking examination, and provided he can win his patient's confidence, is capable of unearthing the cause of the trouble. This is why, we repeat, caution, tenderness and consideration are so essential on the part of the bridegroom. The marriage lines do not give the man *carte blanche* to do as he chooses; if the bride's modesty and instinctive resistance raise obstacles that are too great for him to seduce her, consummation of the marriage is better postponed for a night, for several nights, or even for weeks, until she has accustomed herself to physical contact and learned to desire actual penetration. Life is long, and here more than ever ' it pays to wait '. An approach that is too desultory may also have regrettable consequences; gentle persuasion is very necessary and a woman, even when surrendering, wishes to some extent to be conquered. But between loving conquest and ruthless invasion there is a vast difference, and it is for the man to gauge when the time is ripe to effect connection, that is, when his bride's resistance has become no more than one of the ' eternal feminine's ' many wiles.

* * *

In addition to this modesty and shame—one of the characteristics of virginity—young wives suffer also from a number of other inhibitions. Many girls brought up in an austere atmosphere of false modesty are often seized with a fear that borders on panic when, for the first time, they have to undress in the presence of a man or let themselves be undressed by him. In such a case the best course is to let the bride undress by herself and to return to the room when she is in bed; meanwhile the most elementary tact requires that the man should undress in his dressing-room or in the bath-room. After a time this reticence will disappear, especially rapidly if the love-making has been tender.

Sometimes, however, this reluctance to undress in front of the husband has an altogether different reason. Such is the case of women who have, or believe they have, an imperfect figure, ugly breasts, birth-marks or other defects. The experience of family physicians and particularly of psychologists goes to prove that such fears may develop into *idées fixes*—not only in the woman but in the man as well. Women consider their breasts their weak point; men dread being regarded as a hairy ape or of having their penis thought small. Needless to say that in nearly every case the consequences of the fear are much more serious than the defect itself. Sagging breasts do not affect married happiness nearly so much as does the mental equilibrium of the woman obsessed by the thought of them. Fear, shame, resistance, hypersensitiveness, even hysteria, may be the result of such slight imperfections and poison a human life. If her husband happens to look at her breasts she will try to guess what he thinks of them and wonder whether he is making any comparisons. If, on the contrary, he pays no attention to them, she will be no less disturbed by the thought that he is repelled and is sparing her through a sense of delicacy.

In this case as in many others, it is not the actual defect, but a form of hypochondria, which overshadows the woman's happiness. One must guard against complicating life by such inhibitions; the attraction between two human beings is rarely founded on the hope of contemplating a classical figure; the spiritual element enters into it in just as large a proportion and amply balances any possible physical disappointment.

There are of course breast, leg, or hair fetichists. It may happen that a wife loses all charm for her husband through having cut her hair short, or that she is hopelessly disillusioned on realising that her husband has a paunch which had been well disguised by his tailor's skill. But in the long run, surprises of this nature, when one accepts them sensibly, play a far less important part than one might at first imagine.

It is true there are men who will on no account marry a ' poor figure' whatever the mental attractions may be; but if they do, they will soon find that physical defects can be more than compensated for by mental assets. Plastic beauty and its erotic value are mainly a question of taste, and men are not infrequently attracted by withered breasts; sex-appeal is, as we know, subject to fashion and to the æsthetic standards of class, so that it can answer to widely divergent definitions.

*　　　*　　　*

Obviously when a woman cannot rid herself of her *idée fixe*, but is conscious of it all the time, the above considerations are of little use. Here again it is for the man, by his tact and understanding, to avoid any unpleasantness. If he sees that his wife is really afraid of showing herself naked before him, he must not insist; to do so would be just as unfortunate as to attempt to rape her. In general one should not ask one's partner to undress in front of him during the first weeks of marriage unless she shows her wish to do so.

If one of the couple has some slight physical defect the other should on no account show any surprise, as this

[217]

might wound and actually induce a sense of inferiority. If the defect is found really objectionable, a suitable opportunity must be awaited to mention it and if possible have it corrected. In any case even a joking allusion to it should be avoided, because even that can provoke in an otherwise normal individual a real trauma.

We may mention that most men are particularly sensitive where the size of their member is concerned. Misplaced vanity and the respect that surrounds sexual athleticism make most men desirous of having a large penis. But even if the penis is comparatively small, and the vagina large, there are suitable attitudes (straddling or side positions) which will compensate for the disparity; the woman can also contract the vaginal muscles—a thing which most women learn easily—or apply an astringent solution, preferably under a physician's directions to insure proper use. These three methods will largely make up for the deficiencies of nature and ensure perfect enjoyment to both partners. Barring actually pathological cases, a penis below average size is no obstacle to normal coitus; besides, we know that men possessing an unusually large penis may be more or less impotent, while very much less favoured individuals are often the most accomplished lovers.

As an instance of this actual psychosis, I shall quote the case of one of my own patients.

He was twenty years old the first time he visited a prostitute, and she laughed at him because of his small member; the same thing happened the second time he went to a brothel. His vanity was so deeply wounded that for years he abstained from all sexual relations and even gave up the idea of marrying. He then fell violently in love with a girl but dared not propose to her. One day he took her to the theatre, and after having seen her home he felt so desperately lonely that he went to a cabaret for a drink and fell an easy prey to a prostitute. No sooner was he alone with her in her room, than he realised the situation and started for the door, whereupon the woman began to question him, and he ended by confessing his obsession. 'Why,' she exclaimed, 'but your organ is no smaller than that of other men! I know many who would like to have one like it.' The young man dressed quickly and rushed to another prostitute to have her authoritative opinion! When she had confirmed her 'colleague's' verdict, his obsession left him, his outlook changed radically and he decided to marry. He is to-day the happy father of two children.

In this case it would be difficult to decide whether the penis developed later than usual or whether the first prostitute merely made fun of his inexperience; the fact remains that he spent the best years of his youth under the shadow of his obsession.

The Indian love breviary *Kama-Sutra* points out, and with good reason, that there are many women who cannot endure a large penis, while many men prefer a woman with a rather large vagina.

In conclusion, we shall again repeat that an ironical remark, whether deliberate or not, can spoil a whole life by inducing a sense of inferiority or neurotic anxiety, and must therefore at all costs be avoided.

*   *   *

After this digression we shall now return to the problem of defloration.

We have already said that it must in no case be a rape, and that the man must on the contrary apply all his tact and skill to persuade his bride to co-operate with him in the culminating act. In other words, he must by caresses and love-play stir her passion to the required pitch; on the first occasion this needs more delicate handling than later on, when her initiation will have been completed.

Granted all this, there still remains a last obstacle, the hymen.

In many cases it is either wholly lacking or hardly perceptible; we have previously remarked that it can be so constituted as to allow penetration without being broken, owing to the size of its opening or to its elasticity. The absence of bleeding during the wedding-night is therefore no proof that the bride was not a virgin; hence, the barbarous custom of both primitive and civilised peoples of making a public exhibition of those bloodstains, as an indisputable token of the bride's virtue, is not only repugnant but is moreover founded on a grievous error.

Nevertheless, defloration is normally accompanied by slight hæmorrhage and discomfort. The maidenhead may even be so resistant that its rupture causes acute pain, in which case medical advice will be necessary.

The technique of defloration requires the same fore-play as the emotional preparation of the young wife for the consummation of her marriage, because the ensuing sexual excitement stimulates the glandular secretions, which act as a lubricant and assist the penetration of the penis into the vagina with a minimum of discomfort.

Professor Metschnikoff has propounded the following interesting theory on the primitive significance of defloration:

'During the childhood of the race, boys and girls had sexual relations at a very early age, when the male organ was not fully developed; the hymen then presented no obstacle but on the contrary rather added to the enjoyment because it allowed penetration without rupture.'

There are many indications to support this theory, and

the following remark of Dr. Van de Velde must be understood in this light:

‘ The breaking of the maidenhead must be achieved by distending and not by puncturing it.’ The same authority gives much interesting advice on this subject in his *Ideal Marriage*. He thus describes the attitude which Eastern people consider most suitable to defloration:

‘ The woman should lie across the bed, the upper part of her body as low as possible, her sacrum on the edge or even a little over the edge of the bed, her legs slightly apart, her feet touching the floor; the bed must not give at the edge and must be high enough for the man to reach the woman when standing between her knees. True contact between the bodies is of course impossible; the man bends forward and rests on his hands.

‘ This method has anatomical advantages; to begin with, increased stimulation of the clitoris is ensured; then, at the moment of intromission the penis has to change its almost vertical direction for a practically horizontal one; it is thus thrust forward, as much by its own elasticity as by its prominence, towards the woman’s pubic arch, and can slip into the vagina along the anterior wall of the latter by merely distending the free edge of the hymen, which is not torn until the body of the penis penetrates. In the usual position, the rupture of the hymen is more brutal and painful because the thrust is made directly from the outside by the glans of the penis.

‘ However rational the above attitude may be, it can hardly be envisaged by our young couples! The young husband must nevertheless endeavour to introduce the penis along the anterior wall of the vagina, so that he deflorates his bride by distending the hymen instead of rupturing it. The simplest method consists in adopting the normal attitude so that penetration will take place

[221]

from above; in this way the woman's pubic arch will deflect the angle of erection and force the penis into a semi-horizontal direction.

' As the penis is forced in, as indicated above, it distends the anterior edge of the maidenhead, which finally breaks. This involves, of course, a certain amount of pain, but not more than is quite bearable in a normal case. It can be reduced to an instant's duration if the man, on feeling the obstacle to deeper penetration, reacts with a sharp thrust; if at the same time the girl does not recoil to avoid the pain, but on the contrary thrusts her pelvis forward to meet it, defloration is instantaneous and penetration complete. The ensuing hæmorrhage is very slight and stops of itself. Usually all that is necessary is to keep the thighs pressed close together so as to avoid the sore parts being touched. It is extremely rare that medical assistance is needed.'

The ' sharp thrust ', or we might say the ' *coup de grâce* ', to the hymen must be delivered with the greatest care. If the resistance is abnormally strong and the pain acute, it is advisable to postpone any further attempt until the next day. We have already stressed the fact that defloration need not necessarily be accomplished on the wedding-night. As Omar Haleby, the Oriental love expert, said, ' Thou shouldst proceed with gentleness and caution, and not try to force by violence the resistance of the closed corolla. Learn to control thy impetuous desire, and if nature made thee too powerful, hesitate not to put off till the morrow, or even the day after, thy attempt at defloration '.

Indeed, a brutal first penetration can be extremely harmful to a woman and bring in its train consequences both physiological and psychological. Cases have been known where the violent introduction of the penis caused grave lacerations of the genital parts. In contemporary medical literature, 157 such cases have been recorded by Neugebauer, and a dozen by Lothman. Therefore, although defloration is usually an ' operation ' without danger, it can nevertheless have disastrous results if performed too inconsiderately.

In this connection we quote an extract from an Englishman's autobiography related by Havelock Ellis in his book *Sexual Education*. It is a wonderful example of masculine tenderness and of love-inspired consideration during the wedding-night, rewarded by a happy conjugal life. We must note that in this case it was not only the woman who was a virgin, the man too was without sexual experience, an exceptional thing in our times:

' We were married. I had always imagined what a shock her wedding-night must be for a girl with any sensitiveness, even if she were in love. I therefore adopted an attitude of " expectation ". Our first night consisted simply in sharing the same room. We had discovered the French kiss, but it did not have the same effect on her clitoris as it did later on, whereas it caused me to have an emission. We spent several nights together, I sleeping outside the bed-clothes. Then very naïvely she finally asked me to get under them. I had taken good care to undress in the dark. From time to time our bodies touched; and then, it being full summer, we threw off the sheets. Some inborn instinct inspired me to caress and kiss her breasts and this made her quiver. I had learned from books the meaning of this symptom and I touched her " love flesh ", as Walt Whitman so beautifully expresses it. Little by little I went on exploring without hindrance from her; I found the way, instinctively my fingers took the required position, my lips touched hers, our tongues met, her whole body was shaken by tremors, she held me tight for a moment and then sighed deeply.

' I concealed my emission as best I could; neither of us dared speak and I could not say how long we remained thus.

[223]

When I again had an erection I drew her to me, lifted her thighs and explored the vestibule, into which I introduced my glans; I then began a rhythmic movement and found I could penetrate just deep enough for the foreskin to be pushed back between her compressed labiæ. We kissed again and our orgasms came simultaneously. The same thing happened on the following night. But when I tried to penetrate deeper, she recoiled as though I were hurting her. Knowing now how far I could go, I introduced just enough to induce the orgasm; but at that moment she pressed me closer and I felt something give way, though only slightly. It took a whole week, with an interval caused by menstruation, to penetrate fully without her recoiling.

' I am glad to have begotten our first child under these conditions, that is, without having forced its mother, and to have thus cemented our mutual confidence for all time.

' I am now 60, she is 61; we are still in love with each other, although I do not pretend that sexual feelings have been the predominant ones in our life.'

What follows the breaking of the maidenhead?

Usually the woman does not derive full enjoyment from her first intercourse, nor does she reach her climax. Pain, and particularly the fear of pain, shyness, and modesty, prevent the complete abandonment necessary to the orgasm; also, the man, mentally and physically tired out by the deflorating process, may not be able to control himself and ejaculation occurs almost immediately. The act thus curtailed rarely suffices to induce the woman's climax, and even if she is deeply stirred emotionally, her sensations are so blunted by the above-mentioned inhibitions that her chances of complete satisfaction from the first connection are very small.

This is the actual reason why many women, although in love with their husbands, say that they expected some‧ thing quite different and were disappointed.

Such disappointment is hardly avoidable. Exaggerated erotic phantasies in young girls are the counterpart of a false sexual morality and a hypocritical upbringing. Even if reality proves superior to phantasy, it never has the same aspect as the exalted day-dreams of these young girls. But the young woman will easily console herself for her disappointment, and willingly exchange those dreams (often accompanied by masturbation) for a loving husband's caresses; and in the end she will find reality even more attractive than fiction, provided she has the good sense not to judge by her first night and to let intimacy take its course. It is therefore advisable not to make a point of bringing about the orgasm on the first night.

Satisfaction never results from a forced attempt but comes of its own accord at its own appointed time. Mechanical irritation of the genital parts must be guarded against after they have been injured by defloration; at the most one may risk caresses in the surrounding regions if the woman is too manifestly unsatisfied.

In most cases the pleasure derived from love-play and the tenderness which accompanies the first surrender are enough to overcome the first difficulties, and the woman, full of those new sensations, will not resent her failure to reach her climax. Even if she is a little disappointed, her husband's tenderness and a delicate explanation will readily restore her serenity.

Indeed, the art of love, like every other art, requires, paradoxically enough, both patience and abandon. We shall therefore close this chapter with the following great saying:

' The fruits of love, like all fruits, become more tempting if one dallies before plucking them.' (Nicholas Chorier.)

Editor's Note.—In order to spare the bride the fear of being hurt, and the bridegroom the fear of hurting her, and both the fear of leaving embarrassing tell-tale bloodstains in a strange bed—for perhaps the majority of honeymoon 'first-nights' are spent away from home—the hymen may be dilated by a doctor beforehand. Among educated people in this country, this practice is becoming ever more common, on account of its many advantages. It not only removes the fear and embarrassment mentioned above, but, if the hymen is really difficult to dilate, it is better that the unpleasant memories connected with defloration should be attached to a stranger—the doctor—rather than to the husband. In addition, if it is done a week or more before the bridal night, the parts have time to lose their soreness before the first intercourse takes place. There is still a further advantage: after the doctor has dilated the hymen, he can, if the bride wishes it, fit her with a contraceptive appliance, and instruct her in its use, so that she is able to take contraceptive precautions even at the first intercourse. If the young couple do not wish pregnancy to occur immediately, the fear of an unwanted pregnancy may spoil the perfection of intercourse at the very beginning of marriage.

Surgical defloration is best carried out under gas and oxygen, and takes only a few minutes. It is sometimes done by snipping the hymen with the scissors, but a much better way is to dilate it gradually, by means of a set of graduated glass vaginal dilators, which are smeared with an antiseptic lubricant before insertion. If the doctor can get some idea of the thickness of the husband's erect penis it will guide him in deciding to what extent he should dilate. Of course the little operation should be carried out with strict aseptic surgical precautions.—N. H.

BOOK III

PROCREATION

BOOK III

CHAPTER XVI

THE MIRACLE OF PROCREATION

The path taken by the seminal fluid. Extra-uterine pregnancy. Development of the fertilised ovum. Development of the mother's body. Development of the embryo. Disorders of pregnancy and changes in the appearance of the woman. Physical and psychological symptoms of pregnancy. Calculation of the date of confinement. Spurious pregnancy.

WE have already seen that in the course of copulation about 200,000,000 spermatozoa reach the vagina and try to join the ovum. From the vagina they have to make their way through the cervix into the uterus, sometimes even up to the fallopian tubes to the abdominal extremity of the latter. The ovum and the spermatozoa may meet in the oviduct, where impregnation takes place; the ovum and spermatozoon are attracted to one another and their conjunction establishes fertilisation. There are several possibilities: the fertilised ovum may lodge itself in the uterus (which is normal and most frequent), on the ovary, or in one of the fallopian tubes, or even in the abdominal cavity. These three latter alternatives constitute what is called extra-uterine pregnancy, classified as ovarian, tubal and abdominal. Extra-uterine conception may endanger the expectant mother's life and manifest itself in pathological phenomena, the most serious of which is a rupture of the tube; surgical intervention is generally indicated in such cases.

In a normal pregnancy, the ovum soon establishes
contact, through the uterine mucous membrane, with the
woman's blood circulation, which supplies it with everything
that it requires for its development. The impregnated
human egg becomes large enough to be visible to the naked
eye only three days after impregnation, when it has a
diameter of .04 in.; by the seventh or eighth day, it has
reached .15 in. We see that in its first days the growth
of the embryo is extremely rapid. The rudiments of the
spine, the head and the heart are soon distinguishable,
those of the arms and legs by the end of the first month.
At that time the embryo is about .5 in. long. At the end
of the second month, it is already 1.5 in. long, but it is
still impossible to ascertain the sex, which does not become
apparent until the fourth month.

As regards the development of the mother's body, a
solid mass composed of blood-vessels forms on the wall
of the uterus, where the ovum has fastened itself. This
mass grows steadily and takes the shape of a disc about
1.25 in. thick; it is called the placenta. Throughout
gestation, one side of the placenta adheres to the inner
uterine wall, while the other side connects the fœtus with
the uterus through the umbilical blood-vessels. By this
means the fœtus is nourished and supplied with oxygen.
The tube which connects the placenta with the fœtus, and
brings to the latter the nutritive fluids which are furnished
by the mother, is called the umbilical cord, or more simply,
the cord. Many women think that if they eat a great
deal during their pregnancy, the fœtus will become so
large that delivery will be difficult. They are quite mistaken, since it is solely through the blood-vessels that the
child is nourished, and the quantity of food which the
mother takes has but a slight influence on the composition
of her blood. There is therefore no reason why a pregnant

woman should diet; barring exceptional cases, she may eat what she likes and as much of it as she wants, without danger of increasing the ultimate size of the fœtus.

Between the placenta and the fœtus, and enclosing the latter, is a membrane filled with liquid, which is called the amniotic sac.

At the end of the third or the beginning of the fourth month, the fœtus is four inches long and its sex is no longer in doubt. From that time, an analysis of the woman's blood may give the doctor certain indications as to the sex of the child*.

During the fourth month, the amniotic fluid increases considerably; the embryo is now about six inches long, begins to move about, and the hair and nails appear.

About the fifth month, the fœtus reaches ten inches in length and becomes increasingly active; the adipose tissue develops, and the fœtus loses its terrifying aspect. By the ninth month, it measures from 17 to 24 inches and in appearance is much the same as after birth. It is no exaggeration to say that during the development of the embryo a revolution takes place in the mother's organism.

It begins with facial alterations. Circles may form around the eyes, and the jaws appear more prominent in the more or less thin face; blotches may also make their appearance. The breasts swell, the nipples enlarge and become hyper-sensitive, the areola darkens. After the third month, a slight pressure on the breasts is frequently sufficient to squeeze out a few drops of milk.

The volume of the uterus naturally increases with that of the fœtus. After the third month, the woman's abdomen begins to bulge, the expanding uterus pushes upwards

* *Editor's Note.*—These analyses and their interpretation are at present only in the experimental stages, and it is too early to place any reliance on them. It is probable, however, that they will become of practical value in the near future.—N. H.

and sideways all the organs which normally fill the abdominal cavity. The intestines are compressed and their
specific movements, so important during digestion, are
hampered. It follows that constipation is, so to say, a
frequent corollary of pregnancy, and that several disorders
of digestion are apt to appear; for instance, burning
sensations in the stomach, loss of appetite, etc. The
upward pressure reduces the volume of the thorax; we
cannot go into the details of this process and its manifestations, but shall merely mention that this pressure
may cause respiratory troubles (shortness of breath)
and also disturb the circulation (varicose veins, phlebitis).
Certain renal (kidney) disorders are also noticeable,
but it has not been ascertained up to now whether
they are caused solely by disturbance of the circulation,
or by various toxins automatically secreted during pregnancy. It is, however, a fact that there is often a certain
quantity of albumen in the urine of a pregnant woman.

Many women, already worried about the distorted shape
of their body, are still more perturbed when they notice
the appearance of discoloured patches on the groins.
After delivery this pigmentation fades, but not without
leaving traces. Physicians of all times have tried to
obliterate these; hitherto, however, without success.

The sexual organs are also modified during pregnancy.
The cervix and the vagina soften and the vulva becomes
a deeper colour. In fact, those are the first conclusive
signs of pregnancy.

A woman knows that she is pregnant by the cessation
of her menstruation; this is, however, by no means an
infallible sign, because it may occur for a multitude of
other reasons, while women actually pregnant have been
known to have a slight menstrual flow at their usual period.
The indisputable signs of gestation are the heart-

beat and movements of the fœtus; but these can be diagnosed only after the fourth month. The psychological
signs of pregnancy are a change in disposition and a perversion of tastes. During the first months, many women
feel depressed and ailing, and this depression may not
disappear until they feel the movements of the fœtus, when
they know for certain the reason of their discomfort.

It is generally believed that 'quickening' starts exactly
half-way through the period of gestation and that one
can reckon the date of delivery by it. But this can only
give an approximate date and no more, as the time of
actual impregnation is not capable of being determined
unless it happened after a single copulation; even then, it
remains somewhat uncertain, as we shall see. In short, it
is very difficult, if not impossible, to forecast accurately the
date of delivery.

The usual base of reckoning is from the end of the
last menstruation. This is not an exact indication; an
appreciable period may elapse between ejaculation and
impregnation, since, under favourable conditions, the
spermatozoa can exist for several days in the genital
system of the woman. Many gynæcologists rely on a
table of reckoning to fix the day of birth; the gestation period being 280 days (ten lunar months), they add
one year, minus three months, plus seven days, to the first
day of the last menstruation. If, for instance, a woman
began menstruating for the last time on February the 2nd,
1932, one year hence would be February 2nd, 1933, minus
three months would give November 2nd, 1932, plus seven
days would point to November the 9th, 1932, for the event.

The heart-beats of the fœtus become audible toward
the fifth month and grow clearer every day; they are easily
differentiated from those of the mother, their rate being
about 140 beats per minute.

While on the subject of pregnancy, we must mention the phenomenon known as pseudo or spurious pregnancy. It may appear not only in hysterical or mentally deranged women, but also in perfectly normal subjects; the woman thinks herself pregnant but her state is purely imaginary. Such an aberration may have either physical or psychological grounds. For instance, menstruation may stop for several consecutive months for other reasons than pregnancy; if in the meantime there has been intercourse, the woman will naturally imagine herself pregnant and the physician's assurances cannot always dispel her belief. This phenomenon is particularly frequent at the time of the menopause among women who long for a child. At that period, menstruation becomes irregular, the abdomen becomes distended, and tumours often develop on the fallopian tubes or in the uterus, all of which helps to confirm their suspicions. In some cases, the nipples have been known to exude a few drops of milk, perhaps owing to stimulation of the mammary glands consequent on repeated manipulation by the woman. It is easy to imagine the joy of a woman who has vainly desired a child, and who, just as she reaches the threshold of old age, and thinks that her sexual life is at an end, finds herself to all appearances pregnant. She clings desperately to the slightest hope, to the least sign of gestation. If her physician tries to undeceive her, she refuses to believe him and goes to another one. How could she possibly believe him when she no longer menstruates, is clearly growing larger, can feel the embryo (which is in reality a tumour), and actually notices a milky discharge from her breasts?

It is not a rare occurrence for such a woman to commit suicide when she is finally faced with the truth. The doctor must act with the utmost caution and use the greatest tact in enlightening his patient.

Another cause of imaginary pregnancy is fear of a real one. Young girls or women who have been indulging in clandestine sexual relations are sometimes subject to this phenomenon. Menstruation having stopped for some reason, under-nourishment, for instance (as during the last war), to which is often added psychological factors such as remorse, the woman thinks herself pregnant; she then rushes to some quack to be relieved of the ' unwanted ', and whatever he may prescribe for her never fails to have the desired effect!

CHAPTER XVII

BOY OR GIRL?

Science and superstition. Can the mother by her mode of life influence the sex of the embryo? The sex of the child is determined at the moment of conception. Male and female spermatozoa. The race to reach the egg. Statistics, theories and experiences. The rôle played by the vaginal secretion. In Great Britain one hundred girls born as against one hundred and five boys. The work of Professor Unterberger of Koenigsberg. Influencing the sex of the offspring. Alkalinity of the vaginal canal favours the production of males.

THE question whether the expected child will be a boy or a girl interests all parents. It is the first question which the mother asks the doctor or the nurse. While it is the fervent wish of almost every father to have a son, many a mother would rather have a daughter, because a boy's upbringing is troublesome, while a daughter remains more of a companion.

The parents' social status is often an important factor. Noble families, for instance, want an heir, and so does a peasant; but in the former case it is a question of safeguarding the inheritance. Sometimes it is a matter of misplaced pride.

It is easy to understand why the question of the sex of the unborn child has always occupied the mind of the medical world. As usual, superstition has played its part alongside science, as, for example, in certain country districts where the peasants believe that in order to have a boy it is enough to have intercourse with one's boots on; in Southern France, and Italy, quacks assure the farmers that an infallible way to secure the birth of a boy is to wear one's hat during coition. In certain sections of Poland, the peasants cohabit in their Sunday clothes when they desire male progeny.

So much for superstitions. Where scientific theories are concerned, the most favoured one is that the sex of the fœtus does not develop before the third month and that until then it is bisexual. In fact, the actual sex of the child only begins to become apparent after that period, but it is fixed from the moment of conception. We emphasise this fact because some mothers have a deep-rooted belief that their mode of life (diet, exercise, etc.) can influence the child's sex; they maintain that the latter being undefined until the twelfth week of pregnancy, it is possible to influence the course of nature during that period. Over-feeding is held to be conducive to a girl, under-feeding to a boy; but the opposite doctrine is equally favoured.

Reliable statistics of a number of pregnancies, observed from a dietary standpoint, and compiled by competent scientists, have proved that the mother's regimen during the first weeks has no influence whatsoever on the sex of the embryo.

This conclusion is confirmed by the American physician Wilson, who has established that sex is determined at the moment of impregnation and depends solely on the spermatozoon and the ovum concerned.

Does it depend on one or both? The latest scientific researches tend toward the conclusion that, whereas the ovum plays next to no part in the formation of the child's sex, it is quite otherwise with the spermatozoon.

We have seen in the preceding chapter that of the

millions of spermatozoa entering the vaginal cavity at the moment of ejaculation only one fertilises the ovum, and it is that one which determines the future sex of the embryo.

Let us remember that of all those spermatozoa some are male and some are female, that all of them reach the vagina simultaneously, while a single one only is destined to reach the ovum. If in this ' egg-race ' a male spermatozoon arrives first, the future baby will be a boy; in the contrary event it will be a girl.

How could one predict the winner of this contest in which there are over 200,000,000 competitors, each of them visible only through a strong microscope, and endowed with a velocity which, toward the end of the course, is but a mere fraction of an inch per hour? Thus put, the problem is revealed in all its complexity, and so too is the considerable part played by chance.

Modern science has nevertheless succeeded in securing certain data which have a direct bearing on the question. It is now believed that the male germ is more active than the female; by more active we do not mean that it moves faster, but that it is more vigorous and can better overcome obstacles. If, therefore, extraneous circumstances (mode of living, alcohol, etc.) have an adverse effect on the process of reproduction, a male spermatozoon, being more resistant, is more likely than a female to reach the ovum.

The German scientist Blum has made interesting experiments in this connection. He made a number of male mice intoxicated and then put them with females. This resulted in the birth of 120 males to 100 females, as against 80 males to 100 females in normal circumstances. This seems to indicate that an intoxicated man is more likely to beget a boy than a girl.

Some statistics show that first-born children are more frequently male than female. As it often happens that the bridegroom goes in to his wife after having freely imbibed at the wedding feast, this seems to bear out the experiment with the mice!

This, however, does not appear to be sufficient to account for the fact that males predominate among first-born. We know, however, that the genital organs of a woman who has just lost her virginity present more obstacles to the progress of the spermatozoa, because they are narrow and obstructed by the remnants of the hymen; this would also explain why the more active male spermatozoa have a greater chance of reaching the ovum first.

Another widespread theory is that sex is determined by the difference in temperament of the couple. Some scientists have gone so far as to state that when the man is much older than the woman, he is more likely to have male issue, whereas a similarity in their ages favours female offspring. Statistics in no way support this thesis.

Breeders have noticed that sexually overtaxed male animals most often beget females, and that when in possession of their full vigour they produce males. Applied *mutatis mutandis* to man, this curious theory would imply that, in the course of a love-night, impregnation following the later intercourse would produce a boy. For this reason certain people advise the use of a contraceptive for the first sexual acts but not for the later ones. This theory is too weak to stand serious examination.

According to another theory it is the woman's nature which determines the child's sex. Although the ovum is quite sexless, some cases seem to prove the influence of the whole female sexual apparatus. This would explain why in certain families one sex clearly predominates over the other, and why this hereditary tendency is transmitted through the women.

Recent researches have led to the following possible

explanation: The rôle of the ovum being excluded, we must turn to other parts of the female organism. We know that the vagina secretes a certain acid and that this acid has a definite action on the spermatozoon, which it can harm or even completely destroy. The composition of this acid may be influenced by hereditary factors and, because of its acidity, the female germs succumb while the more vigorous male ones survive. This would be a very plausible explanation of why some families ' run to boys ', instead of girls.

*   *   *

From the foregoing it is clear that our present knowledge does not enable us to influence the sex of the child. The only positive result so far reached—though still contested —is that based on the intoxication of the male prior to intercourse. But this method can on no account be recommended because of the pernicious effects of alcohol and the subsequent accidents which it may cause.

Some physicians have attempted to change the composition of the vaginal secretion. The results are most problematical owing to the infinitesimal quantities on which they have to operate and which make it almost impossible to gauge the doses suitable to such or such a case. According to statistics, there are in Great Britain 105 boys for every 100 girls born.

It follows that each couple has about 52 per cent. chances of having a boy, and all the resources of science are helpless to alter those figures by so much as .1 per cent.

To all those who to-day wish to influence the sex of their unborn child, science can but answer in the words of Dante: ' Abandon hope . . .'

Editor's Note.—Recent work done by Professor Unterberger, of Koenigsberg, suggests that we are at last in a position to exercise some influence on the sex of the child. It was found that, in a good many cases of sterility, the vaginal secretions of the woman were too acid. As it was thought that the sterility might be caused by the acidity, efforts were made to counteract the acidity of the vaginal secretions by the application of alkaline substances just before intercourse. Among the cases in which this procedure resulted in fertilisation, a very large proportion of the offspring was found to be male. Further investigation seems to show that alkalinity of the vaginal canal favours the production of male offspring, and quite a number of specialists in many countries now advise some sort of local treatment with suitable alkaline douches or powders, if male offspring is desired. The success of this treatment varies with the substance used and the manner of its use, and it is still too early to make a final and definite statement as to the value of the treatment. But the evidence available seems to indicate that some procedure of this kind, properly carried out, is favourable to the production of males.—N. H.

CHAPTER XVIII

HYGIENE OF THE PREGNANT WOMAN

Pregnancy not an illness. Vomiting in the pregnant woman. Other disturbances. Diet during pregnancy. Clothing and hygiene of the body. Sexual intercourse during pregnancy. Effect of physical work on the pregnant woman. Dangers of overwork. Necessity of consulting a doctor.

PREGNANCY is not an illness. Every expectant mother should bear that in mind. Health means the harmonious co-operation of all the internal and external organs of the organism. When this harmony is disturbed we have illness. Pregnancy is not characterised by a lack of harmony, but by a change of harmony, in the female system. Some physicians go so far as to state that pregnancy establishes in a woman's body the very harmony that it requires for its free physiological development.

Evidently this change from normal to pregnant harmony puts a certain strain on the system, and the corresponding transformation causes all manner of discomforts, one of the most widespread of which is ' morning sickness '.

This phenomenon has given rise to a number of scientific theories, the most probable of which is that it is due to a form of intoxication. Certain products of the embryo are toxic to the woman, and as they pass into her blood they give rise to intoxication, which manifests itself in vomiting.

If not very violent, it may be considered a normal symptom of pregnancy, which can be allayed by rest and massage of the abdomen. In more serious cases the mother brings up everything she takes, however carefully selected, and a mouthful of plain water or tea is enough to start spasmodic vomiting. Increased salivation and froth at the corners of the lips are further symptoms of the acute vomiting of pregnancy. The patient grows visibly thinner, her muscles become flaccid, and if treatment fails to give relief the woman's health is seriously threatened. In extreme cases the interruption of pregnancy becomes necessary.

In about ten per cent. of pregnant women the kidneys secrete a certain quantity of albumen which is found in the urine. This is due to a special form of intoxication, doubtless consequent on organic exchanges in the embryo. The symptoms, which at first are not apparent, are a slight œdema of the genital parts, the hands, the legs and the face. Besides vomiting, there is trouble with the sight, fainting-spells and various forms of cramp; all these may have fatal results. As the external signs of this complication do not appear until a somewhat later stage of the disorder, it is essential for pregnant women to have a regular analysis of their urine made.

Among other pregnancy troubles must be mentioned varicose veins. They are due to a disturbance in the circulation of the blood, and while very frequent during pregnancy they usually disappear immediately after delivery.

Apart from a few exceptional cases, these troublesome symptoms of pregnancy usually take a mild form; this is why it is more important to devote more space to the general hygiene of the expectant mother than to her possible illnesses. Leaving, therefore, complications to the physician's care, we shall limit ourselves to routine advice.

[243]

As regards food, a pregnant woman should have a very varied diet in which mineral elements, chiefly iron and calcium, predominate. These two elements are indispensable to the formation of the child's structure: a considerable reserve of them should also be allowed to accumulate in the mother's system, as the maternal milk, which is to nourish the new-born child, is ordinarily very poor in calcium and iron. We repeat therefore that a varied diet, with a minimum of albuminoids, and consisting principally of fruits and fresh vegetables, is the appropriate one for the expectant mother and the most suitable for the development of the embryo. We must also emphasise the fact that the pregnant woman should not always indulge her thirst*, which is often very intense at this time, lest she put too great a strain on the blood circulation, which already carries a heavier burden than normally. The abuse of alcohol is most unfavourable to the development of the fœtus, as is also the exaggerated use of coffee and cigarettes.

*   *   *

As regards the bodily hygiene of the expectant mother, great attention must be paid to the care of the nipples. They should be prepared at an early stage for their future rôle, and be bathed daily with tepid water and a pure soap to prevent cracking and roughening; once or twice a week they should be rubbed with an astringent, and daily anointed with lanoline or cocoa-butter in order to make them resistant and supple at the same time. Lack of such care may make nursing very painful for the mother, and may even render an early weaning necessary.

Particular attention, too, must be given to the bowels,

Editor's Note.—This must not be taken to mean that the pregnant woman should cut down her fluid intake unduly. She should drink six glasses of water per day, in order to facilitate flushing of the kidneys, and to ensure that the motions shall not be unduly hard and dry.—N. H.

all the more so since constipation is one of the usual accompaniments of pregnancy.

Clothes should be adapted to the change in the figure. All constrictions must be avoided. It is above all important to support the heavy breasts with a well-fitting brassière, so that they do not drop. When the abdomen is particularly large, a special belt is required, to prevent the fœtus from moving into an unfavourable position as the date of delivery draws near. It must, however, be remembered that a badly fitting belt may have the opposite effect. If, for instance, it is too tight, it will press on the womb and may result in a bad presentation.

*　　　*　　　*

A much discussed question is that of sexual intercourse during pregnancy; it is difficult to answer it simply, and generalisation is impossible.

There is no doubt that the uterine contractions which accompany strenuous coitus can provoke a miscarriage. As we know, female animals avoid all contact with the male while they bear their young. This would seem to indicate that nature is opposed to sexual intimacy during pregnancy.

On the other hand, relations between human beings are much more complex and other factors must be taken into consideration.

Our civilisation is founded on monogamy, of which one of the main principles is conjugal fidelity. But if the husband is separated sexually from his wife for months, his fidelity is put to a severe strain and the most united home runs the risk of being broken up. On the other hand, it has been proved that a woman's sexual desire may increase during pregnancy. Havelock Ellis quotes in this connection a letter which he received from a mother: ' I have had only one child, but I can say that while I was bearing it my longing for intercourse was stronger than it has ever been during the rest of my life '.

In other chapters we have seen that the fear of pregnancy prevents a great many women from abandoning themselves to sexual enjoyment; once a woman is pregnant this inhibition no longer exists.

But although we have made these reservations to our initial statement, it is a fact nevertheless that coitus may be as harmful to the mother as to the child. It is well known that the mucous membrane of the genital organs become much more delicate during gestation and therefore more subject to lesions. Infections and inflammations are, then, a not infrequent result of coitus.

Let us balance the pros and the cons of sexual intimacy during pregnancy. From the woman's point of view it is not indicated because of the dangers which it presents, miscarriage being one of them. As, however, couples cannot or will not give up sexual relations for such a long time, the physician's advice can be summed up as follows: if absolutely necessary, intercourse may take place during the first six or seven months of pregnancy, provided the greatest care and hygienic precautions be observed. In the chapter on the sexual act we have described the most suitable attitudes to be adopted*.

*   *   *

* *Editor's Note.*—I definitely disagree with this view. In my experience, coitus, provided it be carried out with reasonable gentleness, has no ill-effect on the normal pregnant woman. She already has quite enough to put up with as a result of her pregnancy, and if she is to be deprived of sexual satisfaction for a period of many months as well, pregnancy will become even more unattractive than it already is. Some women, who tend to miscarry easily, may be well advised to abstain from intercourse, either only at those times when, if they had not become pregnant, their menstrual periods would have been due, or, in a very few cases, at all times during the pregnancy. But such cases are the exception, and not the rule.—N. H.

We shall now give the figures of statistics which we owe to Latourneux. This physician and scientist has recorded the weight of 732 new-born babies, and found that the children of 137 women who during pregnancy had done heavy physical work, mostly of a domestic nature, weighed on an average 3,081 grammes*. In the case of 115 women whose occupation was more or less tiring (dressmakers and milliners), and who during the last months of their pregnancy had been unable to take the necessary rest, this figure rose to 3,130†. It must be noticed that the constitution of women accustomed to heavy work is generally more robust than those of the latter type. One might have expected that their children would weigh more than those of the weaker women. If, therefore, the first lot of new-born babies weighed less than the second lot, it must be attributed to overwork on the part of their mothers during pregnancy. Latourneux compiled a comparative scale of newly-born babies of both classes whose mothers did not work during the last months; the results confirmed his thesis, since the average weight in the first class was 3,319 grammes‡, that is, half a pound more than in the case of women who worked to the last, and 3,218§ in the second class, which refers to children of mothers doing sedentary work.

In conclusion, the weight of a new-born baby whose mother performs heavy work to the end of her pregnancy is about half a pound less than that of a baby whose mother takes the necessary rest; we also see that not only heavy work but even less fatiguing work, such as that of a seamstress or milliner, also lowers the weight.

* Approximately 6 lbs. 12¾ ozs.
† Approximately 6 lbs. 14½ ozs.
‡ Approximately 7 lbs. 4¾ ozs.
§ Approximately 7 lbs. 1½ ozs.

We have given a good deal of space to these statistics because many women believe that comparatively light work, like sewing or office employment, does not affect the development of the fœtus. It has, on the contrary, been proved that any professional occupation, whether regular or occasional, influences it. To believe that the new-born baby's weight is of secondary importance would be a mistake, as the less the new-born baby weighs the less its resistance is during the first months, when it is subject to so many adverse influences.

Scientists and gynæcologists have proved by statistics that women who work a great deal during the later months of pregnancy frequently give birth prematurely, generally ten to twenty days earlier than women who take the necessary rest. To be born prematurely means to be physically inferior; hence the much larger infantile mortality rate among the working classes than among the more leisured ones.

The above considerations come within the sphere of social welfare. In this book we do not intend to discuss sexual problems from that angle.

The practical conclusion from what precedes is that every pregnant woman should, at any rate during the last two or three months before birth, avoid all fatigue. This does not mean that an hour's sewing or light manual work is harmful, but the thing to be avoided above all is regular professional work, however light it may appear.

On the other hand, overwork during the first two months is just as dangerous owing to the risk of miscarriage which it presents. This applies not only to actual work but also to any kind of strain, such as riding, dancing, jumping, long rail or motor journeys; any muscular effort, like lifting a weight or any straining to move the bowels, may displace the uterus and thereby affect the embryo. Not for an instant should an expectant mother forget that her heart has to supply two circulatory systems and is therefore constantly overworked; consequently she must avoid any additional burdens. Cases of sudden death from heart-failure are not infrequent among pregnant women.

One must, however, not conclude that a woman must spend her period of pregnancy glued to her chair; this would cause excessive corpulence and overtax the heart, besides making delivery all the more difficult. Outdoor walks and mild exercise are indispensable, as also are recreation and a regular mode of life.

We shall end this chapter with an important piece of advice. So soon as a woman notices symptoms of pregnancy she should call in her physician for a general examination, but particularly of the heart, kidneys and lungs. Serious and often fatal complications can be avoided by timely medical treatment.

CHAPTER XIX

THE PSYCHOLOGY OF THE PREGNANT WOMAN

Bizarre cravings of the pregnant woman. The lady who ate one hundred and forty cakes. Cravings of the woman and cravings of the child. Suggestion and auto-suggestion. Superstitions. Effect of nervous shock. Kleptomania and the Napoleonic code.

ONE of the most interesting phenomena, and perhaps the most difficult to explain psychologically, is that commonly known as the ' cravings ' of an expectant mother, meaning thereby the irresistible longing which she feels for certain foods and drinks; sometimes she longs for something which normally would not even tempt her, sometimes she merely develops a passion for one of her favourite dishes.

Those longings may also be so extraordinary as to be inconceivable in a person in a normal state of health. Havelock Ellis, the doyen of English sexology, relates cases of pregnant women who ate ravenously sand, coal, ashes, or pieces of metal. Others are attracted by repulsive things, like human excretions, spiders, toads, etc.

Those are, of course, exceptional cases which come within the domain of pathology. Most pregnant women crave for sweets, fruit, and acid vegetables.

In medical circles the case is recorded of a lady of social standing who in one day ate no fewer than 140 cakes. Among fruits, apples and cherries are most craved for, while oranges and lemons take second place. Pickled cucumbers and tomatoes hold the record in the vegetable world.

There is even more variety among liquid cravings, but milk, coffee, liqueurs, and vinegar, seem to be the favourites.

The phenomenon may be inverted, in which case the patient develops an invincible repugnance for things which she usually likes, and to such an extent that their very odour upsets her.

The study of the cause of those cravings has given rise to numerous theories, none of which is quite satisfactory.

Some physicians hold that the organic changes resulting from pregnancy, and the corresponding alterations in glandular functioning, require the supply of certain elements hitherto unnecessary for the system. Another interesting theory is based on the observation that these longings are mostly for foods which children prefer (sweets and fruit), and it concludes that they correspond to an organic need in the child. A mother's craving would thus be justified by her instinct, and would be really the craving of the fœtus.

This theory is quite plausible where such longings are for normal nourishment, but it does not explain freak desires like those which we mentioned above.

It seems to us that suggestion and auto-suggestion may account for many fancies during pregnancy. The woman has heard that her mother, her friends, her neighbours, had cravings when pregnant, and she somehow feels compelled to have them also. It is, besides, a widespread superstition that the absence of cravings in the mother is a bad omen for the unborn child. We have taken from Havelock Ellis an example of this belief, which refers to the Duchesse d'Abrantès:

' The duchess tells in her memoirs how a craving was forced upon her, when first she became pregnant, by the anxious care of her parents and of her husband, Marshal Junot. Although she was constantly suffering from nausea, she had no cravings. One day at dinner, when her pregnancy was already far advanced, her mother suddenly put down her fork and exclaimed: " I have never asked you what your craving is! " The duchess answered that she did not have any, and was spending her days and nights being sick. " No cravings," retorted her mother; " this is impossible. I shall certainly speak to your mother-in-law." The two old ladies put their heads together and then explained to the prospective young mother that an unsatisfied longing could make a monster of the child; her husband in his turn began to inquire daily about her cravings; her sister-in-law told her all sorts of stories about children born with marks on that account. The duchess began to be afraid and to wonder what she ought to be longing for, but she could think of nothing. At last one day, when she was sucking a sweet flavoured with pineapple, it occurred to her that this was a delicious fruit which she had never seen, pineapples being then very rare. Thereupon she began to crave for it, all the more when she was told that at that season of the year it was unprocurable; she then felt that she must have a pineapple or die, and the marshal scoured Paris offering twenty pounds for one, but in vain. He succeeded at last in obtaining one through Madame Bonaparte, and arrived home just as his wife, still talking of pineapples, had retired for the night. He entered her room with it, to the great delight of the duchess's mother, who had herself in the course of one of her pregnancies had a longing for cherries in January, so that her child had been born with a strawberry-mark, scientifically called a "nævus". The duchess thanked her husband effusively and prepared to eat the fruit, but Junot stopped her by saying that Corvisart, the imperial physician, had told him that she must on no account eat it at night as it was very indigestible. The duchess gave up the idea and spent the night hugging the pineapple. In the morning, her husband came in, cut it up himself, and offered her slices of it in a china bowl; whereupon the duchess felt a sudden violent revulsion and found it absolutely impossible to touch the fruit. Persuasion proved useless; the pineapple had to be taken away and the windows opened because the very scent upset her. The duchess adds that ever since then, although she liked the flavour of pineapple, she could never eat one without forcing herself. We might add further that she became insane in her old age.'

This is an interesting instance of suggestion, and we do not think we exaggerate when we say that a third person's influence can, to a great extent, determine a pregnant woman's cravings.

It has also been said that to satisfy the cravings prevents morning sickness, but it is difficult to see what foundation there is for this assertion. One thing seems to be certain, cravings cannot be attributed solely to suggestion, because the peculiarity is as well known among primitive peoples as among civilised ones; certain native tribes regard them as sacred wishes. In short, while we do not know the biological reason for such symptoms, we must accept them as facts and deal with them accordingly.

Another equally strange phenomenon of pregnancy is the belief that an object which makes a strong impression on an expectant mother can affect her unborn child's physique. Such is the case with hare-lips, strawberry-marks, nævi, ill-formed ears, etc. More serious congenital disfigurements have also been attributed to the same cause.

One can but smile at such nonsense. There is no direct relation between the fœtus and the mother's nervous system; moreover, the psychological as well as the physiological dispositions are partly determined at the time of impregnation, and the fœtus's evolution follows more or less an appointed path. In fact, if we study the origin of nævi and the like, they can almost always be traced to heredity.

It must nevertheless be admitted that a fright or a nervous shock may possibly influence the evolution of the fœtus, in spite of the absence of direct connection between the two nervous systems. It is presumed that this repercussion is transmitted by the circulation. As a matter of fact, we know that all changes occurring in the internal secretions of the maternal glandular system leave traces in the blood, and consequently in the nutritive elements transmitted to the embryo. Should the expectant mother be subjected to serious worries or reverses, her child will probably be extremely nervous. Hence the necessity to avoid all annoyances.

It is difficult to credit the extent to which superstitious beliefs concerning pregnancy have taken root even in cultured circles. The author knows a woman, one of the socially elect, who used to spend whole days before paintings of the great masters in the Louvre, so that her child would 'have the face of an angel'! The tragic part of the story is that the baby was born hydrocephalic and died within two days.

In America, white women are said to have given birth to coloured children because during their pregnancy they looked too much at negroes. If the husband persists in believing this, it is not for us to disillusion him; we will merely offer him a piece of advice: he had better keep his wife from too frequent contemplation of negroes if he does not wish to have a coloured heir.

But a truce to banter! We must speak of another psychological phenomenon very frequent in pregnancy, namely mental troubles. They are most characteristic during the first months of pregnancy, and generally take the form of a fear of death which degenerates into melancholia. However, once the woman has felt the quickening or, later, after delivery, this disturbance usually vanishes, but not always; we know of cases of incurable melancholia, hysteria, and epilepsy, occasioned by pregnancy, but these disorders were very probably latent, and pregnancy only served to hasten their development.

Among the psychological disorders that may affect a pregnant woman, we must mention also kleptomania, which is not of infrequent occurrence. Fortunately, the objects of this morbid covetousness are almost always sweets or fruits, so that the thief absolves herself on the plea of the irresistible urge of her 'craving'. The French revolutionary law of Germinal 28th, Year III, provided partial immunity for this kind of larceny, but the Napoleonic Code repealed this enactment.

CHAPTER XX

'IN SORROW SHALT THOU BRING FORTH CHILDREN'

Preliminary symptoms. Onset and duration of labour. Dilatation of the neck of the uterus. Contractions of the uterus and of the abdominal wall. Delivery of the baby. Expulsion of the placenta. Twins. Possible complications. The Cæsarean operation. Hygiene of childbirth. Pros and cons of using an anæsthetic. Ligature of the umbilical cord. Twilight sleep. The most modern method of alleviation.

'The critical hour is drawing near.' It is in some such way that we speak as a rule of the hour of delivery. But how fortunate for women if it meant literally only one hour of labour.

During the last six or eight weeks of pregnancy, a woman feels at times that her abdomen is swelling and hardening. This sensation lasts only a few moments and causes no pain. It is due to slight uterine contractions which are the forerunners of true labour. When the latter actually sets in, these contractions become more and more frequent and violent, and enable the uterus to expel its contents into the vagina and thence into the outer world.

There are many theories concerning the beginning of labour. The one most generally accepted is that the accumulation of toxins produced by the fœtus irritate the uterine muscles, and thereby induce the first labour spasms, with their accompanying pains.

The majority of pregnant women anticipate the moment of their delivery with much anxiety. It should be noted that the natural nervousness with which women are attacked at that time, gives them the impression that their delivery is too long delayed. Soon, however, the contractions to which we have referred become intensified and assume the characteristics of actual labour, which means that momentarily acute pains alternate with periods of rest. These pains, which at first are easily borne, become more acute, and the quiet intervals between them shorter and shorter. The muscles of the uterus have begun their work, and do their utmost to expel the fœtus as quickly as possible, but the task is more difficult to accomplish than the woman would wish.

Clinical experience has shown that a first labour generally lasts from eighteen to twenty-four hours at least. For women who have already borne several children, the time is usually reduced to nine or six hours, sometimes to even less.

In the chapter describing the female genital organs, we mentioned the neck of the uterus, or cervix, which in the latter part of gestation is 2.2 to 3.5 inches long and the diameter of a pencil. It is through this narrow passage that the child's head, which is from 5 to 5.5 inches in diameter, must make its way (head presentation being normal). It is therefore not to be wondered at that it need hours for the cervix to dilate sufficiently, since each uterine contraction, always accompanied by a pain, expands it by a mere .04 inch or so. Fortunately, here again nature has taken good care to facilitate this painful process as much as possible.

Delivery is a complicated affair which we cannot examine in detail within the scope of this book. We shall merely mention that it progresses by stages. Fifteen to twenty days before delivery the uterus drops, which gives the mother a certain amount of relief. It means that the fœtus has started on its way, and some physicians consider this occurrence the first stage of birth. The second, or labour proper, consists in the automatic uterine contractions which we have mentioned, and in the patient's conscious efforts to contract the abdominal muscles; these 'bearing down' efforts cause the cervix alternately to contract and to expand, and are accompanied by a discharge of blood-streaked mucus. After a time, the bag of waters breaks, and this allows the head of the fœtus to get nearer to the vulva; the latter gradually expands until a new effort allows the head and neck to pass through; another pause, and the next effort brings forth the shoulders; then follow the back, the buttocks, and finally the feet. The mother now experiences immense relief and feels that it was worth while enduring so much for the sake of the tiny being, whose only link with her now is the cord.

Even though the baby is born, however, there still remain in the uterus substances which, now useless, must be expelled in their turn.

This is the last stage of delivery. It occurs from fifteen to thirty minutes after the birth of the baby, following a uterine contraction which detaches the placenta, drives it through into the vagina, and out. This may be accompanied by a hæmorrhage, and therefore requires the same care from the physician and nurse as the delivery itself.

Subsequent births follow practically the same course, except that, as we have previously explained, their duration is distinctly shorter. The fœtus meets with weaker resistance, the cervix and the vagina expand a great deal more quickly, and the mother as a rule suffers much less.

There are cases, however, in which the first confinement progresses without accident, while the second is considerably more difficult. The simple explanation of this is that, as a rule, the second or third child is much larger at birth than its predecessors.

It must also be remembered that the normal head presentation is not an unvarying rule; pelvic, breech, or transverse presentations are a frequent complication.

There still remains to mention the bogy of all pregnant women, twin births. Obviously, the simultaneous delivery of two children is an impossibility, and the births must take place in succession. In the majority of cases twins are not nearly so fully developed as a child which has had the maternal uterus all to itself. In the case of twins, conditions differ in accordance with whether they have developed from two ova, or from a single one which has divided after impregnation. In the former case, there will be two placentas and two bags of waters; in the latter case, there will be only one placenta, that is only one source of nourishment, and only a thin membrane separating the embryos. In any case twin births entail two ruptures, and one or two deliveries, according to whether one or two ova were involved. The sex of twins produced from a single ovum is always the same, while that of twins produced from two ova is nearly always different.

The process of birth, which we have just described, naturally has a profound effect on the general condition of the woman during confinement. The enormous effort required of her affects the heart and the lungs; her pulse is very fast and her breathing very rapid. Throughout labour she may perspire profusely, and there is a considerable expenditure of physical energy, her mucous membranes are parched and she suffers from an intense thirst. The obvious reaction is complete exhaustion and, as delivery always involves a certain loss of blood, therefore of heat, the patient not infrequently shivers, and needs plenty of covers. In this description we have not given details of all the attention required by the mother, but have limited ourselves to a broad outline of the actual process of delivery.

We shall now give a brief list of possible complications.

We have already seen that the fœtus, instead of presenting itself head foremost, may present other parts of its body, as for instance the face, which however hardly constitutes a complication; pelvic and back presentations are much more difficult and require the assistance of an obstetrician to prevent accidents. A series of complications occur in certain women in the form of narrowness of the pelvis, especially in those who in childhood suffered from rickets. In other cases—happily very rare—there may be stricture of the uterus, cervix or vagina, cancer, fibroid tumours; or an unusually difficult presentation requiring a surgical operation or even a Cæsarean section.

This operation, which was already known in antiquity, consists in opening the abdomen and the uterus and extracting the fœtus. It owes its name to the story that Julius Cæsar was born in that way. At the time when surgical precautions left much to be desired, this operation was considered one of the most dangerous, and often ended fatally; nowadays it presents scarcely any danger, and, even taking into account the most extraordinary cases, the proportion of casualties is less than two per cent.

In conclusion we shall give a few indications of the hygiene to be observed during the confinement. The principal aim is to avoid all danger of infection. As soon as labour begins, the patient is given a low enema and a lukewarm bath; the pubes are then shaved, thereby removing a source of infection, and the genital parts are soaped, and bathed with an antiseptic solution. Care should be taken not to touch the vagina except with strictly clean hands, and even then preferably rubber-gloved. All persons not actually concerned must be forbidden the room; they would be of no help whatsoever to the patient; on the contrary, they might cause infection by stirring up dust. The doctor and the nurse will of course endeavour to alleviate the suffering of the patient. A problem which until a few years ago was keenly discussed by obstetricians was whether these pains could be prevented, or greatly relieved, by anæsthesia or semi-anæsthesia. Some practitioners uncompromisingly adhered to the Biblical precept 'in sorrow shalt thou bring forth children', and explained their attitude on the ground that the uterine contractions are caused by the pains, and that to lessen the latter would involve weakening the former, thereby needlessly prolonging labour.

The truth is that the pains are caused by the muscular contractions, and the fact remains that, even if partial anæsthesia prolongs labour appreciably, the general condition of the patient who has been anæsthetised is much better than that of one who has had to bear the full brunt of the pains. It seems therefore that an anæsthetic administered during the final pains is indicated, in view of the beneficial relief which it affords.

After birth, the child is left to rest for a few minutes between the mother's legs, until cessation of the pulse in the cord shows that the child has begun its independent life. The cord is then tied and cut. Once severed from its mother, the child is placed in a bath at 100° F. and afterwards oiled. The mother's genital parts are washed with an antiseptic solution, and examined by the midwife or doctor, to ascertain whether there has been any laceration of the perineum, a not infrequent occurrence at a confinement. She is then given something warm to drink, a hot-water bottle is placed at her feet, and she is left to rest and recuperate.

As regards the nourishment of a woman during labour, if she has any appetite, a little milk, coffee and milk, or tea, with perhaps a little crustless bread. Her thirst will be best quenched by cold tea or pure water. Sparkling waters, black coffee and alcohol are not advisable. Alcohol in particular dilates the blood-vessels and increases the risk of hæmorrhage. The attending physician is alone qualified to prescribe it in exceptional cases, such as an over-protracted labour, to prevent the mother's collapse.

Editor's Note

Since the introduction of chloroform, about a century ago, many attempts have been made to alleviate the pains of childbirth. Many drugs have been used for this purpose. But most of them have had the disadvantage that they not only stop the mother's perception of the pain, but also diminish or stop altogether the muscular contractions of the uterus. In addition, some of them have an unfavourable effect on the child.

Some twenty-five years ago a method of relieving the pains of childbirth known as 'twilight sleep' was elaborated. This consisted in the injection of a combination of two drugs, morphine and hyoscine, during the latter part of labour. If carefully carried out, this method alleviates or entirely removes the mother's pain, without materially slowing up the process of birth. But the morphine tends to dull the child's respiratory centre, so that there may be some difficulty in getting it to breathe after it is born.

More recently a much better method has been worked out, in which neither morphine nor hyoscine is used. The mother is allowed to have the early, mild pains, but when the mouth of the womb is sufficiently dilated she is given an intravenous injection of one of the barbiturates (a group of drugs of which, perhaps, veronal is the best known). She immediately falls into a deep sleep and no longer perceives the pain. In spite of this the muscular contractions are not slowed down at all, and the drug exerts no harmful effect of any sort on the child.

This method not only relieves the mother of pain, but has the additional advantage that, if the child's head is big or the mother's passages narrow, labour may be allowed to go on longer, in order to allow for moulding of the former and stretching of the latter, so that the baby may be born naturally, instead of the doctor being compelled, by the thought of the mother's pain, to drag the baby out with forceps before the moulding and the stretching have taken place.—N. H.

CHAPTER XXI

THE CARE OF THE MOTHER IN CHILDBED

Duration of the lying-in period. Hygiene of the woman during her confinement. Importance of the digestive and renal functions. Puerperal fever. The reappearance of menstruation. Sexual intercourse after the confinement. Is the nursing mother capable of conceiving? Danger of too frequent confinements. Maternal love and sexual love. Can the child dispense with breast-feeding? The sacred duty of the woman.

THE critical moment has passed. For nine long months a mother has carried her child; for nine long months she has impatiently awaited it, and now it has arrived; her suffering is over and forgotten, and nature sets to work to bring her sorely taxed body back to its normal state. The first question to be decided is whether the recovery of the genital organs after a confinement requires a prolonged rest in bed, or whether one or two days are sufficient.

Three or four years ago, gynæcologists were of the opinion that four days' rest was ample. A normal confinement, they said, is not a pathological case, and therefore it would be out of place to treat the young mother as an invalid; they also referred to the fact that rest after a confinement is unknown among primitive peoples and animals, where the females resume their normal existence immediately. It is also not unusual for a peasant woman to undertake heavy work twenty-four hours after confinement.

All these instances would tend to prove that a protracted

rest is counter-indicated and liable to cause complications, such as, for instance, phlebitis (thrombosis in the legs).

The more modern discoveries of science, however, have radically altered this doctrine, which experience and reason have disproved. The genital organs, already relaxed and distended through pregnancy, are extremely weak after parturition and need to be strengthened; a woman who gets up too soon after her confinement runs the risk of a displacement or of a *prolapsus uteri*.

It should also not be forgotten that the strain of labour exhausts the woman's system, and that the first days of suckling the infant are also very tiring; complete rest is therefore essential. So far as the danger of phlebitis is concerned, the patient can avoid it, even though in bed, by beginning the day after delivery to make some easy movements which flex and extend the legs. The repetition of this exercise several times daily, together with some massage, from the soles of the feet to the hips, should prevent any circulatory trouble.

In our opinion the young mother ought to rest for seven or eight days, and ten to twelve if there has been laceration of the perinæum.

The question of rest being thus settled, we now come to childbed hygiene.

The function of the bowels and the kidneys is the most important consideration. The abdominal wall having been abnormally distended, the muscles are unable to perform their accustomed work; as a result constipation is a frequent aftermath of pregnancy, and may give rise to grave disorders. The use of purgatives, however, is not advisable, because they may affect the composition of the milk; for this reason enemas are to be preferred. The passing of urine must also be attended to, in order to avoid the unpleasant consequences of an over-full bladder pressing on the uterus. If urinary troubles do arise, and a hot compress or poultice over the region of the bladder does not give relief, a catheter must be used.

Another complication of birth is so-called milk-fever, a misnomer for puerperal fever, which is due to infection, often by the doctor or nurse. Whenever a patient suffers from an infection involving a high temperature, people attribute it to everything except the nurse's negligence. There is no such thing as milk-fever; if therefore the temperature rises, it is a sign of infection or of some other serious illness, and a doctor must be called in immediately; not to do so is extremely dangerous, as the least delay may prove fatal.

When the placenta comes away it leaves a wound on the inner wall of the uterus, where several blood-vessels burst; the contraction of the uterus after the pains are over partly closes this wound and restricts the hæmorrhage; during the next few days the wound heals and a new mucous membrane grows over it. This process is accompanied by a serous discharge, which is called *lochia*; during the first day, this consists of pure blood; it then becomes mixed with mucous secretions; between the eighth and the fourteenth days it assumes a viscous and purulent appearance. By the twentieth day it stops, or more exactly, the vaginal secretions resume their normal aspect. The lochia therefore merely show that the wound in the uterus is not yet healed and must consequently be considered a normal manifestation.

The uterus contracts simultaneously with the healing of the wound. Fourteen days after delivery it is only twice as large as before pregnancy, and four weeks later it has resumed its normal size, which is then one-quarter to one-half larger than a virgin womb.

If the mother nurses her child, menstruation does not

usually appear till after the child is weaned; this is a sign that the genital organs are once more normal.

Before ending this part of the book, it is advisable to say a few words on the care of the abdomen after confinement. As previously stated, during pregnancy the abdominal wall is considerably stretched to make room for the enlarged uterus. After birth, the abdomen ought to resume its normal shape; this is not merely an æsthetic consideration (which no sensible woman will ignore), but one also of health, because a distended abdomen can give rise to a number of intestinal troubles, besides favouring a defective position of the embryo in the next pregnancy.

Leaving out of account exceptional cases, the simplest attention is enough to restore the young mother to her normal figure. All chemists and orthopædists stock special abdominal bandages for this purpose. Actually, nothing has such a good effect as massage. The heavy breasts should naturally be supported by a suitable brassière.

* * *

Obviously, a couple with the most elementary æsthetic sense will not consider having sexual relations after the confinement and during the succeeding weeks. The lochia and their pronounced odour should alone be a sufficient deterrent. Experience shows nevertheless that there are human brutes who force intercourse on their wives even at the beginning of labour, or within a few days after delivery. The woman is really equally to blame for thus submitting, whether it be through weakness or fear that her husband will seek satisfaction elsewhere.

Apart from æsthetic considerations, however, sexual intercourse during the first weeks following a confinement should be prohibited on purely hygienic grounds. Enough to mention the extreme susceptibility of the genital organs to infection. Obstetricians record cases where premature intimacy has resulted in such severe lesions that death has followed. We have shown that the uterus takes six weeks to contract completely, and it is desirable that no intimacy should take place during that period.

When, however, the confinement takes place without complications of any kind, intercourse may be allowed as early as the fourth week, provided the greatest precautions are taken.

A husband must not forget that coitus may so affect the mother's already strained nervous system, that it will bring about a lasting repugnance to the sexual act, which will be difficult to overcome.

Intimacy too soon after childbirth is also undesirable from the standpoint of the next pregnancy. Women fondly imagine that whilst nursing they are immune from the consequences of sexual intercourse, and can indulge in it to their heart's content. The fact is that, although less probable during lactation, impregnation is by no means impossible. The ovaries are likely even at this time to resume their normal functioning, and ovulation may take place. In fact it is by no means unusual for pregnancy to occur again before the menses reappear. This is possible if the ovum is already ripe and becomes fertilised, before menstruation is due.

Another pregnancy occurring a few months after a confinement may present a serious danger to the organism, in that it may prevent the normal development of the organs, disturb the harmony of the female body, and bring about premature old age. The strongest constitution cannot withstand the physical and mental strain of pregnancies following one another in rapid succession; an exhausted woman has not much chance of bearing healthy children. Statistics record a 20 per cent. mortality before the fifth year among children born after less than an interval of one year; this figure is reduced to 11 per cent. for children born after an interval of two years. This amply illustrates the necessity of allowing enough time for the mother's organism to recuperate.

A woman's sexual feelings are often greatly in abeyance while she is nursing her baby. This is not due only to the drain on her physical energy, but also to the temporary predominance of her maternal instinct. We have unfortunately no space here in which to enlarge on the question of the relation between maternal and wifely love; but the husband should remember that his wife's sexual remoteness at this period is due to psychological, and not to physical, reasons, and he should regard with indulgence the dual rôle of mother and wife which she is called upon to play.

A woman must not let the mother altogether submerge the wife in her, lest she lose her husband. It is by no means rare for a father to hate his child for being the unconscious means of depriving him of his wife's love.

This is, of course, an exceptional case; an understanding husband will not insist too much on intimacy until the baby is weaned, and a sympathetic wife will endeavour not to show her lack of sexual interest in the man, whom she continues nevertheless to love. Only in this way will the couple succeed in preserving their happiness, the primary condition of which is a satisfactory sexual relationship.

This state of affairs may also be reversed; there are many instances of women who do not enjoy sexual intercourse until after they have had their first child, while it not infrequently happens that a man is repelled by a nursing mother. Maternal duties are not always an adjunct to feminine charm, and there is nothing particularly attractive in the *chloasma gravidarum* (discoloured blotches on the skin) or in the intensified secretions of the sweat glands.

The relations between husband and wife after the birth of
their child are therefore a matter which requires delicate
adjustment.

*   *   *

Nursing hygiene is outside the scope of this book; all the
same, we cannot omit to raise a question which is essential
to the welfare of the new-born baby: ought a woman to
breast-feed her baby, or can the latter be equally well
raised on cow's milk or patent baby-foods?

When my patients ask me this question, I invariably
answer that the child *can* dispense with maternal milk,
but that it has a lasting effect on its ultimate development.
To believe that maternal milk can be replaced by patent
food is trusting science too far; as regards cow's milk, it is
essentially adapted to the calf's requirements but lacks the
elements necessary to the more highly evolved human
organism.

Here again statistics show how much larger mortality
is, among children deprived of maternal milk. A gynæcologist, Vitrey, has calculated that it reaches 33 per cent.
as against 12 per cent. among breast-fed babies.

Havelock Ellis has compiled another interesting statistic
on the subject. An inquiry among a group of athletes
showed that out of 150 members, 65 had been breast-fed
on an average for six months; among the best subjects,
72 per cent. had been breast-fed on an average for nine to
ten months; in the group of 65 who were less athletically
developed, 57 per cent. had been breast-fed on an average
for barely three months.

It is true that the nursing period is a very trying one
for young mothers, who, in order to fulfil their mission
worthily, must give up all pleasures. But what mother
will not willingly forgo these for the sake of her baby?

CHAPTER XXII

PREMATURE LABOUR, MISCARRIAGE AND ABORTION

Definition of abortion, miscarriage and premature delivery. Causes of miscarriage. Symptoms of miscarriage. Causes of death of fœtus. Artificial interruption of pregnancy a criminal offence in most countries. Soviet Russia the exception. Necessity of enacting legislation similar to that of Soviet Russia. Opposition of the Church. Indications that warrant interruption of pregnancy. Illegal methods. Dangers attendant on interruption of pregnancy except by a competent surgeon.

IN the preceding chapters we have described normal pregnancy and confinement. This chapter will be devoted to cases where the pregnancy does not go on to full term. The word *abortion* should be used when the pregnancy ends before the completion of the first three months. During the second three months the termination of pregnancy is spoken of as a *miscarriage*. During the last three months, when the child is *viable*, or able, under favourable circumstances, to survive in spite of its untimely birth, we speak of *premature delivery* or *premature labour*.

These are the correct definitions of the terms which we have used. But in general parlance, many people use the word 'miscarriage' to describe a pregnancy which has terminated prematurely quite spontaneously, and the word 'abortion' to describe one which has been terminated artificially, whether by the use of drugs, by operation, or by other means. Instead of miscarriage, they may call the spontaneous and premature termination of pregnancy a 'mishap'.

The problem of abortion and miscarriage is a complex one and the causes many and various. Some women are incapable of carrying a child to full term, and always miscarry. This may be due to some abnormality in the woman herself, or it may be primarily due to the male—for instance, he may have infected her with syphilis. Many miscarriages are due to the fact that the woman's genital organs are infantile, that is to say that their development has been arrested at a stage short of maturity.

Besides syphilis in the man and infantilism in the woman, other affections may cause miscarriage in spite of the doctor's efforts to prevent it. In such a case the couple is fated to remain childless in spite of the woman becoming pregnant frequently. Once the doctor is convinced that this chronic condition exists, he should interrupt the pregnancy at the earliest possible stage. Since the woman cannot carry the fœtus to full term, the sooner the miscarriage occurs the better it will be for her health.

A fact worthy of note is that there are some women who can only carry female children to term, and who always miscarry if the child is a male.

Many miscarriages are quite accidental, so that a woman who has had perfectly normal pregnancies and confinements on previous occasions, on another occasion has a miscarriage, and in future confinements she is quite likely to have a normal pregnancy again.

There seems to be some special tendency to miscarriage during first pregnancies. This tendency may depend in part on the fatigue and excitement of the honeymoon, especially if it is accompanied by a long voyage, with the rush and hurry of sightseeing, change of climate, unfamiliar food, and, as it often is, with somewhat excessive use of alcohol. But more important is the fact that many newly married women have genital organs which are still not fully developed. Especially the internal genitals may be as yet incapable of carrying the fœtus to term. Later, as a result of regular sexual relations, the organs may develop so that the woman is capable of a normal pregnancy.

Spontaneous miscarriage is not, of course, limited to the first pregnancy. A woman may miscarry after having experienced a number of perfectly normal pregnancies and confinements. This may be due to accident, to nervous shock, to sudden fright, or other psychological causes, to excessive physical fatigue, especially the lifting of heavy weights, or over-vigorous indulgence in sport. Violent sexual intercourse may also interrupt the pregnancy. A miscarriage commences by bleeding from the uterus, through the vagina, and this may go on without interruption, or it may stop for a time and then begin again. It will be accompanied by pains in the lower abdomen and back, similar to those of a full-time confinement, though less severe. The pains are the expression of uterine contractions, which result in the opening of the mouth of the womb and the expulsion of the fœtus into the vagina. After the fœtus is expelled the bleeding becomes less, unless the placenta or after-birth is retained in the uterus, and in this case bleeding may be prolonged and dangerous. In all cases of miscarriage, a doctor should be summoned, who will decide whether the miscarriage is complete or incomplete, and whether the uterus needs emptying and scraping. The scraping of the uterus is known as *curettage*.

Proper hygiene during pregnancy will tend to render miscarriage unlikely. When the first symptoms of a miscarriage appear the woman should go to bed and rest, and put herself in the hands of a doctor, who may still be able to prevent the premature termination of the pregnancy.

Premature labour presents symptoms not unlike those of miscarriage. It is particularly common in cases of twins and also in cases where the amniotic fluid is excessive. The onset of labour is generally announced by a slight hæmorrhage. If the amount of bleeding is considerable a doctor should be called at once, lest the mother's life should be endangered. In some cases Cæsarean section may be necessary in order to save the life of the mother or of the child, or of both.

Sometimes the child dies in the uterus. This is particularly likely to happen if the mother is gravely ill, whether from syphilis or from any other cause. It may occur too if the child's blood supply is interfered with, for instance if the umbilical cord is too long and becomes knotted. The child may move in such a way that it ties a knot in the cord, or the cord may become twisted around the child's neck. In such cases the child involuntarily commits suicide, so to speak.

The mother suspects the death of the child when she no longer feels it moving. After a while she feels that she has 'a foreign body' inside her. If expulsion of the dead embryo does not take place soon, the woman may exhibit symptoms of intoxication—headaches, nausea, vomiting, etc. This is because decomposition has begun in the uterus, and in such a case it will be necessary for the doctor to remove the uterine contents without delay.

If the fœtus dies during the first half of pregnancy, the mother will not yet have felt any movements and will therefore not notice their cessation. In such a case death of the fœtus will only be suspected when it is noticed that the mother's abdomen is not increasing in size in the usual way. The mother may also notice some of the symptoms of intoxication mentioned above, or she may not. Once the death of the fœtus is established, the uterus should be emptied.

* * *

We have now to consider the question of artificial interruption of pregnancy. We use this term to cover all attempts, by any means whatever, to expel the fœtus before it is viable. In most countries interruption of pregnancy is a legal offence, punishable with heavy penalties, except where it is necessary to safeguard the life or the health of the mother. In Soviet Russia, interruption of pregnancy by a properly qualified medical practitioner, in a public hospital, is permitted during the first three months, if the mother desires it. One or two other European countries have enacted legislation somewhat similar to that of Soviet Russia, and there is a growing body of opinion, both among the lay population and in the medical profession, in many other countries, favouring such legislation.

Nowadays there is a constantly increasing feeling that the State has no right to interfere in the private life of its female citizens to prevent them having a pregnancy interrupted if they wish to do so. Many sociologists proclaim the principle which has been aptly phrased by Victor Margueritte '*Ton corps est à toi*' (Your body is yours). They claim that there are many other reasons, besides the health of the mother, which may render the interruption of pregnancy desirable. Thus in our society an illegitimate child is itself subjected to many disadvantages, and its birth may mean social or economic ruin for the mother. Even in the case of a married mother, the economic circumstances of the family may make it undesirable that she should have a child. The economic circumstances may not enable her to support it properly. She may already have as many children as she can support and care for. Many married couples can usefully rear three children, but are quite unable to support six and rear them properly. It is better to have three healthy children well cared for, well brought up, and given a good start in life, rather than six ill-nourished, unhealthy, and badly equipped for the struggle for existence.

This view is opposed principally by religionists who consider that sexual intercourse is only justified when it is carried out with the intention that it shall result in the production of offspring. They consider that intercourse for its own sake, as an end in itself, for the purpose of obtaining sexual pleasure, is a sin. Once impregnation has occurred they regard any interference with the life of the fœtus as an even greater sin. The Catholic Church goes so far as to forbid the interruption of pregnancy even where it is known that its continuation will involve the death of the mother.

Except for Soviet Russia and the other States mentioned above, most States regard the embryo as a living creature, and its destruction as akin to murder.

Apart from the objections of the Church and State, opponents of the legislation of abortion produce other reasons for their attitude. They say that a woman who wishes to have her pregnancy interrupted is frivolous and selfish and lacking the maternal instinct. Most gynæcologists are requested, with surprising frequency, by married women in excellent economic circumstances to terminate pregnancy.

It is a mistake to think that abortion occurs more frequently among the unmarried than among the married. The statistics of many gynæcological clinics show that the majority of abortions occur among married women.

The writer's point of view is that interruption of pregnancy is always an evil, and should be avoided unless for the purpose of averting a more serious evil. It is an evil because it entails the interruption of a physiological cycle, which begins with impregnation and is not completed until the child has been born, suckled, and weaned. The beginning of pregnancy has brought about a whole train of changes in the mother's body, and the sudden interruption of these, if pregnancy is artificially terminated, is not favourable for her health. *But interruption of pregnancy may be necessary or desirable in order to avoid even greater evils.* The mother's health may already be unsatisfactory, and the continuation of the pregnancy may endanger it even more than would the interruption. She may be fatigued by excessive or over-frequent childbearing, so that she needs an interval for rest and recuperation before the next child is born, and in such a case abortion may be the less of two evils. One of the parents may be suffering from some disease which is likely to be transmitted to, or to damage, the offspring, and in such a case the risk to the mother's health may be a smaller evil than the risk to the future child. Or again, the economic disadvantages, for the parents, or for the already existing children, may be a greater evil than the termination of the pregnancy. In every case where the mother demands interruption, all the circumstances of the case should be carefully reviewed before a decision is made. And if, after mature consideration, interruption is seen to be the smaller evil, the writer considers that the law should permit it. It must be remembered that the legal prohibition of abortion has very little effect in actually preventing abortion. Its effect is rather to induce people to terminate pregnancy more dangerously, by illegal means, than if termination were permitted. Until recently, legal termination of pregnancy was carried out only when the mother was gravely ill, and the mortality and morbidity (death and illness), which sometimes

[277]

followed, were attributed to the interruption of the pregnancy. But the careful observation of hundreds of thousands of cases in Soviet Russia has shown that if the operation is carried out in healthy women, by competent surgeons, with proper surgical precautions, the mortality and morbidity sink almost to vanishing point.

We are therefore forced to the conclusion that the dangers hitherto observed were due rather to the ill-health of the mother, or to the way in which it was carried out, than to the termination of pregnancy itself.

Since the law in this country forbids abortion, women who are determined not to go on with their pregnancy have recourse to illegal methods of attaining their end. They take all sorts of drugs which have a reputation for terminating pregnancy—large doses of quinine, ergot of rye, powerful purgatives, and many other substances, many of which are actually poisonous in the doses used. Some women abort easily, and find such drugs successful. But in the majority of women the drugs damage the health and do not cause abortion. Many women think that a doctor, and especially a gynæcologist, knows some harmless and certain prescription for terminating pregnancy. This is not so. Any drug which brings about abortion can only do so by poisoning the mother to a greater or lesser degree.

The less reputable chemists and drug stores sell pills and potions for the purpose of procuring abortion, and charge very high prices for them. They are usually unsuccessful. Such preparations are usually advertised as being good for 'female irregularities' or 'female ailments'. Their main purpose is to bring money to the seller, but they are of little use to the buyer.

When drugs fail, many women attempt to bring about an abortion by lifting heavy weights, shifting heavy furniture, violent skipping or other exercise, jumping off tables or downstairs, or other strenuous physical efforts of this kind. These efforts are seldom successful, and the woman is much more likely to break a limb, or do herself some other physical harm, than to succeed in her endeavour to interrupt the pregnancy.

Many women are so desperate as to attempt to bring about an abortion by giving themselves vaginal, or even intra-uterine, injections; or they try to push crochet-needles, skewers, button-hooks, hatpins, and other such objects, into the womb to kill or break up the embryo. All such manœuvres are extremely dangerous and may result in septicæmia (general blood-poisoning), or peritonitis, or perforation of the uterus.

Other women go to shady doctors, nurses, midwives or other persons who make a trade of procuring abortions illegally. Since any doctor who is convicted of an illegal abortion is not only imprisoned, but also deprived of his licence to practise, it follows that no ordinary competent doctor, who can earn his living in a legal manner, will *transgress* the law, whatever his views on the desirability of *changing* the law may be. Professional abortionists, therefore, whether medical or non-medical, are usually more or less incompetent.

They cannot carry out an illegal operation in any good hospital or nursing home, and are therefore compelled to carry it out under unfavourable surgical conditions, without adequate assistance, and almost always without proper precautions in sterilising the instruments and other materials used. Under such conditions there is always grave danger of perforation of the uterus, and even graver danger of infection.

If a woman is determined not to go on with her pregnancy, these dangers—of which, indeed, very few women are aware—will not deter her. The net result of the legal prohibition of interruption of pregnancy is, therefore, not to prevent abortion, but to force the woman to have it done surreptitiously and dangerously, instead of openly and safely.

The danger attendant on interruption of pregnancy, when it is carried out legally, by competent surgeons, under proper circumstances, is practically negligible. The danger of abortion when it is carried out illegally, by incompetent persons, under improper conditions, is very great indeed.

One of the most unfortunate results of the present state of the law is that many women, whose health is such that termination of the pregnancy on medical grounds would be quite permissible, do not realise that they could have the operation done legally; and they endanger their health, and even their life, by putting themselves in the hands of an incompetent charlatan.

It is important to point out that medical opinion, concerning the grounds on which interruption is justifiable, has changed very much during the last few years. Ten years ago, in England, a woman had to be almost on the verge of death from tuberculosis or kidney disease or heart disease before any reputable doctor would advise or perform interruption. Nowadays many conservative specialists consider that interruption of pregnancy is justifiable, if it is carried out for the purpose of safeguarding the health, and not only the life, of the mother. A study of the Proceedings of the Royal Society of Medicine, the Medico-Legal Society, the British Medical Association, and similar medical groups, shows unmistakably that, while the law has remained unchanged, the medical interpretation of the law is gradually but continuously being extended.

If interruption of pregnancy is properly carried out there is scarcely any risk that it will render the woman incapable of having children later on. But among the dangers of illegal abortion, the likelihood of sterility for the rest of the woman's life is one of the greatest.

BOOK IV

THE IMPERFECTIONS OF LOVE

BOOK IV

CHAPTER XXIII

HAS A WOMAN HER DAYS OF IMMUNITY?

The course of the spermatozoa. Vicissitudes of the ovum. Favourable and unfavourable days in the menstrual cycle. Absolute certainty not possible. An example.

DOCTORS are so often asked this question that we cannot ignore it altogether. It is a particularly vital problem to people who are prevented by religious principles from using contraceptive methods, because if women have their periods of immunity, it would then be possible to cohabit, without fear of procreation, while still keeping the law. If there were definite periods when a woman could not be impregnated the parents would be able, when the advent of another child was undesirable on account of the health of the woman, to indulge without risk in the sexual act, and the sperms would be deposited in the vagina according to the dictates of religion.

Before answering that question it might be well to describe the process of fertilisation.

We have seen elsewhere that the spermatozoa, suspended in the seminal fluid, progress partly through their own activity and partly through the uterine suction, and that they finally reach the womb and then the ovaries. If they meet a ripe ovum the latter becomes impregnated. If they do not, they follow their course through the fallopian tubes into the abdomen, in which they die and are resorbed.

[283]

A spermatozoon probably takes about thirty-six hours to make its way from the mouth of the womb to the abdominal cavity. If however the chemical environment of the uterus or of the fallopian tubes is favourable, they may survive as long as eight or ten days while waiting for the ovum. So much for the career of the spermatozoa.

As regards the ovum, it reaches maturity about twelve to fourteen days after the *beginning* of menstruation; when the graafian follicle which contains it breaks, the ovum leaves the ovary for the abdominal cavity, in which it becomes fully ripe. It then progresses towards the fallopian fringes, through which it enters the oviduct and eventually reaches the uterus. This journey probably takes from two to three days, and if impregnated the ovum fastens itself on to the inner wall of the uterus. This would therefore happen between the fourteenth and seventeenth days after the beginning of the last period; impregnation would thus take place normally between the twelfth and seventeenth days,* always counting from the same date. If, for instance, the last period began on March 3rd, ovulation will take

* *Editor's Note.*—All sorts of different days have been described as 'safe' at various times and by various authors. The latest, and probably the best, authority on this aspect of fertility, is Dr. Knaus of Gratz in Austria. He believes that in women who have periods at intervals of 26, 27, 28, 29 or 30 days, impregnation is only possible between the eighth day after the beginning of the menstrual period and the sixteenth day after the beginning of the menstrual period (thus if a woman began to menstruate on the 1st January, Knaus believes that she could only be impregnated from the 9th to the 17th January). This rule makes no provision for women who menstruate oftener than every twenty-six days or less often than every thirty days. Nor does it make any allowance for the fact that a woman who normally menstruates at intervals of from twenty-six to thirty days may, owing to some accidental factor, have her ovulation at an earlier or later date than is normal for her, and thus become susceptible to impregnation on a day outside the days mentioned in Dr. Knaus's calculation. To sum the whole matter up, one must say that, while impregnation is less likely to occur on the days regarded by Knaus as 'safe', the possibility of error is so great that it is unwise to trust to the method at all.—N. H.

place about the fifteenth. The process just described is schematic. We know that an orgasm is accompanied by strong muscular contractions of the internal genital organs, and that these may induce premature ovulation as early as the sixth or seventh day of the cycle. The ovum may also remain some time in the ovary after maturing and start on its journey a few days late. Many women also ovulate late, so that the ovum is also late in reaching the oviduct and does not come within range of the spermatozoa until nearly the end of the cycle.

The foregoing explanation makes it clear that no particular time of the cycle can be considered 'safe' with any degree of certainty. We have seen that coitus can bring about the release of an ovum as early as the sixth or seventh day, and that, on the other hand, retarded ovulation can postpone the period when impregnation is most likely to occur until very near the end of the menstrual cycle. Cases are also known of the ovum surviving menstruation. In these cases impregnation may occur even during that period, a phenomenon rendered possible by the ability of the spermatozoa to remain alive in the uterus eight or ten days.

There are, of course, women who are immune on certain days of their cycle; for instance, those whose ovulation occurs later than the average, say on the twentieth day, have small chances of being impregnated during the first weeks. In the same way, when ovulation takes place before the twelfth day impregnation is unlikely to occur shortly before the next menstruation. But we repeat that no set rule can be formulated regarding a woman's immunity at any time.

Without claiming the infallibility of our statements, we can set down some observations which are valid for average cases:

I. In the majority of women the spermatozoa are likely

to meet an ovum capable of being impregnated between the twelfth and seventeenth days of the cycle. This period is therefore that of greatest susceptibility.

II. Between the sixth and twelfth days coitus may bring about impregnation, firstly because the spermatozoa retain their vitality for seven or eight days, and thereby render conception possible for about a week after the sexual act, and secondly because the contractions set up by the orgasm may result in advancing the date of ovulation.

III. Between the seventeenth and the twenty-second days the risk is as great as between the sixth and the twelfth, owing to the possibility of a delay in ovulation.

In short, impregnation is most likely to occur between the twelfth and the seventeenth days; between the sixth and the twelfth, and the seventeenth and the twenty-second this risk decreases the further one gets away from the date limit, that is to say, the earlier coitus takes place before the twelfth day and the later after the seventeenth. Before the sixth and after the twenty-second day pregnancy is unlikely but not impossible.

As an example let us take a normal menstrual cycle lasting twenty-eight days; if menstruation began on March 3rd the days between the third and the ninth, and the twenty-sixth and the thirty-first are those of least susceptibility; on the days between the ninth and the fifteenth, and the twentieth and the twenty-fifth the chances of impregnation have greatly increased and are greatest between the fifteenth and the twentieth.

Once more we draw the reader's attention to the schematic character of these data. One must not rely on them blindly, because experience has proved that in practice *impregnation may occur at any time during the menstrual cycle and even during menstruation.*

CHAPTER XXIV

THE DESIRE FOR CHILDREN
(The Curse of Sterility)

Social considerations. The craving for motherhood. The desire to procreate in the man. The sterile marriage. Vaginismus. Dyspareunia and lack of anatomical adaptation. 'Seminal immunisation.' Sexual infantilism in the woman. Diet and fertility. Anatomical abnormalities. Infection of the genital organs. Surgical operations. Artificial methods of impregnation.

IF we were to study the problem of procreation from all its angles, this chapter would become a treatise on Eugenics and Social Economics. This latter aspect alone constitutes a vital question for some countries, either from the point of view of over- or under-population.

A great deal has been said and written concerning the average number of children which, in normal circumstances and all things being equal, a couple ought to bring into the world to fulfil its obligations to society. At first sight two seems to be the answer, since there will be no decrease in population if each individual leaves one successor. A closer study of the question shows that two children would not be sufficient if one takes into account infantile mortality, sterility, and celibacy, all important factors which must be taken into consideration if a stationary population is to be maintained. Actuarial calculations have given the number of three or four children as the

nearest average below which no couple should fall if they
wish to fulfill their procreative mission.

We are speaking, of course, of a normal couple, because
to some women repeated pregnancies and confinements
may be injurious, and that is a matter of primary importance.

Leaving out of account the social problem, we shall
pass to the purely individual factors which induce a couple
to have children.

As regards the woman, her longing for children is an
obvious fact since her organism is essentially fitted for
maternity. To be a woman practically implies motherhood, or, as Sellheim very aptly puts it: 'Every woman is
a potential mother and every mother is a self-expressed
woman'. The organic need of children, which is latent
in every woman, is so imperious that prolonged enforced
sterility drives her body to revolt, and this revolt may
manifest itself in a number of disorders and growths (cysts,
fibroid tumours, myomata) which, some authorities believe,
may be traced to compulsory inactivity of the genital
functions.

The physiological need of childbirth is reinforced by a
psychological one no less important. The desire for
maternity is born in the need to protect a weaker being,
and since this need cannot find expression in relations with
the husband, it leaves, if unsatisfied, a void in a woman's
life. The torment of a woman who knows definitely that
she is irrevocably sterile is indescribable; she goes from
physician to physician and willingly submits to risky
and even dangerous treatment; the modern thwarted
mother appeals to the physician as her primitive sister
yielded herself to magic practices in order to become fruitful.
The longing for children is particularly intense in the
domesticated woman, whose life, unlike that of her husband,
is not filled by professional activities; the need for *some*

activity makes itself felt in the long run, and, the care of children being the occupation most suited to her temperament, she will seek an outlet for her energy in that direction.

Thus, in order to preserve her physiological and psychological equilibrium, a woman, to whichever social stratum she may belong, needs children.

In man, the desire for children is much less instinctive and more reasoned. We can distinguish two factors in man's desire for offspring; the first, generally found among happily married men, is a corollary of what we have said concerning women: a loving husband feels, or at any rate understands, that his wife needs to become a mother in order to reach her full development, and it is for her sake that he also wants children. His love also looks for a new mode of expression, and besides desiring the mistress-wife, he wants to worship the mother-wife as well.

The second factor is of a more selfish nature, even if one sets aside the social standpoint, which is more developed in man than in woman. First and foremost, there is the wish to manifest his virility in a concrete form, a wish which can only be fulfilled in the form of progeny. Then material considerations come into play; a sensible man wants to secure a support for his old age, or an heir to his estates, or a male descendant to bear and carry on the name of which he is proud. Such is the composite prompting which impels man to fill his procreative part; we may also mention the unconscious urge to perpetuate oneself which is innate in every human being.*

---

* *Editor's Note.*—It is necessary to draw attention to the fact that the majority of children are conceived, not as the deliberate result of the wish of the parents to procreate a child, nor even as the chance result of the parents' indifference as to whether a child should result from the sexual union or not, but in spite of the parents' deliberate wish that the act should remain unproductive. Too few parents, among those who do wish to have offspring, trouble to ask themselves what sort of hereditary

All this exemplifies sufficiently the unhappiness that can
overwhelm a normal couple when they find themselves
condemned to sterility. The most passionate embraces
lose their savour when the partners are obsessed by the
thought of their disappointed vanity; they lose the joy
of life, and neurasthenia, particularly in women, is not
infrequent. To fill the resulting void they spend themselves in social or professional activity.

We shall see later on that couples who remain childless
after several years of married life and believe themselves
definitely sterile need not abandon hope, because modern
science has now at its disposal various and certain measures
to remedy this deplorable state. But the first step is to
find the cause responsible for sterility.

* * *

We shall first study the case where sterility can be
attributed to both partners, an instance, so to say, of conjugal
sterility. Everybody knows what has been called incompatibility of temperament. It is an old story as yet insufficiently
explained. There are beings who cannot adapt themselves
to each other and the general lack of harmony prevents
conception without any apparent anatomical or biological
reason. According to a sentimental theory, it is love that
is lacking, but this is immediately disproved by the number

endowment they have to offer to the child which they procreate. And
even among those who set out with the best motives, who deliberately
procreate a child with the definite intention of doing the best they can
for it, few realise fully the enormous responsibility of parenthood. Parents
seldom realise that they are betting, so to speak, with the child's money.
If things go well, if the particular horse which they are backing wins the
race, so to say, the child will collect the winnings. But if, as is infinitely
more likely, their horse does not win, it is the child who is the loser.
I know of nothing more necessary than a constant insistence on the
responsibility that parents owe to their children, to replace a good
deal of the orthodox insistence on the duty a child owes its parents.
—N. H.

of anything but loving couples who are distinctly prolific. On the other hand, a woman may remain unimpregnated in spite of regular intercourse with her husband over a period of years, and yet prove fertile at the first attempt with another partner; in such a case we must not overlook the importance of the rôle played by the orgasm in impregnation. We are not propounding here the superstition that a woman cannot conceive unless she reaches her climax, but an actual fact founded on the specific reaction of the feminine organism, that the orgasm appreciably assists impregnation. There is no doubt that the secretions from the genital glands and the muscular contractions of the uterus are apt to draw the spermatozoa into the uterine cavity. It follows therefore that a couple whose sexual relations are not satisfactory are less likely to have children than a couple in physical harmony. One cannot in that case speak of sterility, but of incompatibility; that is to say, lack of harmony during intercourse.

With this may be associated other disturbances of sexual life which prevent a couple, neither of whom is, truly speaking, sterile, from having children. One of them is *vaginismus*, a psychological rather than a physiological disorder which manifests itself in an automatic contraction of the vagina as a kind of instinctive defence against coitus; we shall examine this peculiarity in detail in the chapter on feminine frigidity. In the main it is the man who must be held responsible for *vaginismus*, and often because of his behaviour on the wedding-night. Obviously a constricted vagina does not lend itself to normal intercourse or to the transference of semen into the uterus. So far as treatment is concerned, *vaginismus* is more a case for psychology than gynæcology; there are, however, appliances which can be used to stretch the vagina and give satisfactory results. In any case a couple who detect signs of this disorder must not hesitate to consult a physician in order both to avoid sterility and to safeguard their happiness.

A less frequent cause, in which the fault lies equally with both partners, is that of badly adapted external genitalia. It sometimes happens that a somewhat long but otherwise normal vagina is coupled with a rather short penis, and this anatomical disproportion proves a mechanical obstacle to impregnation. It is not an insuperable difficulty but it greatly diminishes the chances of procreation.

A special category is formed by those cases in which sterility, although directly due to an infection in the wife, is actually attributable to sexual habits for which the husband is at least equally responsible. Certain imprudent activities, especially if they are repeated, expose the delicate female organs to lesions which may result in sterility.

One of the most widespread of these habits is the systematic practice of *coitus interruptus*. Intended as a temporary contraceptive, it often succeeds too well and ends in permanent sterility. By preventing the orgasm by abruptly breaking off connection at the very moment when the whole feminine system is prepared for it, *coitus interruptus* may give rise to hyperæmia of the feminine genital apparatus and in time can endanger ovarian function and even affect the mucous membrane of the uterus. Some gynæcologists go so far as to attribute to *coitus interruptus* those uterine tumours which are so prejudicial to impregnation.

Other contraceptive methods can also have an unfavourable effect on a woman's sexual life, unless they are applied with all due care. The strictest hygienic and sanitary care must be used at all times or irritations and infections, the consequences of which are numerous and dangerous, may result. Even douches or sprays, quite harmless and often indicated, may be responsible for inflammation of the mucous membrane if too strongly medicated.*

A husband's hastiness or brusqueness in effecting connection during pregnancy or too soon after delivery may also give rise to disorders and eventual sterility, by lacerating the tissues, which are at that time particularly fragile.

Many other ailments known as 'feminine' are attributable to the husband, who only too often takes liberties outside the home and brings back a germ which will cause sterility. Sometimes he is unaware of what has happened and only recognises his own infection when his wife becomes ill. The symptoms manifest themselves far less acutely in the woman, and when she consults a physician it is often too late to prevent sterility. In such cases it is obviously unjust to tax the wife with a misfortune for which her husband alone is to blame.

A somewhat peculiar phenomenon is that known as 'spermatic saturation'. Neither of the partners is sterile, yet the desired children do not arrive (this occurs generally after a first birth). It is said to be due to incompatibility between the male and the female cells resulting from an excessive quantity of seminal fluid in the feminine organs; it is a sort of immunisation, somewhat similar to vaccination, in which the spermatozoa play the part of bacilli. This constitutes a mild case of sterility and is easily remedied

* *Editor's Note.*—The writer of this chapter is right to insist on the necessity for cleanliness in relation to the use of contraceptives. But the vagina is fortunately pretty resistant to infection. It must be, to withstand the constant danger to which it is subjected by the insertion of the average man's penis. Only a sexologist, perhaps, fully realises the extremely dirty condition in which most men, even those who bath every day, are accustomed to keep their genital organs. And the same is true of most women. What is wanted is a good deal of plain speaking about the necessity for hygiene of the genital organs. Daily cleansing of these organs is at least as necessary and desirable as daily cleansing of the teeth.—N. H.

by discontinuing sexual relations for a time; a complete separation is still more efficacious, because the eventual reunion creates psychological and physiological conditions favourable to conception.

Finally, a couple not strongly endowed with the power to procreate, handicap their ability if they have intercourse in unfavourable attitudes, like those which do not allow deep penetration or which allow the spermatozoa to flow out of the vagina. If to this 'tactical error' is added coitus at the time when ovulation is in abeyance, a normal couple may remain childless for a long time and believe themselves sterile.

In this connection it may be interesting to note that one of the many superstitions concerning the sex of the unborn child attaches particular importance to the moment of impregnation. For instance, people believe, without any foundation, that sons are conceived immediately after menstruation; those who ardently desire a son and heir select, therefore, that period. But it requires only a slight knowledge of the female genital mechanism to realise that at that time it would be exceptional for the female organs to contain ripe ova and that the mucous membrane is not ready to receive a fertilised cell. Small wonder that couples who adhere to this superstition practically condemn themselves to sterility.

The foregoing shows what flimsy reasons can be the cause of sterility; this should encourage all those who have vainly been desiring children to consult a gynæcologist before despairing.

We now come to feminine sterility proper, and we must here distinguish between the incapacity to conceive and that to carry a child to its full term. The latter case is more frequent than is generally believed. The repeated miscarriages which follow in the train of certain diseases, chiefly syphilis, are symptomatic of this particular kind of sterility. When abortion occurs at a comparatively advanced stage of pregnancy, the case is clear and the physician's diagnosis easy. But numerous young women have a miscarriage without knowing it. Menstruation a little more copious than usual after a few days' delay, is very often nothing less than the expulsion of an impregnated ovum by an under-developed uterus. Once diagnosed, this can be cured by appropriate treatment.

For the most part this points to a common but temporary abnormality, genital infantilism in the woman; the immature organs cannot carry the child to its full term. This form of sterility may be cured by time; it has also been successfully treated by vibratory massage of the uterine muscles and the mucous membrane; performed *per rectum*, it has the twofold advantage of avoiding sexual stimulation and of being practicable even in a virgin in whom pre-nuptial symptoms revealed a condition of genital infantilism.

If a very young wife, say of sixteen, seventeen, or even twenty years, does not conceive, her husband would be wrong in concluding she was sterile; normal menstruation at that age is no proof of genital maturity. Dr. Van de Velde explains in a striking manner the causes of infantilism:

'The recent increase of female infantilism seems to be to a great extent due to over-population in large cities, where intellectual and cultural work, irrational feeding and professional duties have resulted in a generation of physically deficient women. A sex has been evolved by this abnormal expense of cerebral energy so degenerate from the point of view of physique that it has automatically lost most of its procreative capacity. This constitutional and sexual inferiority, caused in one generation by abnormal conditions of living, is transmitted to the next in an increased form and ends in creating, particularly among women, a human type which is either sterile or unable to stand the strain of pregnancy.'

The general physical condition, which depends on the manner of living, is a factor of primary importance for the woman who wishes to bear children. Van de Velde alludes in the foregoing paragraph to diet; this is a much neglected point which bears directly on our subject, because diet affects the whole organism and not least the genital functions. An insufficient supply of vitamins handicaps fertility by throwing the ovarian cycle out of gear. A diet restricted exclusively to certain articles of food is deleterious because a proper proportion of each vitamin is indispensable to the maintenance of the equilibrium of the organism. Aside from vitamins B and C, vitamin E is the most favourable to fecundity. It is contained in corn, in yeast, and in fresh fruits. Experience has shown that these elements considerably stimulate the functioning of the ovaries. It is therefore easy to cure this type of sterility, since treatment is simply a matter of diet.

In general, malnutrition impairs fecundity; hunger has a definite effect on the internal organs. According to Stefko, the Russian famine gave rise to severe genital disorders which took the form of changes in the graafian follicles; the germ cells degenerated into connective tissue, which obviously is not conducive to reproduction. During the last war, when there was a shortage of food in most countries, amenorrhœa (absence of menstruation), which is the most striking symptom of sterility, was very common.

Conversely, the proverb 'too much of a good thing is as bad as not enough' applies to fertility in so far as over-feeding is capable of weakening genital activity to such an extent that sterility may follow; an obese woman, among other drawbacks of her pathological state, suffers from a weakened capacity to conceive, as had been proved beyond all doubt by experiments on animals. If the suppression of certain vitamins in the animals' food retards the advent of rut, an excess of those vitamins prevents reproduction. Other sexual anomalies associated with signs of obesity always arouse the physician's suspicions; the two things are so closely allied that with the menopause and the cessation of her reproductive activity, woman has usually a tendency to stoutness.

In short, anything which affects the general health also influences fertility.

'Among the chief causes of feminine sterility we shall mention the noxious atmosphere of cities. Nerve-racking professional and semi-professional occupations, prolonged residence in unhealthy localities, the lack of exercise or excessive indulgence in sport, an abnormal mode of living and unsatisfactory hygiene, sexual excesses, all contribute to deplete the feminine organism. Man being endowed with a stronger genital stamina, his testes can more readily produce a new supply of cells as soon as living conditions become normal again, whereas the woman's organism is more susceptible to adverse factors and recuperates more slowly. The ovaries, its most vulnerable part, lose their capacity for cell production if illness or untoward circumstances are prolonged. The number of follicles in an ovary being determined at birth, the destroyed ones cannot be replaced and complete sterility ensues.'*

A whole series of anatomical disorders can also render sterile a woman whose genital glands are otherwise normal. Lesions of the vagina and of the vulva, tumours, neglected lacerations of the perinæum, a vagina too long or too short, and malformation of the hymen, constitute so many obstacles

* Van de Velde: *Fertility in Marriage*, Covici-Friede, N. Y.

[297]

to conception. With regard to the internal organs, various abnormalities can prevent the spermatozoa from reaching their goal; the most common is prolapsus or retroversion of the uterus, etc., particularly after the first confinement. The resulting sterility is easily remedied by massage, the use of a special pessary, and the adoption of a suitable attitude during coitus, in accordance with a specialist's advice. More complicated cases, like the occlusion of the fallopian tubes, require surgical intervention; in recent years this has proved most successful.

In addition to the anatomical obstacles to conception, it is necessary to stress those due to deficiency of the glandular secretions; any disturbance of function in the thyroid, the ovaries, or the suprarenals may result in sterility; such cases are sometimes treated successfully by opotherapy. This treatment consists in giving suitable hormone compounds (ovarian, thyroid, adrenalin), which are sometimes efficacious. Hyperacid vaginal secretions destroy the spermatozoa; this is soon detected by an analysis, and neutralised by douches of a solution of bicarbonate of soda or other alkaline substances.

Sterility becomes an extremely serious matter when it is due to a specific inflammation of the mucous membrane of the uterus, of the oviducts or the ovaries. Although we shall study these infections in the chapter on venereal disease, we must outline them here in view of their immediate connection with sterility.

Gonorrhœa, syphilis and other venereal diseases are not the only specific causes of infection; the latter is not infrequently an aftermath of abortion. Anyone aware of the doubtful methods and rudimentary antisepsis of professional abortionists will not wonder that infection, in addition to traumas, usually follows their good offices. During pregnancy, the mucous membranes are particularly susceptible to germs, and to many abortionists asepsis is unknown; for that matter, a normal delivery presents the same dangers, but it is usually performed under scientific conditions. For the same reasons, the strictest cleanliness in sexual relations is specially advisable for a few weeks before and after delivery; the penis is eminently liable to deposit in the vagina germs which will generate puerperal fever, the outcome of which, if not fatal, is frequently sterility.

If infections were always treated in time, they would not be so serious; but their painless character at the beginning is their chief danger, since they are too frequently overlooked; by the time they have reached a more acute stage and a doctor is called in, there is no alternative but to remove the affected organ in order to stop the spread of the disease. If only some of the organs are removed and the woman is still capable of intercourse and further pregnancies, she will have been let off lightly. But, only too often, gonorrhœal and other infections compel the surgeon to take drastic action and remove the ovaries, the fallopian tubes and the uterus.

Sterility, however, is such a painful mental affliction to a young woman that scientists have endeavoured to find a means of enabling her to conceive in spite of everything. This is a recently developed branch of surgery which has already proved wonderfully successful. Our repeatedly quoted authority, Dr. Van de Velde, is one of the pioneers in that domain.

If the fallopian tubes have to be removed, the surgeon tries to leave enough of the oviduct and to modify the tissues in such a way that, even in its reduced form, the tube will still be capable of transmitting the ova from the ovary to the uterus. In the case of an ovariotomy, the patient may be given another chance, by grafting on to the

stump of the oviduct part of the excised organ, or by grafting
it into the wall of the uterus. If this is possible with a fragment of the diseased ovary, there is nothing against it; the
case becomes more delicate if it is a question of grafting
foreign ovarian tissue. This operation has been performed by
several surgeons and the patients have given birth to perfectly
sound children; but it raises difficulties of an ethical order;
since the ovary produces the ovum, in case of pregnancy
the patient may justifiably feel that she is bearing a strange
child. This idea is capable of influencing her for the rest
of her life so that she is unable to regard the child as really
her own. From a legal point of view, it is the woman who
bears who is considered the mother, and a child grown from
a grafted ovary is strictly legitimate.

The surgeon's intervention is needed in numerous other
cases of sterility. Cysts and tumours which cannot be
treated medically have to come under the scalpel. Lately
efforts have been made to cure sterility, due to constitutional
disorders, by X-raying the ovaries; this treatment is a
double-edged one, owing to the difficulties of properly
regulating the doses; the sensitiveness of the organs varies
greatly in individuals and a radiation which helps one
patient may harm another. Then, too, even if the patient
is unharmed by the treatment, the ova may have been
damaged; X-ray applications have caused congenital mal-
formations. This therapy must therefore be applied with
extreme caution, for even sterility is better than giving
birth to a monstrosity.

From this brief survey of the different causes of sterility
in a couple, and in women in particular, it appears clearly
that sterility is necessarily incurable only in the case of absolute genital abnormalities (lack of a vital organ, herma-
phroditism, etc.). In the great majority of cases suitable and
patient treatment, or an operation, may enable a woman to

become a mother. Dr. Van de Velde has classified as follows the cases of sterility which a physician may be called upon to treat:

I. Is the formation of the ovum abnormal? If so, is it attributable to a constitutional defect or to an inflamed condition of the ovaries?

II. Is the uterus sufficiently developed and large enough to give the fertilised ovum its required nourishment and the embryo the necessary shelter until fully developed?

III. Are there any obstacles to the fusion of the ovum and the spermatozoon?

IV. Do voluptuous sensations fail to evoke a feeling of receptiveness, and, if so, what are the psycho-sexual reasons for it?

V. Have the couple been committing technical mistakes during copulation? Have they chosen a time unpropitious for impregnation?

In any case the popular tendency to throw all responsibility for the sterility of a couple on to the woman is clearly unjust. It is founded on a very primitive process of reasoning: 'it is the woman who ought to bring children into the world; this one does not, therefore she cannot'. Experience has proved that, leaving out those cases where the husband's fault is indirect, it is a venereal taint in his blood which by setting up inflammatory conditions in the wife is responsible for the childlessness of a large proportion of couples. Further, whereas a frigid woman is not necessarily sterile, an impotent man nearly always is. Impotence is commonly associated with the inability to have an erection, but it can assume a variety of other forms, as, for instance, hyposecretion of the endocrine glands. We shall pursue this subject further on.

A comparatively new treatment of sterility is that

known as artificial fertilisation. It may be required by the man, by the woman, or by both, according to whether it is due to a malformation of the penis, or a malformation or chemical defect of the vagina, the cervix or the uterus. The process is applicable if there is no apparent cause for sterility and if the cells of both partners are found to be normal. Obviously, artificial fertilisation is contra-indicated if there is a hereditary taint in either family or if, without being actually ill, the woman's ova are degenerate.

Artificial fertilisation consists in inseminating the uterus by a process other than coitus. The sperm is usually introduced directly into the uterus, sometimes it is deposited only at its mouth; the former method is obviously surer. In general, this method is better the more closely it imitates a normal sexual act, freed from the particular defects of the couple concerned. Some practitioners who hold that the woman's orgasm is a great aid to fertilisation recommend that she be sexually roused before the operation. As this implies coitus, it may give rise to a somewhat delicate situation entailing the settlement of details important to the success of the experiment. We shall again quote Van de Velde:

'The question of where artificial fertilisation shall be performed, that is, whether it shall take place at home or in the physician's surgery, is important. The practitioner is naturally perfectly willing that his surgery be used, with all the necessary appliances. In my opinion, however, the main objection to this is that the patients are much less at their ease there than in their own home, a factor which cannot be overlooked in view of the necessary emission, stimulation of the woman at the right moment, and her eventual rest in bed. Whenever it can be done in the patient's home it will therefore be preferable for the doctor to take his instruments and perform the operation on the edge of a table or a bed, instead of on a gynæcological chair. In fact, a surgeon has often to perform far more difficult operations in his patient's home, whereas in this case it is simply a matter of introducing the nozzle of a uterine syringe into the cervix.'*

The author goes on to recommend that normal coitus be performed at home while the doctor waits in the next room. At the proper time he will join his patients, place the wife in the obstetric position, draw into his syringe some of the seminal fluid left in the vagina, and, after having drawn down the lower cervix by means of forceps, will introduce the nozzle into the mouth of the uterus and inject the fluid.

This procedure is not without its inconveniences, but they are comparatively easy to circumvent. On the other hand, there is the distinct advantage of having secured a favourable environment for the spermatozoa.

Some practitioners prefer to collect the sperm in the course of a *coitus interruptus*, using for that purpose a suitable vessel. Others resort to coitus with a sheath, which facilitates the transfer of the sperm.

Another very practical method is masturbation, which is used when normal coitus is impossible. This has the disadvantage of offending the æsthetic sense of the couple.

It sometimes happens that the man's semen does not contain the live spermatozoa needed for artificial impregnation. One then punctures the epididymis, in which there is always the possibility of finding some live cells; they are then mixed with some prostatic secretion, without which they have no motility; this secretion is placed in the vagina, where it is left during intercourse.

* Dr. Van de Velde's works are published in America by Covici-Friede, N. Y.

Some gynæcologists have pushed the process further and have tried to scatter the semen across the uterus as far as the fallopian tubes, even to deposit the sperm in the neighbourhood of the ovaries. These methods are not of very great practical value.

Needless to say, the selection of an appropriate time for artificial impregnation is as important as for a natural one. Experience has shown that operations performed between the eighth and the sixteenth days after the beginning of menstruation give the most satisfactory results. The failure of one operation must not discourage the couple, since, after all, this is only an imitation coitus, which is also liable to fail. The couple may require to have the operation repeated two or three times, which they will not hesitate to do if they have had the good fortune to meet a physician whose tact did not make the process repugnant to them at their first attempt.

Editor's Note.—There is a proper systematic procedure which should be carried out in every case of sterility. First of all, the husband's semen should be examined to see if it contains a sufficient number of healthy sperm cells. If this examination gives a satisfactory result, the next step is to examine the wife. The vaginal and cervical secretions should be examined by a pathologist; an injection of Lipiodol or some other similar opaque substance should be made into the uterus while the patient is under the fluorescent X-ray screen. With this technique the progress of the fluid into the uterus and through the fallopian tubes can be followed. If the tubes (one or both) are seen to be blocked, the pressure can be increased gradually, the danger from too great a pressure being avoidable since the whole thing is done under the direct ocular observation of the surgeon. And, of course, other obstacles to fertility must be searched for. A systematic investigation of this kind will succeed in bringing about cure of the sterility in a surprisingly large number of cases. The Lipiodol injection is particularly valuable, not only for diagnosis, but also for the cure of certain cases of tubal blockage.—N. H.

PUBLISHERS' NOTE

As the original Chapter XXV written by Dr. Norman
Haire for the English edition might possibly have come
in conflict with the United States laws concerning transmission of contraceptive information through the mails,
the American publishers of The Encyclopedia of Sexual
Knowledge have substituted a chapter from another
hand. The present Chapter XXV contains views and
opinions with which Dr. Haire is in strong disagreement,
and is not to be considered as representing Dr. Haire's
viewpoint. The reader will bear in mind, therefore, that
the statement of authorship contained in the preface to
this edition is erroneous to this extent.

THE PUBLISHERS

WHEN WOMEN SHOULD NOT PROCREATE

WE now approach a chapter whose subject matter is bound to arouse the keenest kind of interest, since the question of birth control constitutes a vital problem in all civilised countries. In an earlier chapter we made the statement that, while the problem had a political and social bearing, its medical aspect was what chiefly concerned us. Which is our reason for stating at the very outset that any artificial interruption of pregnancy, any obstacle placed in the way of fertilisation, is contrary to nature. It is true that we are ignorant of nature's ultimate goal, just as we are ignorant of the ultimate goal of our own existence here, but our observations in the field of the vegetable and animal kingdoms do teach us that we are here to reproduce, and that it is our duty, our biological mission, to leave progeny. There are, as a matter of fact, certain living creatures—in the insect world, primarily—which are born, grow to maturity, reproduce and die. With us this aim manifests itself in the instinct which impels us to have children. The normal, healthy individual, living under acceptable conditions of existence, feels the need to procreate and to establish a home. Without children, life seems devoid of charm or meaning. The child complements the human being, and experience has shown us that there is no operation from which a woman will shrink in order to satisfy her natural instinct for children.

From the purely medical viewpoint, therefore, everyone

should be advised to found a family. Only thus can the individual achieve complete fulfilment, find a support for his old age, perpetuate his own life in that of his children, who are not only his flesh and blood, but his spirit and his thoughts as well. Women are not truly women until they have become mothers. Men do not actually reach maturity until they have acquired the responsibility of a family.

*   *   *

Tuberculosis is the most decided contra-indication to pregnancy. The danger here is so grave that every possible measure should be taken to prevent fertilisation. The process of gestation considerably aggravates the tuberculous condition by fostering the spread of the disease which, superficially cured though it may be, is likely to become active once more. Some women have sufficient resistance to hold the malady in check during pregnancy, but with the arrival of confinement, when a supreme effort is demanded of the organism, the enemy takes the upper hand.

As to kidney disorders, a distinction should be drawn between pre-pregnancy affections and those whose appearance coincides with pregnancy.

As a general thing we know that, when a woman suffering from nephritis becomes pregnant, the prognosis is unfavorable. The outcome, in cases where nephritis develops only in the course of pregnancy, presents a far more complicated problem and involves the necessity of distinguishing among the various types of the disease—an examination too lengthy for the limits of this chapter.

Ordinary cardiac ailments present no special danger to pregnant women. But when the heart muscle itself is affected or when, even before pregnancy, an œdema of the feet, irregular respiration and so on are noted, these symptoms indicate that the heart is incapable of performing its task properly, and the danger becomes accordingly greater.

In other words, though a small motor may suffice to drive a car over a long stretch of years, that same motor, attached to a heavier vehicle, may refuse obedience or even cease functioning altogether.

Returning to diabetes, of which we have already made mention, its complications may well prove dangerous during the period of confinement. Fortunately, however, diabetic women rarely become pregnant, since the uterus, impregnated with sugar, is practically incapable of nidation.

Exophthalmic goitre, varicose veins, epilepsy, biliary calculus, cyclic vomiting, of which we have spoken elsewhere, and finally, affections of the female genital organs, also previously mentioned, are likewise contra-indications to pregnancy which should prompt husband and wife to forego children.

For the sake of future generations, it should also be borne in mind that mental disorders, syphilis, alcoholism, hemophilia and nervous diseases are scarcely desirable legacies to hand on to one's offspring.

*　　*　　*

We have just stated that, in certain cases, the birth of a child involves danger for the mother, the child or both. In such cases—but in such cases only, in order to avoid gambling with a human life—the advice of the physician who counsels against procreation should be followed.

We have had occasion to state, in other sections of this volume, that at such times the use of preventive measures becomes imperative. In our opinion, the physician has no right to indicate such measures to any healthy married couple; once convinced, however, that the mother can be protected against fatal complications in no other way, it becomes the physician's duty to recommend these measures.

We must, on the other hand, point out that any assistance gained through medical advice is only relative, that there exists no unfailing method of preventing conception, and that the devices and preparations thrown on the market amid such a storm of ballyhoo exploit to a greater or lesser degree the credulity of the public.

The physician alone is competent to determine whether or not a couple should, for reasons of health, have recourse to preventive measures and the physician alone should decide on the most appropriate method in each case.

* * *

Before considering and discussing the advice likely to be offered by physicians, in order that we may appraise such advice in the light of the latest scientific discoveries, let us rapidly review the process of fertilisation. During the sex act the semen of the man is deposited in the vagina, whence it is drawn up by the uterus. In the uterine cavity or in one of the Fallopian tubes, the spermatozoa encounter the ovum expelled by the ovary, and the impregnation of the egg is accomplished. The fertilised ovum is deposited in the uterine mucosa, where it effects its nidation. Pregnancy has begun.

If this complicated series of events and its logical consequences are clear to the reader, he will understand that, to avoid conception, the meeting of the spermatozoa with the ovum must be prevented. Since time immemorial all sorts of methods have been applied to that end, but it is our purpose to discuss here only the most important. The oldest and most widespread of these methods is *coitus interruptus*, wherein the man withdraws before the climax has been reached. The Bible itself contains an allusion to this practise in the passage on Onan: " And Onan knew that the seed would not be his; and it came to pass, when he went in unto his brother's wife, that he spilled it on the ground, lest that he should give seed to his brother". Since this method requires no special knowledge, no appliances nor medicaments, it has gained wide favor in every stratum of society, with the result that 40% of all married couples—if we are to credit statistics—make a regular practice of *coitus interruptus*.

Because of the very vogue enjoyed by this practice, however—to which people resort without consulting their physicians—we consider it necessary to point out its disadvantages. *Coitus interruptus* greatly diminishes the enjoyment to be derived from intercourse and works harm on the nervous system. Its after-effects are characteristic in that they fail to make their appearance immediately. A neurosis may develop later, however, which it would be difficult to cure. In addition to these nervous affections, all sorts of physical disturbances may occur to destroy the joy of living. The normal reactions during the act of intercourse itself are often so profoundly affected that a lengthy course of treatment is required to restore them to their natural state.

Nor should the immediate discomfort of this method—which compels the man to withdraw before his desire is gratified—be overlooked. His pleasure is merely a half-pleasure; as for the woman, she generally fails to achieve the orgasm and frequently finds it necessary to resort to masturbation to induce satisfaction. In short, *coitus interruptus* constitutes anything but a perfect method of sexual union. Countless households have gone to smash against that reef. The husband prefers to turn to other women with whom such measures are not needful, and the wife's sex life is vitally affected by the abnormality of the intercourse.

Nor are the couples who engage in this harmful practice entirely secure against surprise, and the woman who least expects it may one day find herself pregnant. Should the man withdraw his penis from the vagina one tenth of a second too late, this will suffice to deposit two drops of semen at the opening of the vagina. Because of the extra-ordinary motility of the spermatozoa, no more than two drops are needed to bring about conception. There is also the possibility that a few drops of semen may adhere to the extremity of the penis after the first coition, and unless the penis is very carefully washed, these particles may re-main in the vagina at the time of the next coition and fertilise the ovum.

Another preventive method commonly employed involves the use of condoms, known also as preservatives. These are made either of rubber or fishbladder, and the chief ob-jection to their use lies in the fact that they considerably reduce the pleasure to be derived from the sex act. They do have one advantage—they protect the user against in-fection by venereal disease.

Coitus interruptus and the use of preservatives comprise the category of contraceptive methods by which the sperms are prevented from entering the vagina—the methods which the man is called upon to employ. We now come to the methods which must be applied by the woman. They con-sist in rendering harmless the sperms which are deposited in the vagina, or in preventing them from entering the uterus.

With this end in view, a series of appliances has been designed, classed under the general head of pessaries. The most common of these are the cap-pessaries which are made of some rigid substance, usually metal, and are shaped like a miniature basin. The vaginal portion of the uterus is covered by this cap-pessary to prevent the spermatozoa from entering the uterine cavity. These pessaries exist in count-less varieties. The most complicated mechanisms have been devised—appliances with valves and springs—which are intended to prevent the entry of the sperms and to allow the uterine secretions to drain out at the same time.

All these experiments, however, have proven themselves, to a greater or lesser degree, failures. A mechanism which would be childishly simple in the world of machines presents insuperable difficulties when it becomes a question of applying it to the human organism. The very first step —that of placing the pessary in the vagina—is extremely difficult. Soft sensitive muscles everywhere, no bones, no solid base of support. The problem of keeping the pessary in the proper state of cleanliness becomes a veritable stumbling-block in the way of its use, since the mucous excretions which attack the appliance form centers of infection. Every "invention of genius" in this field has failed.

Vaginal pessaries, to be at all effective, must not alone be examined by the physician, but must be placed in position by him, since, if they are badly adjusted, they altogether fail of their purpose. Their job is to block up the uterine orifice, leaving no opening, while at the same time care must be taken to prevent the pessary from pressing too heavily against the cervix of the uterus. Yet even when the appliance is properly placed, anything—an overabrupt movement, pressure in emptying the bowels, a contraction of the uterus—may serve to dislodge the pessary from the cervix and force it back into the vagina. Any woman, therefore, who wears a pessary for purposes of health should, before engaging in the sex act, make sure that the appliance is in place by adjusting it with her finger. The pessary should be removed before menstruation, cleansed, and replaced only after the flow has completely ceased. It is inadvisable, moreover, to confine this operation to the menstrual periods, since the uterus is an organ which, like all organs communicating with the exterior, excretes large quantities of mucus (just as the ears excrete wax and the nose mucus). Naturally, the accumulation of these excretions over the sides of the pessary cannot but prove injurious to the health. In any case, it is absolutely essential that the pessary be removed several days before menstruation and not replaced till the menstrual period is over—which provides the added advantage of allowing the genital organs time to rest.

The fact that the pessary is at best a foreign body introduced into the organism—some women will have nothing to do with it under any circumstances—imposes upon the woman for whom it is prescribed the need for scrupulous cleanliness of the genital organs. Opinions vary as to how frequently a vaginal douche should be taken for purposes of feminine hygiene, but there can be no doubt that, when a pessary is worn, a careful daily douche is imperative.

Another type of pessary which has enjoyed considerable vogue for some time is that known as the intra-uterine pessary. As its name indicates, this appliance is placed not in the vagina but inside the uterus, and its popularity is doubtless due to the fact that it need not be removed during the menstrual period and requires changing only once in four months.

This uterine pessary is designed not to prevent the spermatozoa from entering the uterus—its disc-mechanism does not block the entry—but to prevent the ovum from finding lodgment by setting up a permanent excitation which keeps the uterine mucosa in a state unfit for nidation. In our opinion, this is a process not devoid of danger, and there is every reason to believe that this constant irritation may result in the formation of malignant tumours.

The use of intra-uterine pessaries does not, strictly speaking, prevent conception but only the nidation of the fertilized ovum. Therefore it does to some extent constitute an interruption of pregnancy—a culpable offense from the viewpoint of church and state. The use of these pessaries should be limited to those cases in which the state of the woman's health absolutely forbids pregnancy.

All the contraceptive media discussed up to this point make use of some mechanical device to prevent fertilisation, whether the barrier erected be of rubber or metal or some other rigid substance. We now come to the examination of chemical media which, by their composition, are designed to destroy the spermatozoa deposited in the vagina. These are called suppositories and are thrust as deeply as possible into the female genital tract before the sex act. Their effect, however, cannot be relied upon. An example will better serve to illustrate the process. Certain suppositories, if they are to take effect, must first dissolve and produce a sort of effervescence, for which they require the humid atmosphere supplied by the vagina. If, however, there should happen to be an inadequate flow of vaginal secretions and the walls of the organ should remain too dry, the suppositories will fail of their effect.

The toleration of women, where contraceptive suppositories are concerned, varies considerably. Certain suppositories induce excessive flowing in some women, while in others they produce no abnormal reaction. The male urethra too may react in various ways to various preparations. There have been cases, for example, in which the patient, having employed a preparation with a cocoa-butter base, has developed a serious infection of the urethra which spread to the bladder and required several weeks to cure.

There are other products which are introduced into the vagina in a liquid state. This is an advantage, but they too may fail to effervesce. Hence, one has no guarantee that the antiseptic properties of the product will take effect in all portions of the vagina, as they should.

For the sake of completeness, we must touch once more

on the vaginal pulverisers, which spray the organs with an antiseptic powder preparation. This method offers no surer guarantee than any of the others, and its use is still more complicated.

In enumerating these chemical contraceptive methods, we have reserved to the last the process most commonly used—namely, injections applied with a douche bag or a vaginal syringe.

* * *

Surgical sterilisation is often confused with castration, though they involve two totally different processes of intervention. Castration consists of the removal of the genital glands—that is to say, of the testicles in the male and the ovaries in the female. This operation leaves the patient unfit for love and transforms him into a sluggish creature, stigmatised and devoid of sex power. Sterilisation, on the other hand, does not affect the personality of the patient, produces no reaction on the organism as a whole and does not diminish the erotic capacity. The patient is deprived of no organ and the genital glands remain intact. The operation is confined to the insertion of a ligature between these glands and their excretory ducts. Thus, in the male, the passage between the testicles and the penis is blocked— in the female, the passage between the ovaries and the uterus. In the former case, the insertion of the ligature around the *vas deferens*, which is outside the abdominal cavity, presents no special danger. If the operation is skilfully performed, the patient will recover in three days. It is a considerably more complicated business with a woman, since the process of intervention involves organs situated in the depths of the abdominal cavity. Thanks to modern surgical methods, however, this operation no longer presents insuperable difficulties, though convalescence is far slower than in the case of the man and a hospital stay of two weeks is imperative.

If we lay stress here on the process of sterilisation, it is not merely for the purpose of differentiating it from castration, but because it is the one infallible method of preventing fertilisation. It is also the one method which we can recommend with a perfectly clear conscience to women whose state of health absolutely forbids procreation.

Eighteen states in the United States have enacted legislation which provides for the sterilisation of the unfit—cretins, epileptics, alcoholics, paralytics, incorrigible criminals and so on. Among all the thousands who have been sterilised as a result of these provisions, no serious trouble of any kind has been noted. On the contrary, a certain improvement in the mental condition of a number of cases has been established. In Switzerland there have been cases of inveterate vagrants who, once sterilised, have lost their morbid need of change and developed into hard-working, orderly citizens.

Sterilisation through X-ray has certain advantages over surgical sterilisation. It is capable of producing a temporary sterility which disappears when the X-ray treatments are terminated. The method involves disadvantages too, however, which must be taken into account. Its after-effects may be harmful and difficult to check—especially in relation to the secretory functions of the genital glands. Moreover, it is difficult to regulate the dosage of the rays, with the result that a process of intervention intended to bring about temporary sterility will sometimes effect permanent sterility. These two defects in the method render sterilisation through X-ray—at any rate, for the present—practically worthless.

To round out this chapter, brief mention should be made of certain methods which have not yet been sufficiently well tested to have any practical value, but which may play an important rôle in the life of the future. We refer to contraceptive immunisation through a treatment with a hormone base.

This treatment consists of giving the woman subcutaneous injections of masculine sperms in a 1% solution, prepared so as to destroy the spermatozoa. The dose contained in such an injection varies from between 1 and 12 drops. When the maximum dose is reached, the woman is incapable of conception but the treatment is continued. As soon as the injections are stopped, the woman becomes fertile again. Experiments of this sort on women have thus far been infrequent, and most of them have been undertaken in England and Russia. Tentative experiments along the same line have recently been started in America. The results, however, are not yet conclusive. Therefore the method can hardly be considered from the practical angle at this time.

The principle of organotherapy involves the use of hormones of glands of internal secretion—the testicles, for example—which hormones are introduced into the blood stream of the patient. We know that women who engage in sexual intercourse with abnormal frequency (prostitutes) are in some way saturated with sperms, which fact immunises them against their action. It is possible to bring about this state of saturation by artificial application of the sperms to the woman's organism.

Assuming that organotherapic immunisation may develop in the future into a safe and certain contraceptive method, it would still present the disadvantage of necessitating regular injections. A far more practical method would be to have the product converted into the form of pills which, taken internally, would suffice to prevent conception. Injections with a sperm base have the added disadvantage of blunting the woman's libido.

A recent discovery which we owe to Professor Haber-landt seeks to obviate these disadvantages. His preparation is presented in the form of pills, to be taken internally, and his active principle does not borrow its virtue from the sperms but from the hormones of the ovaries of pregnant or nursing women. Since we know that women in either of these conditions are incapable of fertilisation, their hormones have the power of granting immunisation against conception.

While organotherapic methods have not yet been thoroughly tested, they seem to have a great future ahead of them.

It is unfortunate that State and Federal laws in the United States make specific information about the proper use of contraceptives unavailable to the general public. Information of a sort is always available to the educated and the well-to-do although it is often surprisingly inadequate. Doctors are forbidden by law to give contraceptive information except where procreation will seriously threaten the health or life of the mother or result in a deformed or mentally unsound child. Of course many doctors ignore these legal bars. But it is only recently that doctors themselves have had first rate technical knowledge of many contraceptive measures and many doctors have been almost as helpless and incompetent as their patients in this respect. For the great mass of people who cannot afford private medical attention, there is no way of easily obtaining safe advice. This, of course, is particularly true of the really poor who more than any other class need such information for their own and society's economic and moral welfare. The stand of the Catholic Church has been four-square against making available necessary contraceptive information and it is only recently that the Church, realizing the gravity of the general situation, has attempted to find a way out within its own dogmas. The "Rhythm" theory is advanced as a solution. This theory is based on the fairly authenticated fact that every woman has a barren period between menstrual periods. Intercourse at such times will, of course, be sterile, but may be indulged in with the sanction of the Church as containing no unnatural element. The objection to the theory is that at present there is no easy method of discovering when this sterile period occurs in the individual and the further fact that these periods may even vary within the individual. Even though these objections be overcome this method is at best a compromise. Sexual intercourse among healthy and loving human beings should be a spontaneous expression and it is psychically important that this need be satisfied without artificial delay. However, it is far better than a counsel of perfection—i. e. married chastity, which presents unbearable temptations and even if successful, may carry in its train severe neurotic consequences.

CHAPTER XXVI

IMPOTENCE IN MAN

Impotence in erection and impotence in procreation. The four essential factors. Relative impotence. Illnesses and narcotics. Nervous impotence. The sexual act 'by command' and the customs of the Middle Ages. The revolt of the unconscious. Premature ejaculation. Malformation of the genital organs. Aspermia and azoospermia. Difficulties of diagnosis.

WHEREAS one distinguishes in the case of women between sterility and frigidity, all the imperfections of the genital apparatus of man are included in the single term 'impotence'.* The fact that it is the woman who bears the child and brings it into the world has led to a distinct separation between mother and mistress. To conceive, a woman need not be a perfect lover and, although sexually cold, she can make a perfectly normal mother; inversely, a sterile woman can be a passionate mistress.

While impotence commonly implies solely the inability to have an erection, it is often used to include other dis-

* *Editor's Note.*—The writer of this chapter has chosen to include under the term impotence symptoms which would be better treated under two separate headings. *Impotentia cœundi*, or inability to carry out the act of copulation itself, should alone be understood by the English word *impotence*. *Impotentia generandi*, or the inability to procreate a child, should not be included under the term impotence, but should be referred to as male sterility. This plan is in accordance with the general English usage. The plan followed by the author of this chapter, on the contrary, is in accordance with the habit of certain Continental writers on the subject.—N. H.

turbances, notably those in the internal secretions, which give rise to conditions that correspond to feminine sterility. Thus a man who is impotent in the general acceptance of the word, that is, unable to procreate, can be apparently normal during coitus; his childlessness will be imputed to his wife, for no one will ever think of questioning his obvious virility. It will require a physician to enlighten the couple.

The woman's part in procreation is spread over a relatively long period and includes not only conception but also the need to place the fertilised egg correctly, carry it the full term, and bring the child into the world; the man's part consists in a single action: coitus. Hence the energy consumed in that short instant is much more dynamic and its source extremely complex; the anomalies which can occur in the male genital system are consequently numerous and varied.

The normal sexual act by man is accomplished in four phases: sexual desire or libido, stiffening of the penis or erection, ejaculation or emission of semen, and the climax of excitement, or orgasm. Each of these phases is subject to disturbances, and if one of them is absent or incomplete, we speak of impotence. The term is thus an infinitely complex one and has been classified in a variety of ways. As it would be superfluous to take up one after the other all the varieties of impotence, we shall limit ourselves to examining the more common forms and explaining their causes.

Libido in man and in woman arises through the action of the sex hormones; it can never be totally lacking. A man without sexual instincts no more exists than a man without appetite, but his instinct may be diverted and manifest itself abnormally; we have then to deal with a sexual perversion. A man thus affected may not be able to procreate, usually because coitus is repugnant to him.

There are, however, men and women in whom the orgasm is reached by means of coitus, but in whom the culmination of enjoyment is dependent on perverse practices (in the case of a man this can hardly be regarded as proof of impotence). In their book *Sexual Perversions*, Hirschfeld, Abraham and Vachet relate the case of an Austrian cavalry captain who, although happily married, was impotent with his wife, while with prostitutes his virility was unquestionable. The reason for this was that he dared not practise with his wife all the tricks which he allowed himself with professionals. For instance, he was in the habit of winding a string around his penis and scrotum and of indulging in flagellation, cunnilinctus, and pedicatio with a 'godemiché'. It was only after such preliminaries that he could perform the sexual act with success. This is a typical example of partial impotence where libido is aroused only under peculiar conditions.

As regards difficulties of erection, men normally endowed sexually and able to desire a woman passionately are sometimes incapable of erection and of effecting connection. The anatomy of the male genitals, which we have described in the chapter on that subject, shows that erection is caused by an influx of blood into the spongy tissue of the penis (*corpora cavernosa*) consequent on stimulation of the erectile nerves (*nervi erigentes*).

We must here distinguish between relative and absolute impotence. A relatively impotent man can have intercourse only in certain circumstances, while an absolutely impotent one can never have an erection. The former is merely the victim of a passing functional disturbance, generally psychological; the latter case involves organic disorder and, as such, is very much more serious.

General fatigue is the most frequent cause of temporary impotence. When all the functions of a debilitated organism are weakened, the genital functions are no exception. As a Latin proverb puts it in picturesque language: *Sine Baccho et Cerere fugit Venus.* That is, lacking Bacchus and Ceres, Venus flees, or, translated into unmythological language: there is no love-making without food and wine. Even if he escapes impotence, an underfed man is always a poor lover.

Following a wasting illness or a prolonged bout of fever, erection is often impossible for some time; similarly, after a serious surgical operation which has entailed a considerable loss of stamina.

Certain illnesses handicap male potency, notably diabetes and chronic nephritis in an advanced stage; tuberculosis of the lungs at first stimulates the senses and only at the end renders the patient impotent; any disorder causing obesity dulls sexual activity; an excess of fatty tissue is in any case a frequent symptom of genital insufficiency in man as well as in woman.

Every kind of intoxication hampers normal sexual functioning and may lead to impotence, especially in the form of difficulty in erection. Intoxication in certain industries, for instance by lead, mercury, phosphorus, bromide, iodine, etc., are no exception to the rule. Alcoholism, and the abuse of narcotics like morphine, cocaine or opium weaken the sexual instinct and disturb the corresponding functions, although stimulating them at first. Nicotine itself affects the genital secretions of heavy smokers. This form of impotence must be treated casually rather than organically.

Nervous impotence sets a much more complex problem. The man cannot always account for his inability to have an erection and is deeply concerned, although the cause may be quite trifling. Given a sensitive temperament, an unclean room, an uncomfortable bed or an unprepossessing environment, a man may be affected so disagreeably that he becomes impotent; that is why it must never be forgotten that the sexual act is as much a psychological phenomenon as a physiological one. If conditions unfavourable to an erotic atmosphere, such as we have just mentioned, can provoke a biological deficiency, what then of men who have sexual relations with women whom they do not love? Here the slightest defect, an unpleasant odour, an indelicate gesture, a coarse word, even a glimpse of the douche-bag, may be enough to snuff out the flame of desire in the man. To label him impotent would be going too far; nevertheless he is often considered as such, and it is sufficient for a woman to taunt her lover with his momentary weakness, for him to become alarmed and to believe himself condemned to forego the joys of love for ever.

Thus all unfavourable conditions can induce impotence. The knowledge that he is acting 'to order' is equally liable to paralyse the physical reaction of a normal man. Apropos of this, it might be interesting to recall that, according to mediæval legal procedure, a man suspected of having cast a spell in order to prevent the consummation of marriage was publicly put to the test. In the language of this witch-obsessed age, these malefactors were called *noueurs d'aiguillettes*. Needless to add, the fear of being condemned, coupled with the public demonstration of the necessary proof, easily rendered the accused impotent. In his *Tableau de l'Amour Conjugal*, Venette describes as follows the absurdity of such laws:

'Probably not one man in a thousand can emerge victoriously from the public congress. Our natural parts are not always obedient to our own will, much less to that of the judges. They often wilt against our will, and too often they are frozen when our heart is burning. If we are on the verge of being roused, our courage fails us, we are

[323]

seized by fear, hate fills our heart and modesty hampers our freedom.'

Men in general are very sensitive on the subject of their potency. To be considered 'impotent' is to them a stigma, a fact which accounts for the frequency with which they are subject to psychological troubles consequent on being teased. As the process of erection is closely allied to a special nerve reaction, a man, once persuaded that he is incapable of a normal erection, becomes impotent through auto-suggestion. We quote the following from *Sexual Perversions*:

'One of our patients, as a child, discovered that, in comparison with those of his comrades, his penis was relatively small; as a result he was the butt of much teasing. In spite of the fact that the member grew in time to normal size, he was unable to rid himself of his idea of organ inferiority. Fear of being ridiculous kept him from sexual relations until finally he decided to seek out a prostitute, but even with her he remained impotent.

'Meanwhile, having fallen in love with a young girl, he underwent treatment in the hope of being cured of this "shortcoming" which would have prevented his marriage. A friend in whom he had confided sent him to us, thinking that we might perhaps find a remedy for his condition.

'His cure, along purely psychological lines, was a very simple matter. He has been married a year and during that time has never been "impotent".'

Another class of psychological obstacles consists of inhibitions of a moral order. It sometimes happens that a man who is leading a normal sexual life with his wife is seized with a desire to emulate his friends and seeks extra-marital diversion. But he finds himself suddenly impotent; the laughter and the taunts of the prostitute only serve to increase his embarrassment, and he finds it impossible to have an erection. The underlying cause of his impotence is not his wounded vanity, but his unconscious revolt against the escapade, which in his innermost being he finds immoral. It is because his conscience condemns him for having wanted to be unfaithful to his wife, that he loses the power of being so.

The same moral difficulty may confront a man who is having sexual relations with a young girl. Up to a point, his desire has been at white heat, but a sudden realisation of the wrong he is doing upsets the mechanical sequence necessary to the accomplishment of the act.

In addition to moral scruples, fear is a powerful obstacle to normal erection. It may be fear of being watched, or taken by surprise, or fear of scandal in general (performing coitus in the open, or in an unsafe place), or, what is more common, fear of contagion. The mere thought that he is exposing himself to gonorrhœa or syphilis is enough to reduce a man's psychological condition to a point where the *nervi erigentes* (nerves of erection) refuse to obey.

Troubles of ejaculation are sometimes due to the same causes as inability to erect. For the sake of clarity we must distinguish between two kinds of disturbances: involuntary ejaculation and failure to ejaculate.

Premature ejaculation, called ejaculation *ante portas*, is very frequent in hypersensitive men and neurasthenics. It may also occur when a man has long desired a woman and is at last able to possess her. The psychological factor of this sexual excitement may be so strong that the slightest contact is enough to precipitate the climax, and the partner often concludes that he is impotent—unless he hastens to make reparation for his weakness.

These are the main psychological factors which are responsible for premature ejaculation. Van de Velde, writing on sexual abnormalities, says:

[325]

'An attenuated form of *ejaculatio præcox* is found as an individual peculiarity, among men otherwise in perfect health and sexually normal. This applies above all to scientists and artists, who are nevertheless greatly appreciated as lovers by a certain class of women—principally those of an intellectual type.

'Typical premature ejaculation—if not a result of an inflammatory lesion of the upper part of the urethra—is a true sexual neurosis. Its causes are varied and complicated. In agreement with Marcuse, we regard premature ejaculation, in neuropaths, as a failure to realise their desire, or as an unsuccessful compromise between their desire and their fear of sexual relations.

'The anxiety lest he should "not be ready in time", the secret doubt as to his own potency, the fear of being surprised or spied upon, the inner voice protesting against the object of his desire, the consciousness of guilt, the fear of infection or the desire for another person, are some of the psychological factors in premature ejaculation.'

We see therefore that the causes of *ejaculatio præcox* are appreciably the same as those which give rise to difficulties in erection. The pangs of conscience can influence either case. Van de Velde tells the story of a married man who attempted to rape a servant. For the first time in his life he experienced the shame of ejaculation *ante portas*. The subsequent attempts were also doomed to failure. This unaccustomed outcome of intercourse was undeniably due to his unconscious scruples.

The excessive practice of masturbation prolonged beyond the age of puberty is not—as we have pointed out in our chapter on masturbation—an infrequent cause of impotence. By indulging in solitary pleasures, the adolescent is debarred the satisfaction of normal sexual intercourse, and in the presence of a woman, even a loved one, his sexual power may desert him. This is even more true in the case of homosexuals, where the woman does not even inspire passion.

All abnormal practises, from *coitus interruptus* to 'carezza'—the former consisting in interruption of intercourse at the moment of ejaculation, the latter in retarding ejaculation for an indefinite period—may end, in the long run, in the morbid phenomenon of premature ejaculation. It not infrequently happens that where *coitus interruptus* has been practised over a long period of time, the man, even if desirous of continuing the act to its normal conclusion, is no longer capable of doing so.

Even more serious from the standpoint of potency is prolonged abstinence. All functions become weakened after a time if they are not used, just as an organ atrophies if not exercised. Dr. Hirschfeld in his book *Sexual Perversions* cites a case recorded by Mantegazza:

'I knew a young nobleman who, in order to attain to the heights of science and ambition, took the vow of chastity and kept it rigorously until his thirtieth year. His aim achieved, he decided it was time to make up for what he had lost, and thought of love; but love did not answer his call; his most flattering seductions were wasted. Venus' capricious son continued to turn a deaf ear. Finally, he consulted me. I gave him treatment which, although lasting a long time, ended in his being cured.'

Besides organic causes of a general order, and psychological causes, the treatment of which belong to psychiatry, impotence is often caused by malformation of the external genital organs or by disorders of the internal secretions (insufficiency of the testes or other endocrine glands), or, still more often, by a stricture of the urethra or other excretory canals, which hinders ejaculation. Nevertheless, we repeat once more, that in the kind of impotence known as *impotentia cœundi* (incapacity to perform coitus) it is the psychological factors that predominate.

A kind of inferiority complex where virility is concerned, resulting from a traumatic experience in childhood, or from some other disagreeable incident, can make a physically healthy man impotent. Physicians who know these unfortunate men, who consult them about their inability to have an erection, know at exactly what point the case becomes a tragedy. No treatment, no remedy is too costly for a patient who is impotent—or believes that he is. Charlatans and quacks have not failed to exploit this gold-mine, and drugs, more or less efficacious, promising perfect potency to all, however severe the impotence may be, flood the market. The most suspicious man becomes credulous when he has a hope of being cured of impotence.

We come now to the other kind of impotence known as *impotentia generandi* (the incapacity to procreate).

This kind of affliction causes in man a sterility corresponding to the sterility in woman, which we studied in one of the preceding chapters.

Impotentia generandi, whether caused by acquired illnesses or by congenital abnormalities, usually manifests itself in the form of aspermia. This term is not absolutely correct, since it is not usually a case of complete absence of semen, but of an insufficiency of it*. Aspermia may be due to an obstruction in the ejaculatory canals, consequent on inflammation of the genital organs. Coitus is effected normally, but ejaculation occurs after the penis has relaxed, and the spermatozoa therefore rarely reach their destination. Notwithstanding, impregnation is not an impossibility, and sometimes an appropriate position during the

* *Editor's Note.*—Complete absence of semen is known as *aspermia*, and an insufficient amount of semen as *oligospermia.*—N. H.

sexual act will assure the spermatozoa of an entry to the feminine organs. A couple can also avail themselves of artificial impregnation, so that a man afflicted with aspermia need not necessarily be without progeny.

Azoospermia is an affection in which the semen is discharged in normal quantities, but is defective in quality. This anomaly takes several forms. It is known as oligozoospermia when the semen contains only an infinitesimal number of spermatozoa; asthenozoospermia when the spermatozoa have a lowered vitality and die before they are able to impregnate the ova; necrozoospermia when the spermatozoa are devoid of both life and motility.

All these troubles are due to derangements of the internal secretions. In fact, as we have seen in the chapter dealing with the anatomy of the male genital organs, the semen, to be perfect, requires the secretion of several organs (testes, epididymes, seminal vesicles, prostate). But gonorrhœal inflammation is most often the cause of azoospermia. In man, as in woman, this disease is often at the root of sterility.

The task of the physician who is consulted with regard to one of these disorders is delicate. The analysis of the specimen of semen does not always give an exact idea of the seminal fluid which the same individual ejaculates during sexual intercourse. It varies from one day to the next, according to the psychological condition of the man. Finally, the vaginal secretion changes the chemical composition of the semen. Briefly, even if the first analysis shows an absence of living cells, the physician would err in telling his patient that he is sterile. Dr. Van de Velde advises collecting a specimen of the male semen in the vagina after coitus. He cites William H. Cary, who stresses the inadvisability of a too hasty diagnosis. We will conclude with the quotation in question:

'Experiments have shown that in certain cases the semen appears to be very poor in live spermatozoa when collected directly from the man, whereas it shows considerable activity when collected from the vagina, where it has come in contact with the secretions discharged during the course of normal coitus. From this test we learn that, before giving an unfavourable prognosis, we must first of all study the physiological affinity between the male and female secretions.'

CHAPTER XXVII

FRIGIDITY IN WOMAN

The incidence of frigidity. Is frigidity due to civilisation? Tendency to lie about it. Modern Messalinas. Women who are passionate and frigid. Completely frigid women do not exist. Causes of frigidity. Lack of skill. Male potency less important than the knowledge of how to act. Essential condition for the orgasm. The wedding night. The orgasm of the newly-wed. Frigidity and masturbation. Fear prevents the orgasm. The orgasm and conception. The conflict between the sexes. Initiation into the orgasm. 'I cannot' means 'I don't want to'.

OF the various troubles and abnormalities of sexual life, the phenomenon most frequently met with, and least scientifically studied, is woman's incapacity to experience, during the sexual act, the pleasure which nature originally offered human beings as an inducement to fulfil their procreative duty. We say originally, because frigidity seems to be the tax levied by modern times for the refinement of emotional life inherent in civilisation. Among animals a female frigid during the rut period is as unknown as among primitive races. The more civilised man is, the more finely differentiated his love reactions become, and the more subject to disturbances his primitive and natural functions grow. As we have said before, the most common of these disturbances is the frigidity of woman.

The phenomenon is so widespread that a frigid woman is by no means considered abnormal. In certain social strata it is a very common affliction, so much so that the unfortunate women see nothing out of the ordinary in their condition and look upon natural sexual pleasures as 'improper', 'animal', 'infra dig', and 'impure'. They allege that they merely tolerate the amorous advances of their husbands, and submit to them through sheer compliance, without the least pleasure to themselves. They do not understand why so much importance is attached to such things, and are, themselves, quite unable to enjoy them in the least.

We shall see further on, when studying the various causes of frigidity, to what extent those wrong ideas are the result of a sex morality based on lies and dissimulation.

A few statistics will give an idea of the frequency of frigidity. Particularly interesting data have been supplied by universities of post-revolution Russia, where the social upheaval has done away with all prejudices touching the so-called scabrous problem of sex. In 1923, an inquiry at the University of Moscow elicited the following results:

Among girl students who were having sexual relations, only 48 per cent. derived any pleasure from them, 14 per cent. were repelled by intercourse, 29 per cent. remained indifferent, and the sensations of the other 9 per cent. varied according to the woman's sentiments for the man. We thus reach the figure of 43 per cent. frigid women.

Another inquiry made during the same year in the University of Kazan showed 44 per cent. girl students who enjoyed coitus, 34 per cent. who were indifferent, and 22 per cent. to whom it was frankly repugnant: in short, 56 per cent. frigid women.

Otto Adler wrote the following in a book on the deficiency of sexual sensitiveness in woman: 'Out of ten women, four experience no sensation during intercourse, perform it without deriving any pleasure from the man's movements, and have no inkling of the voluptuous sensation which should be called up by the ejaculation'.

The gynæcologist de Brunner writes: 'In the case of 50 per cent. of the women in the Eastern cantons of Switzerland, there is no question of passion in the real sense of the word. I have had several opportunities of observing these women in this connection and I can certify that half our women are ignorant of passion'.

The Viennese neurologist Dr. Stekel, who is one of the best-known pioneers of the scientific treatment of frigidity, estimates that more than 50 per cent. of his patients are 'cold'. True, he deals with subjects suffering from psychological disturbances and who are therefore predisposed to derangements of their sexual life.

Despite the fact that most statistics estimate the percentage of frigid women at more than fifty, we must make two reservations:

Firstly, many women's answers are, consciously or unconsciously, untrue. They enjoy pretending that they are 'frigid', 'misunderstood', superior to 'the low pleasures of the flesh'; what is even more stupid, they are ashamed of admitting to themselves that sex plays an important part in their life. In the latter case they frequently lie unconsciously; we shall have occasion to become more closely acquainted with the type of woman who can have an orgasm, intense almost to the point of swooning, but who afterwards 'does not remember anything' because she will not admit to what an extent she is dominated by the primitive instinct of the female.

Statistics being liable to induce erroneous conclusions, the first reservation to be made, then, is the following: all statistics are misleading, particularly when they are based on statements made by women who were asked to reveal the secrets of their most intimate life. The second reservation consists in recording that, as a collective phenomenon, frigidity varies according to countries and social strata. Thus, for instance, it is more marked among women who, by profession or inclination, belong to the intellectual class. Of all civilised countries, frigidity is most frequent in North America, whereas it is much rarer in all Latin countries, and chiefly in France, where the mechanisation of modern life has fortunately not suppressed love's natural enjoyment.

So, setting aside statistics, we shall start from the vitally important fact that frigidity in woman is the most wide-spread sexual abnormality.

* * *

The foregoing deals with frigidity as though it were a simple phenomenon instead of a complex one. In practice, one has to distinguish between various categories and various degrees of it. In his monumental work entitled *Frigidity in Woman* Steckel makes the following classification:

(1) 'The completely frigid woman': She finds neither pleasure nor excitement in either coitus or love-play.

(2) 'The relatively frigid woman': She is capable of having an orgasm, but only rarely, and then only when certain psychological conditions are fulfilled. Such a woman hardly ever feels desire.

(3) 'The passionate and frigid woman': The prototype of this insatiable being is Messalina. She can never satisfy her sexual needs, because, during the preliminary love-play and the act itself, she is consumed by an insatiable thirst for enjoyment.

The boundaries between these three groups are of course not definitely marked, as is the case with every classification. The human being is compounded of very conflicting elements and he cannot be cast into a mould and labelled. We shall therefore study, not varieties of frigidity, but rather frigidity from a practical angle, by seeking its causes and the means to overcome it.

If the term 'completely frigid' is used, care must be taken to avoid a misunderstanding. Complete frigidity means the lack of voluptuous sensations where normal sexual relations are concerned, and not the absence of the sexual instinct itself. The 'completely frigid' woman, in the sense of one totally incapable of sensual enjoyment, does not exist and never has existed. Sexuality in the broadest acceptation of the term is innate in every being. We have seen, in the course of the development of babies and children, how much infantile voluptuousness differs from adult sexual voluptuousness. We have also seen how the baby's sucking, its restlessness, its anal reactions, are forms of expression of the same sexuality which matures after a lengthy process into what we consider a normal manifestation.

There is no woman in whom 'sex' is wholly lacking; at most it takes in some cases a form different from that to which we are used. Such women seem to be absolutely frigid if the manifestations of their temperament are seen from the angle of normal sexuality. Coitus leaves them quite cold, not because they lack a sexual instinct, but because their particular instinct has taken a certain direction which allows it to be satisfied only in a special manner.

* * *

What circumstances may be responsible for a woman's frigidity?

The most diverse reasons may contribute to prevent a woman finding in sexual relations the longed-for enjoyment. But the main reason is—the man!

In most cases it is he who is responsible for the woman's frigidity, because he does not know how to bring about the reactions conducive to an orgasm. It would, however, be wrong always to tax the man with selfishness or brutality, or to maintain that he does not love his wife. Quite frequently he simply does not know what he should do. Ignorance of the erotogenic zones in woman, and of the difference in the orgasm in the two sexes, is a product of that hypocrisy and prudery which condemn enlightenment in the domain of sex. To pilot a woman through the labyrinth of love to the climax of enjoyment, is an art which requires first and foremost an exact knowledge of female anatomy. Most men are content to introduce their member into the vagina, and there their knowledge of the female erotogenic zones ends. This may be sufficient to procreate a child, but it is often quite inadequate to provoke voluptuous sensations in a woman.

The success of the climax is associated in every woman with conditions individual to her, and it can never be achieved until those conditions are fulfilled. There lies the key to the problem of overcoming a woman's apparent coldness; it is the ABC of love. Doubtless, the majority of men do not know it, but that only goes to prove that twentieth-century man is unlettered in the art of love.

These individual conditions naturally differ in every woman. Sometimes they are easy to fulfil (when, for instance, they consist merely in titillating the clitoris before or during coitus); in other cases they present difficulties, and the requirements range from the absurd to the pathological. The great majority of women, however frigid they may appear, could easily reach their climax if their husband would only take the trouble to explore their erotogenic zones. In the preceding chapter we have seen that these zones include large areas of the skin, the back, the groins, the neck, the lobes of the ears, etc., not to mention such well-known zones as the breasts, the hips, the thighs, and the navel. It is therefore obvious that there are few places on the feminine body which may not, in given circumstances, play the rôle of an erotogenic zone. It often suffices to touch one such important zone during intercourse to induce an orgasm. Obviously, it is not merely a matter of finding such a zone; one must also know how to apply the discovery. Where a violent embrace will sometimes have no effect, a slight touch will provoke ecstasy. In fact, it is a purely personal matter which knows no rules.

The sexual decadence of our time becomes evident when one reads Oriental works, such as the *Kama-Sutra* or the *Anangaraga*, in which we find a description of the thousand 'tricks' to which Eastern people used to resort in order to give their partner full enjoyment; one is amazed at the knowledge these men had of the art of love. It was not the impotent man, who at that time could do nothing to cure his condition, but the man incapable of arousing the woman's passion, who was contemptible in their eyes. They did not look upon the pleasure derived from 'love-play' and healthy sensuality as 'animal', but, on the contrary, regarded intercourse that was joyless, gloomy, and lacking in subtlety as a sordid act. Nature itself proves that man's sexual relations are not intended solely for procreation, since his sexual instincts are manifested at all seasons and are not restricted to certain periods, as is the case with animals.

Any healthy woman would consider it absurd if her husband decided to exercise his marital rights every nine or ten months only.

Once the satisfaction of the sexual instinct has been accepted not only as a means but also as an end, it becomes obvious that the lack of this satisfaction deprives a woman of her natural rights and may besides induce serious organic troubles.

The unsatisfied woman is not only a type familiar to novelists, she is also an object of concern to gynæcologists and psychiatrists. Nervousness, sleeplessness, digestive disorders, sometimes even serious hysterical manifestations, are possible consequences of a woman's permanently unsatisfied state.

We may definitely affirm that a truly happy marriage is practically incompatible with frigidity in the woman. Irritability, bad temper, even physical and emotional estrangement, will break out and may actually disrupt the union, if the woman remains sexually unsatisfied. Yet in most cases neither partner will be aware of the true reason for the failure of their marriage.

We repeat, therefore, that in marriage much more should be expected of the man than mere copulation. He must insure his partner's physical satisfaction as well, and this is always possible unless the woman is sexually not quite normal.

It is not a question of mere virility either; there are sexual athletes who in the course of one night can establish impressive numerical records, while leaving the woman unsatisfied; conversely, rather weakly endowed men may satisfy their mate completely because, where sex is concerned, it is not quantity but quality that counts.

*   *   *

The first condition which a man must fulfil has been previously stated. He must realise the difference between the sensations of a man and those of a woman. Making allowance for exceptions, which are to be found here as elsewhere, a woman requires more time than does her companion to arrive at an orgasm. The apparent frigidity of many women is due to the fact that their partner 'comes' too soon, thereby making it impossible for them to reach their climax. Such cases of frigidity are easily curable: the man has only to prolong the preliminary love-play, to kiss and caress the woman (taking into account her particular erotogenic zones, which he will know from having made experiments), in order to rouse her to such a pitch that she will be already highly excited at the beginning of the act proper. In this way she is given a start, for, as in a race, the aim is not to handicap the weaker competitor— in this case the woman. If such preparations are still insufficient, the man must endeavour to delay emission (this is always possible with a little goodwill) and to avoid having his orgasm until his partner reaches hers.

All this chiefly concerns the simpler cases. We have already seen that in some women the erotogenic zones are so differentiated, that the sexual act itself is insufficient to induce a climax. This is what Stekel says on the subject:

'Very often, frigidity is only apparent in coitus and not at all in the other manifestations of sexual life. It is then not justifiable to speak of sexual anæsthesia; at most one can assume insensibility of the vagina. Anyone with a comprehensive experience of women will have met with such cases. Frigidity then comes within the scope of sexual pathology.'

Indeed, one would do well to consult a physician, preferably a psychologist; in particularly serious instances, psychoanalytic treatment is indicated. There are, however, intermediate stages where a fairly clever man can dispense with the doctor; we refer to women who cannot reach their climax by means of normal coitus, because their chief erotogenic zone is not the vagina. When, as often happens, this zone is the clitoris, the solution lies in titillating the later with the fingers during intercourse, which may be performed *a posteriori*. The matter becomes more delicate if the woman's peculiar make-up requires manipulations which are repulsive to the man (as, for instance, with women of the anal-erotic type). A woman is generally reluctant to express her desires, but if she does and if the man can conform to her peculiarities, he should not hesitate on the grounds of indulging in a 'perverse' practice. After all, the boundary between the normal and the abnormal is mainly a question of custom and definition. (Let it be remembered that in ancient Greece, homosexuality between men and youths was considered the height of sublimity in erotic manifestations and was officially recognised.) What gives joy to a couple without harming outsiders cannot be deprecated. The criterion of normality or abnormality does not rest with preachers, moralists or spinsters, but is entirely a personal matter to be decided by the æsthetic sense of the lovers.

Very often, it is false modesty in the woman and ignorance in the man, which cause the apparent frigidity of the woman, as is shown by the following instance, recorded by Stekel:

'Mrs. H. R. has been married for four years and has never known an orgasm. One day her husband comes home earlier than usual, and after dinner they lie down on a couch. They start playing with each other, and suddenly he performs coitus *a posteriori,* upon which the woman experiences such an intense orgasm that she suspects her husband of having made use of a special kind of stimulation. This he denies and assures her that he did nothing unusual, but her sensation has been so acute that she is obsessed by it; since that day she has an orgasm regularly, and always with the same intensity.'

Thus, a man had been living with his wife for four years and never thought of an *a posteriori connection,* although it was evidently the position suitable to her erotic needs; no doubt he had complained of her frigidity, until the day on which he discovered the egg of Columbus, when the frigidity disappeared as by magic.

*   *   *

Man is the product of heredity and environment. The traits which he inherits at birth determine his aptitudes and inclinations; they are, so to speak, the raw material out of which his environment, that is, his upbringing, contacts and experiences, will build his individuality. In the sphere of sexuality, one also distinguishes between innate and acquired characters. The innate factors, however, only contribute to the formation of the essential disposition, whereas the environment plays the decisive part. The development of man, from the cradle to the age of puberty, is of primary importance to his later sex life; his first specific experience, in particular, will leave an ineradicable impression on his sexuality.

As an example: a little boy sees his governess changing her stockings; the sight of her bare leg arouses in him an indefinite but intense feeling, a mixture of curiosity, fear and excitement. The child may never forget; for him legs and sex may henceforth be inseparably associated and his libido may be characterised by an 'infantile fixation'. All his life, he will be a leg fetichist, even though the picture in question has long been forgotten. The scene will remain buried in his unconscious, and precisely because he does not know the reason of his special propensity he is unable to rid himself of it. Only the modern psychologist, that is the psycho-analyst, can free him by transferring the forgotten but repressed experience from the unconscious to the conscious; by thus bringing it to light he will neutralise its influence. We have unfortunately no space for a closer study of the psycho-analytic theory and we must be content with this brief glimpse of it.

An experience such as that quoted above, which results in

some psychological trouble—most forms of sex abnormality and of feminine frigidity are neurotic—constitutes what is known as a trauma. Naturally, there are many individuals who have experienced some such trauma and who nevertheless have no pathological deviation. A trauma has morbid consequences only in a predisposed subject. It is probable that disturbances of the internal secretions—of the 'sexual chemistry'—have a decisive effect on the development of these tendencies.

The origin of a woman's sexual anæsthesia or frigidity is almost always to be found in some trauma. Sometimes it goes back to a long forgotten period of infancy, more often to the years of puberty; in the majority of cases it coincides with the first love experience, namely the wedding night.

That night nearly always determines the whole future of married life.

'The first occasion on which she surrendered herself is for a woman a major experience; she will never forget the first man to whom she gave herself. If she derives pleasure from him, she will remain eternally grateful; her first orgasm is for her an unforgettable memory. Nothing can erase the imprint of that love, which will linger even if later the man deceives her and makes her unhappy, even if for a long time she has been in love with someone else.

'On the other hand, a woman does not forget the unskilled behaviour of her initiator on the wedding night. If he was impotent, she will always have a certain contempt for him; if he was clumsy, she will never have any regard for him; if he was brutal, love is doomed and his way to her heart closed for ever. . . . But the hurt soul has its revenge, and either illness follows, or the joy of the orgasm, which nature created as love's reward, is not attained. In a man also the wedding night can sometimes cause a trauma, but it is not usually so serious as that of the woman, whose imagination has for some time past been preoccupied by this event, and has anticipated great happiness from it.' (Stekel.)

The Viennese psycho-analyst to whom we are indebted for our knowledge of feminine frigidity gives another striking example:

'A lady came to consult me about various nervous troubles, in particular about her complete sexual frigidity. Before marrying, she had been a perfectly normal girl. On her wedding night, her husband, upon seeing her undressed, exclaimed: 'How short and fat your legs are!' He then proceeded to have intercourse, from which she experienced only pain, and remained completely cold. Subsequent intercourse did not overcome her frigidity; her husband then turned away from her and they gave up sexual relations. She knew perfectly well that the offensive remark on her wedding night was the sole reason for her sexual indifference.'

Whereas this woman *knew* the origin of her frigidity, most of her fellow sufferers are wholly unaware of the cause of theirs, and attribute it to lack of temperament. We have already seen that there exist no really frigid women, only women who have not found the specific means to obtain satisfaction, or who do not want to. We shall return to this question later on.

For the rest, even when all goes well on the wedding night, the climax is not usually reached until a few days, or even a few weeks, after defloration. Leaving out of account the pain, which prevents enjoyment, and which is unavoidable on the occasion of the first penetration, the bride, who has hitherto been practising masturbation, or extra-vaginal stimulation in her relations with men, has to become acustomed to this new form of sexual activity. She must learn to overcome her nervousness, her natural

[343]

resistance and her surprise, in order to give herself up entirely to enjoyment. She must also attain to that physical harmony with her partner which is indispensable for the orgasm.

It sometimes happens that a woman has no orgasm until after the birth of her first baby. In that case one can almost always conclude that she had inwardly revolted against surrendering her body because she considered it degrading. Unconsciously she did not want the orgasm to put the seal on her femininity; but once she had become a mother, she realised the true meaning of her sex and therefore no longer refused to enjoy it.

This example leads us to the domain of Lesbian love, which is so often responsible for a woman's irresponsiveness to man. We shall treat more fully of this phenomenon in the chapter on sexual aberrations, and merely mention here that there are women to whom a chance experience, during their childhood or later, determines a leaning towards members of their own sex. They will, however, not admit it; they insist on being normal beings, they repress their sexual tendency, and marry or have relations with men. In many cases it repays them, because, as we know, human beings are often bisexual, and can therefore derive satisfaction from intercourse with both sexes; there is, nevertheless, always a predominant element. Women whose sex is strongly tinged with Lesbian propensities may adopt a position for coitus which, so to speak, camouflages their feminine rôle: they prefer to be ' on top ', and they are more active during intercourse, in order to have the illusion that they are the one who possesses. A sensible man who detects this tendency, often unsuspected by the woman herself, will, unless it is definitely repugnant to him, let his partner follow her inclination so that she may have an orgasm. A widespread belief is that women who have masturbated a great deal during puberty are unmoved by normal intercourse. The only truth in this superstition is that, in the majority of young girls addicted to masturbation, the clitoris becomes, and remains, even in marriage, the principal erotogenic zone. But the clitoris is not so far removed from the vagina that a skilful man cannot 'kill two birds with one stone'. There is nothing more erroneous than to credit masturbation with the full responsibility for frigidity.

However, the connection between masturbation and frigidity presents yet another interest. As already mentioned, each woman has her own special conditions, which allow the orgasm to occur only if they are fulfilled. 'An intense climax can be reached only when the secret sexual aim of the individual is achieved.' (Stekel.) It is a well-known fact that most women who derive no satisfaction from their husband, seek it in themselves. While masturbating, the woman visualises scenes which she does not find in reality, and these scenes bear precisely on her specific conditions of enjoyment. So long as these phantasies deviate only slightly from the normal, and the man can satisfy her, the woman, having found satisfaction in reality, easily gives up masturbation. But when the phantasies are eccentric and incapable of being realised, the woman will not relinquish her practices, because they are her only means of finding satisfaction. 'A woman is therefor not frigid during the sexual act because she masturbates; on the contrary, she masturbates because she derives no satisfaction, or incomplete satisfaction, from the sexual act.'

Stekel reports the case of a patient, Mrs. I. K., who during the first year of her marriage had never had an orgasm. She did experience slight excitement, but never the full final satisfaction; moreover, she could have an orgasm only by means of anal masturbation; she used her fingers, and believed that the need to do so was a result of the enemas which her mother had given her as a child. One day, her husband, either by chance or owing to an unconscious movement of his wife, effected an anal connection. Her orgasm was so intense that the man, who until then had made fun of his wife's frigidity, was most pleasantly surprised. Stekel adds that they have ever since performed coitus per anum, to their mutual satisfaction. Every man is, however, not capable of satisfying such peculiar desires in his wife*. In this particular case Mrs. I. K. gave up masturbation from the time her fancy became reality.

For many women, chiefly for those whose fathers are particularly strict, the climax is specifically associated with masochistic phantasies. They cannot reach it unless their partner beats and brutalises them. They are usually ashamed to tell their husband, and remain throughout their married life unavowed masochists, who seek their pleasure in masturbation accompanied by dreams of flagellation, rape, and even tortures, which help them to their orgasm. In a masochist, the buttocks are an erotogenic zone of primary importance. We know that in Tzarist Russia the floggings given to women were considered erotic activities. But other parts of the body can also play the same rôle, as in the following instance reported by Stekel:

'A woman, married for ten years and absolutely frigid, had tried several lovers, and despaired of ever having an orgasm. Finally, she met a man of savage temperament who was accustomed to biting his partners' ear-lobes. He did the same to her, but, whereas the other women had

*Editor's Note.—It is necessary to point out to the reader of this book that, however desirable it might be from the medical point of view for a man to indulge his wife's desire for anal intercourse, such an act is a crime according to British law, even where it is performed with the consent of both parties.—N. H.

rebelled and threatened to sever relations, this woman experienced in the pain an intense voluptuousness which induced the orgasm.' It will be easily understood why this lady's husband and previous lovers could not satisfy her. Woman's sexuality is a maze in which man does not always find Ariadne's thread.

*   *   *

In the foregoing paragraphs we have studied the physiological aspects of the problem. We shall now investigate the psychological causes of frigidity. It would be superfluous to emphasise the well-known fact that the orgasm corresponds, not only to a physical state, but to a mental one as well. Proof of it is found among prostitutes, who have repeated intercourse without any reaction, while in the arms of their lover they find the voluptuous pleasure which they do not allow themselves with their customers.

The psychological factor plays the principal rôle in the production of the orgasm. Comparatively insignificant worries may hinder it. The most common obstacle is fear: fear of pregnancy, of disease, of scandal, of one's own passion, which the woman is reluctant to reveal to the man; any fear is a bar to sexual enjoyment. The most common dread is that of pregnancy, which can raise an obstacle, either direct or indirect, through the use of a contraceptive which may prevent the orgasm. Of these the most popular is the condom or sheath, which may interfere with the woman's voluptuous sensations. A gynæcologist has written the following on the subject:

'The least sensitive woman finds the use of sheaths repugnant, however good their quality. She calls them a 'partition wall' which blunts the feeling of direct contact, and stops all the sensations which have such a decisive influence on ultimate satisfaction. In normal intercourse, therefore, this artificial means should not be used.'

Women react in a similar way to *coitus interruptus* or withdrawal. The fear that the dreaded moment will come too soon (before the orgasm) or too late (after ejaculation has begun) absorbs all their attention, so that they cannot give themselves up entirely to their enjoyment, and consequently obtain no satisfaction.

The fear of pregnancy can prevent the orgasm in still another way. It is generally believed that a woman cannot conceive unless she has an orgasm. This theory seems to have been scientifically disproved, but many women still think that they can avoid pregnancy by avoiding an orgasm. This control may be conscious or unconscious; in the latter case its treatment is, of course, far more complex.

Sometimes it is the opposite that happens. Her instinctive fear of pregnancy lets the woman reach her climax, but at its height a constriction of the vaginal muscles ejects the semen; she 'cannot help it', it happens automatically, but is really a reaction of the unconscious ego, which does not want a child.

The relation between sterility and frigidity is therefore most uncertain. The orgasm may either help or hinder conception. The example just given illustrates the latter contingency; the former was dealt with by the royal physician, Van Swieten, in his advice to Queen Maria Theresa when she complained of her sterility, advice which undoubtedly aimed at helping Her Majesty reach her climax; it proved an equally excellent remedy for sterility, for Maria Theresa had eleven children.

On the whole, the relation between orgasm and conception is an individual matter. The secretions induced in the vagina by the orgasm may assist the progress of the spermatozoa, but frigidity seems to be attributable rather to a psychological cause: the woman believes that she can prevent pregnancy by avoiding the orgasm.

The latter may also be prevented by the fear of disease, or of the scandal that would follow the discovery of a clandestine affair, that is to say by a guilty conscience. Prejudice, faulty education, and excessive morality have made of sexual intercourse a sin, for which the woman tries to atone by repressing her enjoyment of it.

Stekel supplies us with an instance of this:

'A working woman, thirty-six years old, complained of sundry nervous symptoms. Her body was full of "pins and needles" which changed to violent itching; from time to time she experienced unpleasant intestinal troubles and had to get up at night; she had anxiety-attacks in her sleep and would wake up with a start. During the day she felt so tired that she could not do any heavy work. Without apparent reason, she was depressed and had bouts of weeping. She admitted to being happily married, although she was not keen on having intercourse: "she did not care for that sort of thing". A closer examination revealed a curious mental process; since adolescence, she had believed that sexual enjoyment was forbidden as a deadly sin which God punishes; she had known violent passion and intense orgasms, but the death of a child appeared to her as a divine punishment for her unchastity and taste for carnal sins.

'Yet she had not enough strength to give them up, until a neighbour told her that sexual excitement was harmful, that it ages one and can have a fatal result. She then began to struggle against her pleasure, and took to praying or thinking of other things during coitus. She succeeded finally in quelling her enjoyment. Her husband had many times to interrupt connection so that she might avoid an orgasm.

[349]

'I gave her suitable advice and freed her from the idea that pleasure is sinful; "God made us this gift so that we could use it with discrimination", I told her, and I quoted the wonderful words of Sheik Neffzawi in his *Perfumed Garden*: "Praise God that He placed man's greatest delights in woman's natural parts, and appointed man's natural parts to be the means of woman's greatest delight".

'I saw the patient again a few weeks later; she had become very fit, and her orgasms had recovered their past intensity. As her husband is quite passionate, they were having daily intercourse . . . and the neighbours were astonished at her healthy appearance: they asked her what miraculous treatment she was following!'

Very often a woman stops before she reaches her climax for fear of her own passion; this is precisely the case with very ardent temperaments. To quote a well-known biblical saying, there is between man and woman a constant struggle that is ceaselessly renewed. The woman will not submit, she rebels against her femininity, her wish to dominate clashes with her desire to give herself. A passionate woman well knows that there comes a moment when she is helplessly at the man's mercy. The popular vocabulary clearly depicts the relative position of the two sexes; the man 'takes the woman, possesses her, crushes her', while she 'succumbs, submits, is annihilated by ecstasy'. The woman knows that with the orgasm her resistance melts, her last defence is gone, she surrenders, she forgoes her personality, 'the man can do as he likes with her'. And this is precisely the cause of her rebellion; she is willing to give herself but not to lose herself, and therefore wants to avoid the orgasm. Her instinct to dominate is stronger than her sex hunger; she wants, while being subjected, to remain unconquered: she insists on keeping her individuality even in bed! Poor woman! She does not know that it is precisely by renouncing the strongest element of her personality that she preserves the essence of her femininity.

Such women are often inclined to devote their love to unhappy or pitiable men, because they can have no pleasure unless they feel themselves superior to their sexual partner. Hunchbacks, sick men, invalids, weaklings, have a peculiar sex appeal for this type of woman. While remaining indifferent in the arms of the strongest man, they reach an intense climax in those of a half-impotent cripple. Such is the idea of Bernard Shaw's *Candida* and the classic example of the type is Mme. de Warrens.

The fight against the orgasm, which is a woman's unconscious protest against man's supremacy, or against giving herself to a man whom she does not love, or to one who behaved brutally on the wedding night, may manifest itself by pains, either in the region of the vulva, in the loins or in other parts of the body. There is no question of real organic trouble; it is a case of a protest against pleasure, a sort of defensive barrier artificially raised, by means of which the woman arms herself against unwanted sensations. The most marked expression of such trouble is vaginal constriction or 'vaginismus', which is the sign of an inner 'no', of the woman's rebellion against sexual surrender in spite of her apparent desire for coitus. Reason may be mistaken, but the body never is, and the latter's expression is pain. As Stekel so aptly puts it: 'A woman's lack of orgasm is always an alarm signal which means: there is something wrong with my love'. Such symptoms are particularly frequent when, after a disappointment in love, a woman has an affair with the first man who comes along, in an attempt to find some substitute for love. She tries to persuade herself that she loves the man, in order to revenge herself on the lover who jilted her, or to prove to herself that her capacity for love was not exhausted by an unworthy object. Her mind tells her that she truly loves this substitute lover, but her body is more truthful and the orgasm is not reached. Unwilling to admit to herself the real reason for the state of affairs, she holds the man responsible, and sees every possible defect in him: he has an unpleasant breath, or a repellent body. The former objection is the most frequent, but constitutes rather a pretext than a true olfactory reaction. A woman who really loves a man always likes his breath . . . or offers him peppermints!

*   *   *

Sexual disorders often appear in a woman's life at the time of the menopause. They are sometimes produced by organic conditions (changes in the internal secretions) or by psychological ones. As a woman feels the approach of age, she may become panic-stricken and wants to have a last fling, so as to drain to the dregs the cup of pleasure before it is too late. As Balzac says, not without cynicism: 'It is only at forty that a woman is really capable of ardent love'.

Whatever the reasons may be, it is an indisputable fact that with the change of life many women find their sexual instinct intensified. But this climacteric may manifest itself, on the contrary, in frigidity; the woman is frightened by the sudden surge of passion within her; shame and self-disgust, due to upbringing and prejudice, make her decide to forgo for ever all carnal pleasures, and she sinks into insensitiveness. This revulsion is often accompanied by religious fervour. The very women who, up to the menopause, have led a dissipated life, when faced by the passion that threatens to overwhelm them, devote themselves to penance, become nuns or sisters of charity and destroy for ever the temptation of the flesh. They generally pay for this drastic cure by hysterical attacks, organic troubles, and a complete upset of their equilibrium.

And now a last amendment to this chapter.

We said that every woman requires specific conditions to reach her climax and that these conditions are essential. We have also seen that these conditions may be situated anywhere in the gamut of sexual life; they run from the innocent yearning for tenderness and caresses, to the most excessive, extravagant and unrealisable phantasies. Often, however, the woman's body accepts a compromise; it is enough that her specific requirements be fulfilled once, for her sexual life to take a normal course. A single realisation of her desire often frees a woman of her fad.

This was the case of a woman who one day came to consult a psychiatrist about her inability to enjoy intercourse. Through her confidences the doctor learned that, in order to bring about an orgasm, she had to practise a sort of mental masturbation, which consisted in imagining that there was a hidden witness to the love passages between herself and her husband.

Who knows what childish memories of her parents' bedroom were responsible for this? We have outlined in a previous chapter the serious traumas which a child can receive from sharing its parents' bedroom. A great many cases of frigidity can be attributed to such experiences during infancy.

The psychiatrist, on consulting the patient's husband, advised him to have intercourse with her under slightly daring conditions. Although very surprised, the man followed this advice, and at the first opportunity had connection with his wife, fully dressed, in the dining-room, where the maid might come in at any moment. As a matter of fact, he had taken good care, unknown to his wife, to send her out. As a result, for the first time since their marriage, the wife had an intense orgasm, which thenceforward was repeated at each sexual act, even though performed in ordinary circumstances. The spell had been broken by satisfying the patient's whim on the one occasion.

We shall close this chapter on woman's frigidity with still one more quotation from the great scientist whose work on this subject has been of invaluable service to humanity:

'From all these cases it is easy to see what an important part psychological factors play in the causation of feminine frigidity. In every instance, it is a matter of an inward "no" which may manifest itself organically. The patient's "I cannot" conceals "I will not" or "I must not". Fridigity shows the extreme dissociation of civilised man, the inner conflict between the self who will and the self who will not, the dilemma, the self-played drama, and the struggle within the personality. The social development of love results in the progressive differentiation of man by increasingly intricate conditions of love. Psychological factors are added to physical ones. The former conceal primitive tendencies, complicate them, and transform them from forces of attraction into forces of repulsion. Modern love must first overcome all constraints, obstacles and opposing forces: it must harmonise itself with the intellect.'

CHAPTER XXVIII

THE ALCHEMY OF LOVE

Virility for sale. Aphrodisiacs throughout the ages. The mania for breaking sexual records. The maze of superstition. Black magic and incantations. Diabolic practices of magicians. Amulets and precious stones. Aphrodisiac properties of certain articles of diet. Good living in the service of the joys of the flesh. Baths, ointments, perfumes associated with love. 'Perfumed flatulence.' Mechanical stimulants. Instruments used for masturbation. How savages ornament their genital organs. Electrotherapy and X-rays. Treatment by virgins and Coué's method. The action of aphrodisiacs. Cantharides, belladonna and mandragora. Hashish, opium, morphine and cocaine. Arsenic and ether.

'OUT of one hundred sexual stimulants, one perhaps is efficacious; but ninety of them are an excellent business proposition.' These words of Dr. Magnus Hirschfeld serve as a very suitable introduction to this chapter, which we shall divide into two parts: in the first, we shall endeavour to guide the reader through the maze of superstitions over which the abstruse, odious and harmful machinations of charlatanism hold sway; in the second part we shall give a glimpse of what modern science has achieved in the field of sexology, making it clear that we are dealing not with worthless panaceas but with scientific medical remedies.

First of all, it should be stressed that, in everything that concerns aphrodisiacs, the ignorance of the great majority of the population has been shamelessly exploited. The

[355]

callousness of vendors, moreover, has been greatly favoured
by the hypocrisy on which sexual ethics are still founded.

In the 'alchemy of love' we distinguish two kinds of
remedies. One is intended to excite and increase the
sexual instinct; the other aims at awakening in one
individual a passion for another. Both may be relegated
to the sphere of superstition. As regards the first, there is
no doubt that there exist methods which are apt to increase
passion in man and woman, to suppress sexual control and
inhibitions, and to stimulate the functioning of the sexual
apparatus. But we cannot emphasise too much the
necessity of distinguishing between superstition and science,
harmless remedies and harmful ones, the danger of the
latter varying, moreover, with the individual.

*   *   *

Let us say, first, a few words on the numerous and
curious reasons why aphrodisiacs have at all times enjoyed
such a vogue.

The most frequent and imperative reason for their use
has always been and still is impotence in man, frigidity
in woman, and sterility in either or both. These questions
have been treated in previous chapters and we shall not
go into them again.

Frequently, the individuals concerned, members of the
privileged classes, have had their senses blunted by idleness
or debauchery, so that although they have a normal constitution, they resort to stimulants to intensify their sensations.
In such cases it is well to note that the boundary between
the use of aphrodisiacs and their abuse is very easily
crossed.

A third class includes people, intellectually and physically
extremely active, who for some reason or other wish to
prove themselves possessed of great sexual potency. Of the
numerous psychological motives which impel a person to

use aphrodisiacs, worries of all kinds and repressions are not the least important.

It would be a mistake to think that 'stage-fright' and sexual inhibitions are exceptional. It is, on the contrary, to their frequency that aphrodisiacs owe their constant success. One has only to read a few novels to find an analysis of the soul of the unfortunate lover who, on being allowed at last to approach the object of his desire, is so overwhelmed by happiness that he becomes temporarily impotent.

In antiquity and during the Middle Ages, the use of aphrodisiacs was often justified on religious grounds. Thus we find that Oriental people harboured a belief that during copulation evil spirits, 'the Djinns', tried to introduce themselves into the female organs in order not only to hinder intercourse but even to attack the embryo. To circumvent this demoniacal interference, people had recourse to various means, the nature of which was partly magical and symbolic, and partly aphrodisiac. Omar Haleby, for instance, advocated beginning coitus with a blessing and calling the name of Allah at the moment of ejaculation. It was he, also, who prescribed the use of aphrodisiacs to the founder of Islam, the prophet Mohammed.

'We must not forget', he said, 'that the Prophet is a human being, affected by the fatigue entailed by his activities, and by the temptations to which he is continually subjected by his numerous wives and slaves, for each of them aspires of course to the supreme honour of uniting herself to God's emissary.'

In this way Oriental polygamy has largely contributed to the ever-soaring production of aphrodisiac beverages and powders.

Another reason for the use of sexual stimulants is the

custom among certain peoples of fixing strictly appointed times for coitus. The observance of such a law often required the help of an aphrodisiac. An instance of this was the obligation to perform the sexual act on certain feast days.

Pedro da Villa Gomez, Archbishop of Lima, relates that in Peru, in olden times, there were special celebrations at the end of December, when the fruits of 'Pal'tay' became ripe. It began with a five-day fast, limited, however, to abstention from red-pepper and sexual relations. After the fast, men and women met, in the scantiest apparel, at a definite place in the orchards. At a given signal, a race was started towards a far-off hill. Every man who during that race succeeded in overtaking a woman had to possess her on the spot.

Jealousy is also at the root of aphrodisiac practices. They say that it was a jealous mistress, if it was not his own wife Lucilla, who gave Lucretius, the author of *De Natura Rerum*, a philtre in order to regain his favours. The poet appears to have died of it.

In modern times, many other motives induce people of both sexes to resort to sexual stimulants. Curiosity, the mania for seduction, the competition for 'records', the stupid bets on the number of exploits performed in one night, and other absurdities, which are too often regarded as inconsequential jokes, play in this respect a far more important part than is generally suspected. This proves how many people there are who do not understand the true meaning of sexual union, side-tracked as they are by the mistaken ethics of present-day society, which hides all sexual matters in the dark. As a matter of fact, morbid lubricity is almost always the consequence of surrounding this natural phenomenon with mystery.

This false attitude of our civilisation toward natural

laws is combined with the habit of deriding and looking down upon people who cannot fulfil their sexual functions in a satisfactory manner. Hence the reluctance of men to seek competent advice on these thorny questions, thus leaving themselves at the mercy of quacks or makers of 'intimate articles'.

Such are the circumstances of the extensive use of aphrodisiacs. As we have seen, the use of them was widespread during antiquity and the Middle Ages, and in our times, in the guise of chemical preparations, they play an enormous part in the life of civilised society. It would, however, be a mistake to regard this as a sign of the decadence of the times.

To a far greater extent than in modern times, instances of this practice are found in the reports of missionaries and ethnologists, who mention preparations of animal or vegetable origin, which primitive races use to intensify sexual desire. These are very often credited with the power of curing sterility, but their composition shows clearly that they are sexual stimulants.

*   *   *

Before describing the more or less superstitious customs which aim at increasing potency and at exciting the senses, it is necessary to say a few words concerning superstition. According to the most widely accepted definition, that of Albert Hellwig, it is 'those elements in popular beliefs which modern scientific concepts qualify as erroneous'. That is to say that certain beliefs, which are to-day classified as superstitions, may a century hence be reinstated by new scientific discoveries. For instance, during the Middle Ages, the genital organs of some animals were frequently used as aphrodisiacs. As a matter of fact, organotherapy has for some time treated impotence in precisely a similar way, using, however, not the penis, but testicular extract. This is, however, a rare exception and he who would prefer a charlatan's science to a physician's may pay dearly for his ignorance and his obstinacy.

Moreover, so-called folk-lore seems to be on the wane. The preparations advertised to-day in the columns of the daily press as 'Nature's remedy' and the 'popular cure' are really not culled from popular wisdom, but emanate from the brain of some obscure quack. In any case, this folk-lore is somewhat unreliable in the matter of aphrodisiacs. Mediæval pharmacology was based on a fundamental error, in that the healing properties of plants were judged by their external characters, their shape, colour, taste and perfume.

For instance, vegetable juices, the smell of which was more or less reminiscent of seminal fluid or of vaginal secretions, plants which with a little imagination might be said to resemble the penis or the vulva, were credited with aphrodisiac properties and used as such by the people. It was the same with animals; particularly intense vitality, an abnormally long or violent period of heat, or a peculiar odour, caused certain animals to be appreciated for the stimulating qualities of their genital organs.

We thus step into the magic circle of philtres, pastes, powders, ointments, and exorcisms, which were in the past pressed into the service of Love. One of the most ancient of the popular sciences dealing with love is that of the Chaldeans, who stimulated their senses by eating the liver or the marrow of young boys. In Rome, the gods were made responsible for any weakening of virility; incantations of all kinds had an amazing vogue. We have already told how Lucretius paid for these practices with his life. Another Roman poet, Horatius, wrote magic recipes in verse, although he himself seems to have been sceptical and sensible about them. In one of his poems he wrote:

' Witches, dreams, magic scarecrows, phantoms, spectres, as well as all their other sorceries, can but make me laugh '.

In the Middle Ages, love-philtres and incantations also played a very important part. Among magic brews, the Italian products enjoyed the greatest favour; they were peddled from country to country by travellers, and in times of popular rejoicings any number of quacks and magicians sold them to the crowd. Incantations were always accompanied by magical formulæ and abracadabras; for instance, a wax effigy of the loved one was made, or more simply a lump of wax modelled to represent his heart; this was heated until it melted, and the person symbolised by the wax-figure was then expected to awaken to love. Such practices were attributed to the Devil's inspiration or 'black magic', as opposed to 'white magic', which was of divine origin.

Mediæval superstitions concerning sexual life manifested themselves even in religious penances. An invaluable document on this subject is the work of the two inquisitors Jacob Sprenger and Heinrich Institoris. It is interesting to see, for instance in Chapters VIII and IX, how seriously they deal with the question whether 'witches are capable, by means of satanic practices, of bewitching the male organ, and finally tearing it off the victim's body '.

The Roman Church, on the other hand, fought energetically for many centuries against all such superstitions and their manifestations. It did not, however, succeed in uprooting from Brittany the phallic cult, which was extirpated only by the French Revolution. The veneration of the *guignolet* in Brest is nothing but a remnant of that cult. According to de la Meuse, there existed in that town a chapel with a phallic statue to which sterile women came on pilgrimage; they rubbed a little dust from the statue and swallowed it, mixed with spring water. The statue was naked with an erect penis, which was replaced when it had been worn out by the devotees.

Cambry relates that in Brittany, after mass, the women used to raise the dust in the Chapel of the Holy Union and blow it over the men; by this means they expected to win the heart of their beloved. Another popular custom consisted in burning sacred images and mixing their ashes with food; this custom has persisted to this day in devoutly Catholic regions. Among so many strange practices, there are a few particularly unappetising ones, as for instance the recipes which prescribed swallowing food previously put into intimate contact with the person desired. In Mecklenburg there is a popular belief that eating an apple soaked in the sweat of the partner's armpit appreciably increases the latter's amorous ardor. Another superstition attributed aphrodisiac properties to nutmeg and other spices which remained in the alimentary tract of the interested party.

What has not man done to propitiate the god Eros! He has let himself be grilled, branded, painted, tattooed, he has resorted to the strangest manipulations, to the most involved formulæ, without ever questioning whether there was any actual relation between the means employed and the effect desired.

On the same plane are charms and amulets, the chief ingredients of which are to this day human blood, hairs, skin and nails. This is mostly a matter for auto-suggestion: it is not the amulet itself but faith in it that brings about the desired result. It is worth noticing that what the midwife or the healer tries to achieve through magical formulæ and impressive procedure, Coué did by very much simpler means.

The same applies to the erotic influence of precious stones. Throughout the Middle Ages, the keenest study was devoted to the magic influence which gems were supposed to exert on their wearer. Already, in antiquity, we know that Cleopatra's habit of dissolving pearls in vinegar was not so much prompted by a display of extravagance, as by the wish to increase her sexual sensitiveness.

Even nowadays one hears of the supernatural power of agate, which is supposed to assist in the success of amorous enterprises, and to insure as well the health and happiness of its wearer. The moonstone is said to possess the power of safeguarding purity, love and faithfulness.

At all times the belief in the extraordinary powers of precious gems has been closely linked with astrology, their efficacy being presumably affected by the position of the stars. Even to-day a great many people are to be found who have faith in all this twaddle.

* * *

To give a complete list of the vegetable products to which aphrodisiac powers were attributed in the past would be far too tedious.

But to give a clearer idea of the superstitions which held sway in this domain, and to reveal the horrible practices of the 'alchemists of love', we cannot forbear devoting some space to certain monstrous recipes contained in the works of Paulinus, the most popular breviary of magic of the Middle Ages. The following are the principal ingredients proposed by the author as aphrodisiacs, and intended to be combined with incantations of all kinds: bull's urine, hen's turds, stag's and hare's testicles, donkey's penis, sparrow's blood and brains, stag's semen, the vaginal secretions of a sow, etc.

One can hardly believe that for centuries people were convinced that all this offal was capable of having a favourable influence on the sexual functions of man. What surpasses belief is that in 1697 the Faculty of Leipzig officially stated that these preparations might be considered 'magical remedies' in the realm of love! Yet the horrible mixtures just mentioned are eclipsed by others composed of human urine and menstrual blood. It is here that scatological chemistry has full scope, although not so much in our countries as in the Orient. In the love recipes of the *Kama-Sutra* and the *Anangaraga* place of honour is given to menstrual blood.

The Church fought mercilessly against these strange practices. The Bishop of Worms decreed severe penances for anyone who dispensed magical brews containing such a component. In this connection, it is interesting to quote a most unappetising process, which Burchardt von Worms describes under the guise of a questionnaire:

'Hast thou done what other women are in the habit of doing? They fling themselves face downward on to the ground, their buttocks bared, and they knead in their anus bread which they will later give to their husbands. The result of this unsavoury procedure was called "love-cake" and penitents of the Middle Ages give us information as to the various ways of preparing such "delicacies"!'

This picture of 'Love as an Art' during the Middle Ages is doubtless not very edifying, but it would be a mistake to think that such practices are inconceivable in our times. There are among our contemporaries clever crooks who, inspired by the old treatises on magic, issue pamphlets of a popular nature which in no way fall short of their models. One cannot emphasise too much the dangers of sexual ignorance and superstition among the masses and the necessity of a wise sexual education.

We are now going to review those aphrodisiacs, the value of which has been recognized by modern science, and which are therefore worthy of attention.

* * *

It is a well-known fact that certain articles of diet

exercise an undeniable influence on the sexual faculties. In certain cases the quantity and quality of food may be a deciding factor in the condition of the sexual system. In this connection vitamins play a leading part.

Before, however, taking up the subject of aphrodisiac comestibles, it might be well to give a definition of vitamins. Vitamins are accessory food factors, deprivation of one or another of which leads to serious troubles in the human organism.

Scurvy, rickets, beri-beri, pellagra, are the immediate results of a lack of vitamins in the diet. Recent scientific discoveries have classified the vitamins as follows: vit. A, for growth; vit. B, anti-beri-beri; vit. C, anti-scorbutic; vit. D, anti-rachitic; vit. E, necessary to fecundity. It is therefore the latter in which we are interested.

Many scientists, such as Evans, Bishop and others, have experimented on animals with a view to demonstrating the influence of vitamin E. Rats copiously fed with it have developed abnormally large genital organs, and rut lasted a whole year even in the case of debilitated specimens whose weight at the time of puberty was but a third of the normal. Those experiments combined with many others have established beyond doubt that vitamin E has, besides its general nutritive value, a special action on sexual function.

There are two ways of increasing the supply of vitamins in the organism: by following a diet in which foods rich in vitamins are given preference, or by taking a cure of vitamins in the form of patent medicines containing concentrated vitamins. Modern pharmacy has brought these within the reach of all.

Let us take in turn the principal articles from the standpoint of their aphrodisiac value. In this respect, spices as seasoning for dishes head the list. Here again we come up against popular superstition; the external appearance of the plant has given certain spices the reputation of being infallible aphrodisiacs. Such is the case of the orchid, the shape of which suggests that of the genital organs.

In modern times, spices have lost much of the favour which they enjoyed in the Middle Ages. Among the most appreciated in cooking nowadays are salt, cloves, thyme, laurel, pepper, paprika and nutmeg. The action of the latter three on the kidneys and genital organs is indisputable. Then come vanilla, saffron, caraway and ginger. It must be remembered, however, that ginger strengthens and regulates the functions of the alimentary tract, improves the general condition, and therefore has a good effect on the sexual functions.

As regards soups, highly seasoned consommés are not without influence on the sexual instinct. Turtle soup and 'bouillabaisse', of which Reboux gives a detailed recipe in his excellent book, also deserve special mention.

Now comes the main item, meat. Already in antiquity they knew how to prepare highly stimulating meat dishes. Ovid praises, for instance, a mess of goose-tongues. Internal organs, such as the kidneys and the liver, have always enjoyed great favour, and still do: their aphrodisiac value has never been overlooked. 'Spanish kidneys' are nothing more nor less than a bull's testicles roasted. Similarly, stews and hashes are often prepared with animal organs, such as brains and testicles, which are known for their stimulating properties. The vogue of shellfish and crustaceans, of fish salads and roes (caviar) is due, without doubt, not so much to their nutritive value as to their action on the sexual function of the human organism. Neither can one ignore the sundry delicacies known under the name of 'patés', the preparation of which is generally based on considerations of an erotic nature. The goose-liver patés, so highly appreciated in certain countries, have evolved from a recipe aphrodisiac in origin. 'Le Vol au Vent à la Cardinal', which consists of fish and crayfish prepared with mushrooms and Béarnaise sauce, is a cunning mixture of stimulating foods. The savoury nature of sauces is intended not only to flatter the palate, but also to stimulate the sexual organs. The most efficacious are Worcester sauce and curry, both of which are especially favoured by connoisseurs.

Eggs are a food intermediate between meat and vegetables. Their nutritive value is universally known, and so are the other advantages of a diet in which eggs play an important part. The Love Manuals of all times stress the value of this food for intensifying voluptuous sensations.

Vegetables as an article of diet are too well known to need detailed study here. As regards our particular subject, carrots, celery, asparagus and mushrooms are to be reckoned with. Mushrooms and nuts have the place of honour in Turkish 'erotic recipes'; Algerian truffles also facilitate coitus, according to a Turkish book, 'owing to their stimulating effect on the brain, and the elasticity they impart to the nervous system'.

Asparagus, notorious for its diuretic action, has since time immemorial been equally well known as an aphrodisiac. An old French recipe advises not to wash or over-cook it, so as to preserve this active principle. Another recipe on the preparation of asparagus ascribed to Sheik Neffzawi is unequivocal in its preciseness:

'He who, after having cooked the asparagus, browns it in fat, dresses it with a mixture of egg-yolks and spices, and feeds regularly on this dish, increases his aptitude for the sexual act and intensifies the enjoyment arising therefrom.'

Among the various salads, we have already mentioned the famous dish of testicles, sliced thin and dressed with

[367]

oil, vinegar, salt and garlic, which one still finds on the menus in Southern states. A salad made of tulip bulbs is also said to possess highly stimulating properties. More commonly used are celery, asparagus, and hearts of artichokes.

A food greatly esteemed in the past as an aphrodisiac, and now for its nutritive value, is honey.

Certain fruits are said to be capable of inducing erotic inspiration. The first on the list is incontestably the tomato, called 'love-apple' in some countries. But this reputation is based mainly on its nutritive value and general wholesomeness.

We shall be content with this brief compendium of stimulating foods. We repeat that their action is chiefly indirect, and that in most cases it is not so much a question of aphrodisiacs, as such, as of a wholesome mixed diet, which stimulates the vital functions.

*　　*　　*

Nevertheless, in speaking of the erotic rôle played by good meat, one should not neglect its liquid accompaniment, it being understood that we are dealing not with magic brews, but with drinks which, in addition to their nutritive qualities, possess stimulating ones which affect the genital organs. Alcoholic drinks are, of course, the most important in this connection. Within the recollection of man, alcohol has always been known as a stimulant, and the modern world has by no means invented the use or abuse of it. All periods provide evidence of alcoholic revels which degenerated into sexual orgies. For the reactions to strong drink are many and various. A joyous conviviality, the unleashing of passion, a sensation of well-being, an increase in imaginative power, and marked stimulation of the genital organs, such are the principal effects which have brought alcohol unequalled popularity.

The abuse of alcohol has, on moral and physical grounds, given rise to bitter controversy. Although it is exaggeration to label the habit of taking a glass of good wine with a meal a vicious practice, over-indulgence is nevertheless harmful. Reactions to alcohol differ very widely in individuals; some men can stand large quantities of it, while others are upset by one small glass. This applies to most artificial aphrodisiacs; that which produces a beneficial effect on the sexual feelings of one man may fail to influence another, or even prove injurious.

Owing to the close connection existing between the digestion and the sexual functions, the absorption of too much adulterated wine produces gastric troubles which paralyse sexual activity.

Among alcoholic drinks, wine, cider, brandy and champagne are definite aphrodisiacs. As regard beer, its value, although very much questioned in this respect, must not be minimised in view of its alcoholic content. Certain mixtures are particularly apt to rouse passion. A glass of cognac with the yolk of an egg and a pinch of paprika is the aphrodisiac *par excellence*. Experts know how to concoct many beverages with carefully selected ingredients which give them a high erotic value. The class of drinks known as liqueurs, which contain 20 per cent. of sugar and 30 per cent. of spirit, is not without interest from this point of view. Liqueurs of vegetable origin, like Benedictine and Chartreuse, which are manufactured by religious orders, owe their origin to the preparation of remedies usually made up by the monks in the Middle Ages. In fact, it was that period which produced the best liquid aphrodisiacs ever made; besides being sexual stimulants, they were efficacious in numerous gastric troubles. As regards the excessive use of alcohol, it might be well to point out its harmful effect on the reproductive cells. The morbid phenomenon which

Forel termed 'blastophoria' carries with it disastrous hereditary consequences. That should be enough to make any inveterate drinker think twice before indulging his craving.

The best known vegetable beverages are cocoa, coffee and tea. From the point of view of sex, the first is negligible; coffee, like tobacco and other narcotics acting on the heart, blunts the sexual appetite. Witness the report of Adam Olearius on his journey in Persia in the middle of the seventeenth century: 'He (the Khan) likes tobacco and inhales its smoke through long pipes plunged in a vessel filled with water; he also drinks a kind of black liquid called Kahowâ, which appears to be a remedy against lasciviousness'.

Tea has no effect on the sexual instinct. Tobacco, however, by means of the nicotine which it contains, has a sedative effect on it. Obviously, by limiting the amount smoked, it is possible to render its ill-effects practically nil.

*　　*　　*

After food and drink come what might be called the external aphrodisiacs, namely baths, ointments, essences, perfumes, etc.

Great importance was given in antiquity and during the Middle Ages to baths, but their action was rather erotico-psychological than really physiological, inasmuch as the main reason for them was to bring scantily clad men and women into more or less close contact in a confined space. There, Eros had an opportunity to enlarge his scope, and he did not miss it. From the start, the custom was to have a staff of the opposite sex to that of the patrons. In ancient Rome, the attendants were slaves, and, needless to say, their services were not limited solely to the exercise of their profession. This is amply illustrated by the literature of the period.

This old custom was revived in the times of chivalry, the only difference being that it was respectable virgins who attended the knight in his bath. The legend of Parsifal is a typical instance of this; Gurnemanz of Graharz orders for the unsophisticated Parsifal the customary rose-perfumed bath; no sooner is Parsifal in the tub than maidens appear to bathe his wounds with their pure soft hands; this they do with great modesty, but the prudish Parsifal sends them away before emerging from the bath and the maidens comply, although unwillingly.

To analyse the social sources to which this quaint custom owed its inception would take us outside the scope of this work. But this much is certain: the custom, in sanctioning a close contact which excited the young knight, while forbidding him the natural outlet for his excitement, was a form of perversion. Such perverse tendencies pervaded the love-life of chivalry, at the core of which we find a curious mixture of sensuousness and sectarian puritanism, against a background of romantic make-believe.

One of the discoveries of that civilisation was the use of public baths, particularly common in Germany throughout the Middle Ages. Heralded by a clarion, the 'bathmaster' announced to the village inhabitants that the hour of the bath had come; upon which everybody undressed at home and went to the baths practically naked. (There were no cubicles, for if there had been, the clothes left in them would very likely have been stolen.) The men went into the baths wearing a suspensory; on their entering, an attendant handed them a bundle of rods, intended for massage; the women's bathing costume consisted of a diminutive apron which usually slipped off the hips. The bathers had to be ministered to by the opposite sex. It goes without saying that the robust waiters and trim waitresses in no way detracted from the erotic atmosphere. So that public baths, as contemporary writers testify, soon turned into brothels or houses of assignation. There is no doubt that it was not so much the water which attracted clients as the prospect of an affair. As a poet amusingly put it:

'Nothing better than a bath for the woman sterile,
For with the water goes company virile.'

*   *   *

One must not conclude from what we have just stated that there are no baths with direct physiological action on the genital functions. The Romans themselves knew the properties of mineral waters, and Islam supplies us with a great many recipes for deriving aphrodisiac benefits from certain mineral waters and other baths wisely prepared. We need only to mention arsenical springs and radio-active baths, the properties of which are known, and which have a favourable influence, indirectly, on the sexual system.

To-day, hydro-therapeutics and cold-water treatments are recognised as a tonic for the nervous system. Spinal douches, when methodically applied with suitably medicated water, are most efficacious in this respect. Sitz-baths, in plain water or with the addition of essences, and cold injections, are equally stimulating; they are used in the treatment of impotence and also as aphrodisiacs.

The preparations added to baths are of various kinds; some natural ones, such as herbs and almond milk or paste, and synthetic ones, the use of which was already known in antiquity. The aphrodisiac value of these preparations is highly problematic.

After the bath come the ointments. It is well to distinguish between ointments which are applied directly to the sexual organs and are intended, by irritating the skin, to increase the sensitiveness of the erotogenic zones, and those the potency of which is mainly due to their perfume. The first group of ointments is usually composed of chemicals which stimulate the parts so that erection follows. Such is the principle of most preparations on the market, including many quack concoctions. Among the Greeks and Romans, vegetable extracts, principally camphor, were in great favour; they were used partly for hygienic purposes, to increase the resistance and suppleness of the skin, and partly to induce local stimulation. Here the ubiquitous cantharides also played its nefarious part and resulted in many cases of serious cutaneous affection. Aphrodisiac salves were also applied internally to the genital parts of women; some of them were astringents for the mucous membrane of the vagina. This is what Poppæa, who became the wife of Nero, advises:

'In order to pass for a virgin, bathe your genitals with a solution of benzoin, which has a milky appearance; dry them with a linen cloth and powder with ground starch.'

The second class of ointments, the virtue of which lies in their perfume, includes scents, essences, and other odoriferous products, generally labelled olfactory aphrodisiacs.

We have previously emphasised the importance of the sense of smell in sexual relations. Hirschfeld and other authorities on the subject are of the opinion that all perfumes were originally aphrodisiacs.

'Bodily cleanliness was not *de rigueur* in the Middle Ages, and this forced women to resort to aromatics, to hide the odour of their natural secretions, which assailed the nostrils disagreeably. Plague and syphilis also required such deodorants. But the very fact that perfumed preparations have been in use for thousands of years, proves that their aphrodisiac value was known so long ago that they cannot have originated in the necessity of concealing the exudations of mediæval diseases. We must also remember that such active agents as musk, amber, etc., have their internal use as aphrodisiacs, so that there is no doubt as to their purpose either in a pure or combined state.'

The history of scents is as old as the world. Henna, myrrh, cinnamon and the like were highly rated in ancient Egypt, whence they were borrowed by the Hebrews. The love stories of the Old Testament are all more or less scented. Esther, for instance, before being received at the court of Ahasuerus, was submitted to a veritable perfume 'cure' which lasted not less than a year; for the first six months she was steeped in balsam and myrrh, and for the next six in various other essences.

In Rome it was not perfumes, but unguents, which were commonly used; in other words, the essences were not dissolved in alcohol, but mixed with certain vegetable oils, with which the body, the face and the hair were anointed, the Romans thereby proving once more their understanding of hygiene, for soap being unknown, they made use of the solvent properties of oil. Hagen calls the Roman Imperial period 'the most highly scented epoch of universal history'. Dufour adds that aromatic baths and massaging with scented unguents were not only the necessary preliminary to amorous frolics; the latter were frequently interrupted to allow of further applications.

It would be superfluous to stress the passion of Oriental people for perfumes. They have made of their preparation a special art, which only the Greek hetairæ have equalled.

During the Middle Ages the knights' ladies were the chief users of perfumes for erotic purposes. Then the discovery of America introduced new scents, as, for instance, vanilla and Peruvian bark. This date marks the opening of a new era in the preparation of aromatics. Italy, the greatest producer after France of all the accessories of love, carried perfume-making to a fine art, while several writers, for example, Saigini Giovanni Marinello, Giovanni Baptista

Porta, and Isabella Cortese, have filled volumes with its numerous processes.

The court of the 'Roi Soleil' was possessed by a veritable passion for perfumes. According to certain writers, the Marquise de Pompadour spent a million pounds a year on scents. The French Revolution tried, as did Parliament in England, to put a puritanical restraint on that orgy, but it succeeded only for a short time; the perfume industry is nowadays an important item of economic life, and its produce is no less appreciated than in the time of Ptolemy.

A few words may not be out of place here concerning the eccentric use made of scent by certain ladies, whose erotic imagination made a few disconcerting discoveries. Beroalde de Verville describes a curious custom which was much in favour among the gay ladies of the sixteenth century:

'She, as chaste courtesans know how, had collected tiny hen-bladders, thin and delicate, and filled them with musk-scented air, according to the perfume makers' process. While the lovely Imperia, with a store of these by her side, held the gentleman in her arms and let him love her, she suddenly took one and squeezed it; as it burst, the gentleman, somewhat troubled by the ambiguous noise, put his head out of the bed. "It is not what you think," the lovely Imperia said; "one should know before fearing." The Sieur de Lierne was thereupon surprised to become aware of a delicious odour, and enquired whether it came from the source which had just made him fear something quite different, to which she replied that Italian ladies ate such aromatic food and used so much scent that they emitted the quintessence of perfume as from "the neck of a retort". Wonder-struck, the cavalier exclaimed: "By our lady, our ladies fart quite otherwise! ".'

These scented vesicles, which were called *pets parfumés*, were quite the fashion not only among courtesans, but also in the best society; they became as extensively used as perfumed cushions and balls, shoes and dresses in Elizabethan England.

Another method of using perfume has been preserved from antiquity up to the present. Three thousand years ago, Egyptian women inserted scented pads into their vagina; this is still done in China and in Italy, as it was by the hetairæ of Alexandria, and by Mme. Dubarry, who employed this device to seduce Louis XV.

There are also perfumes which, instead of being spread over the body in solid or liquid form, are used as vapours or smoke. They were commonly resorted to by mediæval alchemists, who achieved the required results by a judicious mixture of ingredients. They were adepts at exciting the nervous system by this means, thus releasing sexual passions.

Incense was a permanent adjunct of black masses during the Middle Ages, and it still is in corresponding modern assemblies in which it is desired to create an atmosphere of mysticism. The erotic effect of the smoke-laden atmosphere is enhanced by suitable lighting. It is unnecessary to add that the subsequent over-stimulation of the senses is likely to give rise to serious organic disorders, further aggravated by the inhaling of air saturated with heavy fumes. The manufacturers of 'intimate' articles have not failed to take advantage of these exotic fads. As late as 1926 a handbook of 'Magical and Occult Incenses' was published in Germany. Obscure pamphlets and highly specialised shops contribute largely to the fog of erotic superstitions.

* * *

Certain primitive peoples, chiefly in South America and Africa, do not content themselves with incantations and philtres, but increase their sexual enjoyment with the aid of surgery. Operations are performed on both sexes. Those performed most frequently on women aim at artificially extending the clitoris and the labia. This distortion of the female genital organs is called the 'Hottentot apron'. The Basutos carry the process so far that the extended labia can be curled round wooden sticks. Although a woman's genital sensitiveness and her climax during intercourse are supposed to be thus greatly intensified, the main purpose of such an operation is really æsthetic. The elongation of the labia is considered a criterion of beauty among these tribes, while women with their organs thus deformed exert a particular attraction for the male sex.

Even more startling are some of the methods used by the men. They aim at increasing not the man's sensations, but those of the woman, and they generally consist in adorning the penis with wooden, metal, or shell trinkets. Other accessories are fastened to the member without an operation. Such is the 'guesquel' of the Patagonians, which consists of a ring of mule's hair fastened by a string to the head of the penis, so that the hairs point forward. The scientist Stoll comments on it as follows:

'The first time, the native women do not care much for the "guesquel"; it hurts and even causes bleeding; but little by little they get used to it, even in married life. Patagonian women have a somewhat cold temperament, so that the men prefer white women when they can get them; they say that the latter are more excitable and active during intercourse, and that gives them great pleasure; they call white women "corcoveadores", which means "creatures who make faces and wriggle". To induce more liveliness in their fellow countrywomen during coitus, these Indians use the "guesquel"; its effect is such that the women cry, and their orgasm is so intense that they are quite exhausted afterwards. The use of the "guesquel" does not seem to involve any harmful consequences. A well-made "guesquel" is very expensive and often costs as much as two horses!'

In the Celebes and in Java, the natives use similar attachments, but made of goat-skin.

Much less innocuous is the custom of the Batas in Sumatra. They incise the forepart of the penis and insert under the skin flints, shells, or silver or gold pellets; once the wound is healed, the member presents a knobbly appearance.

The most monstrous mutilation is the 'ampallang' of the Borneo Dyaks. The glans, having been flattened between two boards for several days, is then pierced by a bamboo skewer. The passage thus bored is kept open by a pigeon quill, which is never removed until just before connection, when it is replaced by the 'ampallang', of which Miklucho-Maclay has given the following description:

'During work and when moving about the Dyak flaunts a feather in his penis. Before intercourse, this feather is replaced by the "ampallang"; this consists of a copper, silver or golden rod, 1.5 inches long and one-tenth of an inch thick; at one end is an agate or hard metal ball; the ball at the other end is put on after the "ampallang" has been inserted; some "ampallangs" are fitted with revolving balls. The whole contraption is from two to four inches long.

'Dyak wives are entitled to the use of the "ampallang", and they can divorce their husband for refusing to wear it. They are so accustomed to this excitant that they cannot dispense with it. The man introduces it obliquely into the vagina, so that it will take a transverse position.'

A number of native tribes use similar appliances; the Peruvians, for instance, wear a kind of 'ampallang' on which, according to Lindschoten, the balls have been replaced by small spherical bells.

Among primitive races, another procedure, not calculated,

however, to produce a direct, mechanical stimulation, consists in tattooing the whole body of both sexes with a variety of designs.

That savages have not the monopoly of artificial aphrodisiacs is revealed by a closer study of civilised people. Although these do not submit to such painful operations as that required to wear an 'ampallang', a whole branch of modern industry is occupied with the manufacture of celluloid or gold Japanese rings, of 'cuffs' (rings of soft jagged rubber worn in place of the foreskin), of spiked sheaths and spiked finger-caps, all of which are intended to exacerbate sex reactions.

Even tattooing has entered modern life and assumed a distinctly erotic aspect, despite the fact that it originated among primitive races as a mere ornament. Various scientists, including Leblanc and Lucas, have remarked that Paris prostitutes have themselves tattooed to conceal syphilitic blemishes.

Among the artificial appliances used for the purpose of sexual stimulation must be mentioned those employed for masturbating or homosexual purposes. As, however, these are somewhat outside the scope of this chapter, we shall give only a short description of them. They generally consist of either rubber, wax, or composition reproductions of sexual organs, male or female, or in masturbating appliances for women. They are very common in Japan, and are often distinguished by their intricate mechanism. According to Dr. Magnus Hirschfeld:

'One of the most popular mechanical excitants in Japan consists of two metallic spheres the size of pigeon's eggs, called "rin-no-tama", "wat-ama", or "ben-wa". One of the spheres is empty, the other, nicknamed "the little man", contains a smaller solid ball or some mercury, which oscillates at the least motion. The empty sphere is first of all introduced into the vagina as close as possible to the cervix; the loaded one follows. The slightest movement of the pelvis vibrates the spheres and provokes a prolonged titillation not unlike a mild electric current. To prevent the spheres from dropping out, the vagina is plugged with a wad of silk-paper or cotton-wool. Japanese women like to swing themselves in hammocks or rocking-chairs, so as to keep the balls in motion, and enjoy to the utmost the resulting intense sexual excitement.'

Other mechanical apparatuses are designed as auxiliaries in case of complete or partial impotence; their rôle is to facilitate the insertion of the penis where the erection is either insufficient or non-existent. These 'corsets' are of use to men who suffer from only slight disorders and are still capable of beginning normal coitus. More complicated are those intended to induce an influx of blood into the erectile tissues by means of ligatures.

Of all the physiological means at the disposal of modern science, electric radiation is the most worthy of mention. It includes galvanic currents below 5 amp., high-frequency treatment, and Faradisation. They all give very satisfactory results, but present serious dangers to the patient if applied by incompetent laymen or quacks.

These electro-therapeutic methods differ entirely from X-rays, which are never used to augment the sexual instinct, but only to cure pathological impotence. Their application requires a skilled specialist, because X-rays administered in large doses have a destructive action on the germ cells.

*   *   *

A complete enumeration of the psychological methods used throughout the ages to stimulate the sexual instinct would require an encyclopædia of every sphere of activity in civilisation. There is indeed not a single sphere in which sex does not play a part, and in which its erotic effects do not make themselves felt, whether it be in the theatre, literature, fine arts, fashion, etc. We shall therefore limit ourselves to direct psychological methods, from sympathetic cures to hypnotism and suggestion. These methods are explained by the mystic conception which primitive peoples have always had of human will-power. They believe that this will-power could manifest itself only under certain definite conditions accompanied by an impressive ceremonial. When on the subject of superstition, we mentioned the sorceries practised on wax images which symbolised the person concerned. Casting spells by means of the evil-eye, the laying-on of hands, and other magical cures, are only an advanced stage in the evolution of mystical beliefs which go back to the remotest ages.

Another variation of these magic practices is 'shunamitism', which originated in the Bible story of King David's rejuvenation by the virgin Abishag the Shunamite. Shunamitism was a general belief during the Middle Ages and again in the eighteenth century, when the 'roués' imagined that, through her rejuvenating fluids, a virgin could restore to a man his lost virility. There actually were traders in 'shunamites', the most notorious one being Mme. Janus of Paris, who had forty virgins at the disposal of her customers; the price of one night's 'shunamite' treatment was a gold louis. The patient lay beside one of the virgins or, even better, between two of them; all contact was forbidden, and he had to let himself be influenced solely by their fluid. If, however, a 'shunamite' happened to lose her virginity in the course of the cure, the old man had to pay a heavy fine to the matron.

We now come to the question of auto-suggestion, suggestion and hypnotism. We touch here on the subject of supernatural miracles, in which the religious element predominates. Pilgrimages to miraculous statues, processions like those at Lourdes and other places, prove that suggestive treatment succeeds as well with priests as with psychiatrists. The best patients are found among neuropaths or subjects particularly receptive to suggestion. Unfortunately, charlatans as well as priests have taken advantage of this psychological phenomenon.

The application of suggestion and hypnotism to sexual pathology should be strictly confined to psycho-analysts. The layman who dabbles in it risks seriously disturbing his patient's psychological equilibrium; to use hypnotic influence without due qualification ought to be a criminal offence. Auto-suggestive treatment, such as Coué's, has given excellent results, but it is not efficacious in all cases. The first and essential condition of a satisfactory result is faith, and this lifts the problem on to a purely personal plane.

* * *

We should like to add a few more words to what we have already said concerning aphrodisiac substances and preparations. First and foremost comes Cantharides, or 'Spanish Fly', the scientific name of which is *Lytta Vesicatoria*. Antiquity seems to have known how to prepare and pulverise them for aphrodisiac purposes. This preparation has remained in use to this day, in spite of its distinctly harmful properties. The cantharis is a coleopter with a golden green sheen, about three- to four-fifths of an inch long and with a definite specific odour. It is common in Central and Southern Europe and is occasionally seen in tracts where it has been unknown for a very long time. It lives on shrubs and trees during the months of June and July.

To prepare cantharides as it was done in olden times, and still is by modern specialised industries, the trees on which they are found are shaken, the insects collected on canvas, and anæsthetised in ether or chloroform. They are then exposed to the sun or placed in an oven where they crumble to dust. This powder, cantharidine, is the chief ingredient of love philtres. It is a particularly dangerous substance, nine grains of which is enough to cause poisoning, while fifty times that amount in the form of a tincture causes instantaneous death. The symptoms of cantharidine poisoning consist of irritation and inflammatory manifestations, which spread from the mouth to the anus, and chiefly affect the genito-urinary system. It is the latter effects which give cantharides their aphrodisiac value. They take the form of frequent erections, a voluptuous irritation of the urethra, and an incessant urge to copulate.

The use of cantharides has been practically discontinued in scientific medical practice, as small doses are ineffectual, and large ones, while producing the desired effect, cause inflammation of the genital organs and of the kidneys, with the subsequent presence of albumen and blood in the urine. We strongly advise against the use of cantharides in all its forms.

We shall cite as a curious reference, cases of cantharidine poisoning which Cabrol observed in Provence at the end of the sixteenth century. Some women gave their husbands a dish of cantharides in the hope of curing them of fevers. One of the women certified that in the course of two nights her husband performed coitus eighty-seven times and then became ill; he actually copulated three more times during the medical examination. The wife of another of the unfortunate men swore that her husband had intercourse forty times on end, and still remained so excited that he begged the doctor to let him die in his orgasm. Gangrene of the penis was not long in setting in, and he died within a short time.

These reports must naturally be taken with due reservation.

The most generally known vegetable aphrodisiacs are belladonna and the mandrake. From the former is derived atropine, which is much used in modern *materia medica*. Belladonna is an additional ingredient of love philtres, because, thanks to its narcotic effect, it induces hallucinations.

Mandrake has been known for a very long time. According to a legend, of which there are many versions, the semen of a hanged man flowed as the cervical vertebræ snapped, and fertilised the roots of the plant. The mandrake root is thick and whitish, and its forked shape suggests human legs; it is also hairy, so that it has often been likened to the human body. The mandrake legend has inspired *Vampire*, the purely pornographic novel of Hans Heinz-Ewers. Apart from its aphrodisiac properties, similar to those of belladonna, it has no therapeutic value.

The chief modern vegetable aphrodisiac is Yohimbine, which is extracted from the bark of the Yohimboa (Corinanthe Yohimbe) which grows in Africa. The natives have for a long time known the properties of this bark and use it for all sorts of preparations. It plays an important part in modern pharmacology, and is included in varying quantities in most formulæ intended to stimulate the sexual potency of men.

Among toxic substances we shall mention only arsenic and strychnine. The former is such a powerful stimulant that peasants are in the habit of adding some of it to the cattle fodder in order to increase the capacities of their livestock. People use it as a general tonic, especially as a sexual one; it is used not only as an aphrodisiac, but also as a method of developing the bust. Arsenic has also a salutary action on a number of disorders and is prescribed for debilitated conditions. It must be left to the physician to prescribe the dosage suitable to the disease.

Strychnine is also prescribed, but in lesser doses; it is particularly indicated in certain forms of impotence, because it stimulates the reflexes of the spinal cord.

Drugs include opium, morphine, cocaine and hashish. The hallucinations due to opium-smoking have been repeatedly described in literature, and China is notoriously the country of opium addicts; in every brothel, customers are served with 'pipes', and conversely every opium den has at its patrons' disposal the wherewithal to satisfy their stimulated sexual appetites. In the beginning, opium appreciably increases the sexual faculties, but these ebb as morbid organic reactions set in. Impotence then frequently follows.

Morphine has the same or nearly the same effect. In Europe, however, it is cocaine which has become the great scourge since the war. Its regular use leads to terrible consequences. The hallucinations incident to it become more and more fantastic and end in complete physical and mental collapse. As for hashish, it is credited with evoking the most erotic phantasies. (See Baudclaire's *Paradis Artificiel.*)

Even anæsthetics, such as chloroform, ether, and ethyl-chloride, administered during surgical operations, can induce erotic dreams, particularly intense in the case of women. More than one patient on coming to has taxed the surgeon with attempted rape, an accusation which, needless to say, corresponded in no way to reality.

In latter years, a number of legal actions against physicians have been brought by patients who took for reality a figment of their anæsthetised brain. Even if the practitioner succeeds in proving his innocence, he finds it difficult at times to convince everyone; hence the custom of administering anæsthetics only in the presence of witnesses.

To finish let us say a few words about opotherapy. As we have seen, the hormones furnished to the blood by the genital glands eroticise the central nervous system, where the sexual instinct has its origin. This discovery has led physicians to administer extracts of animal genital glands. They are taken from especially strong and healthy subjects, bred under highly hygienic conditions, in mountainous regions; slaughter-houses cannot supply suitable material. The hormones contained in these extracts pass into the circulation and thus supply the required stimulation.

Opotherapeutic preparations, in either powder or tablet form, ought never to be used without medical advice.

Editor's Note.—None of the commercial preparations of the sexual gland extracts at present on the market are of any considerable value, if taken by the mouth, and very few of them have any effect, except a psychological one, when injected. This is especially true of the male sex-gland preparations.—N. H.

CHAPTER XXIX

THE CHANGE OF LIFE IN MEN AND WOMEN

Sexual maturity consequent on changes which take place at puberty.
Ovarian activities. The cessation of ovarian activity known as the
menopause or change of life. Disturbances and symptoms common
at the time of the menopause. The change of life a normal pheno-
menon. Abnormal and troublesome symptoms due to faulty mode of
life or psychological instability. Loss of capacity to conceive not
accompanied by loss of sexual desire. The change of life in men.
Usually later than in women. Diminution in potency but not
necessarily diminution of desire. Decreased activity of the testicle.
Enlargement of the prostate gland. Various forms of treatment.
Diathermy. Grafting. Glandular extracts. Operation on the
sperm ducts.

THE period of sexual maturity, in both men and women,
begins at puberty, directly consequent on the changes
which take place in the ovaries and testicles at that time.

In the female, at puberty and afterwards, the ovary not
only produces an egg, ripe for fertilisation, each month,
but it also elaborates certain internal secretions which
play an important part in the general bodily economy of
the woman, and which, especially, govern the phenomena
of her sexual life. These ovarian activities go on for some
thirty or thirty-five years, and then, in the vast majority
of cases between the ages of forty and fifty, the ovaries
cease or diminish their function.

The change may be fairly sudden, or it may be gradual.

[387]

The elaboration of the internal secretions goes on less actively, and finally ceases altogether, and no more egg-cells ripen.

The period of cessation of ovarian activity is known as the *menopause*, or *change of life*. The woman may notice that her menstrual periods are becoming less frequent, or less profuse, or both; and the change may be gradual over a period of months or years until she ceases to menstruate altogether. In some women the change comes quite suddenly.

The reader will remember that the increased activity of the secretory functions of the ovary caused considerable changes in the bodily economy at puberty. There is an analogous disturbance of endocrine balance at the change of life. Vascular disturbances, such as blushing, hot flushes, and giddiness, are quite common. These symptoms need cause no alarm.

The change of life is a normal phenomenon—just as normal as puberty—and should arouse no apprehension in a healthy woman. If, however, the woman is not healthy, or has not led a regular, moderate, normal sexual life— and this is unfortunately the case with a large number of women in our civilisation—then the change of life may be attended by abnormal and troublesome symptoms of ill-health. Thus many women suffer from excessive menstrual loss at this time, and the periods may appear with excessive frequency. If the woman is ill-balanced psychologically, the strain of the menopause may upset her, just as the strain of puberty may upset an ill-balanced child.

If a woman has had a satisfactory sex life during her years of sexual maturity, she can usually face the menopause without fear. But if her sexual life has been unsatisfactory, she is liable to be seized with panic at the thought that her sexually attractive days, and her powers of procreation, will soon be over: and, in such cases, her psychological balance may be gravely disturbed.

A large number of people seem to think that every woman must expect to pass through grave disturbances of health at the menopause. This is not so. If a woman is ill, either physically or psychologically, at this time, it is a sign that something is wrong, and she should consult a competent sexologist or physician.

Though the woman loses her capacity to become pregnant after the menopause, she does not necessarily, or even usually, lose her sexual desire, though sexual desire generally diminishes in frequency, if not in intensity. Many women, whose sexual desire has been inhibited all their life by the fear of pregnancy, are able for the first time to enjoy sexual intercourse thoroughly, now that the fear of pregnancy is removed. And many women retain their sexual attractiveness for many years after the menopause.

In men, the change of life usually comes later, and much more gradually. Probably the majority of men find that, after forty, the sex urge is less constantly insistent, and they are less able to carry out frequent, and repeated, intercourse. This diminution of activity goes on, with varying rapidity in different men, so that potency diminishes gradually with increasing age. The diminution in potency does not always go hand in hand with diminution of desire, and most men are capable of sexual pleasure, and even of orgasm, long after they have lost their capacity to get a good erection and accomplish penetration.

Thus, a married couple who continue to attract each other sexually in old age frequently carry out some sort of incomplete intercourse, which gives satisfaction to both, although the man may be quite incapable of performing the full sexual act.

ENCYCLOPÆDIA OF SEXUAL KNOWLEDGE

The change in the male is due to the gradual diminution of the internal secretory activities of the testicles. The secretion of spermatozoa usually goes on, though less actively than before, until death, and men of the most advanced age may still be capable of fertilising a woman, even when they can no longer, under any circumstances, get a proper erection.

As the testicle becomes less active, the prostate gland has a tendency to enlarge, and the enlargement may be so great as to cause an obstruction to the outflow of urine from the bladder. Prostatic enlargement may also give rise to sexual irritation, which expresses itself in frequent, and sometimes uncontrollable, desire for sexual intercourse. The sexual delinquencies of ageing men, formerly respected members of the community, are often traceable to enlargement of the prostate. Symptoms of this sort indicate the necessity for medical examination and advice, and operation for removal of the hypertrophied gland may be necessary.

If the change of life, in either man or woman, gives rise to disturbance in physical health, it is possible nowadays to obtain benefit through various forms of treatment, which include the injection of glandular extracts, the stimulation of the ovaries and testicles by diathermy, the grafting of ovaries or testicles into the body of the patient, and in men by a small operation on the sperm ducts.

CHAPTER XXX

THE PROBLEM OF REJUVENATION

Eternal youth, a dream not capable of realisation. The chemistry of the human organism: the glands. The glands of internal and external secretion. The discovery of Brown-Séquard. Steinach's experiments on rats. Voronoff's method. The glands of puberty. The vaso-ligature of Steinach. Is it possible to prolong human life? Rejuvenation of woman and plastic surgery.

OUR survey of the artificial means employed for the purpose of increasing sexual potency brings us to the problem of rejuvenation. The history of the struggle against old age is itself as old as humanity, because it corresponds to an instinct which never weakens. Can we escape senility and remain young to the end? Can life be prolonged? Is it possible to add to our sexual faculties in potency and duration? Is impotence curable by a rejuvenating operation? Such are the questions to which we seek an answer, and this chapter therefore follows on as a continuation of the previous one.

Before dealing with actual rejuvenation, we must say a few words on certain organs, for a long time ignored or unknown by science and recently reinstated: the glands.

We know now that their rôle in the human system is a very important one as centres of organic exchanges. We have the sweat glands, the mammary and salivary glands, the gastric and pancreatic glands, and let us remember that the liver and the kidneys are glandular organs, and that the white corpuscles of the blood, the defence force against infectious diseases (phagocytes), are supplied by the lymphatic glands.

Seen through a microscope, a gland, like one of the salivary ones, for instance, looks like a bunch of grapes; each grape is a gland which generates the secretion (saliva in this case), and its stem is the duct by which this secretion is brought to the main canal and thence into the mouth. Each glandular cell is protected from pressure by a delicate tissue, as a grape by its skin. The salivary gland excretes its product, saliva, which reaches the exterior through the duct; the liver excretes bile, the lachrymose glands tears, and the sweat glands sweat. For this reason, all these glands are called the glands of external secretion or exocrines.

The human body, however, possesses another glandular system, the secretions of which are not excreted through a duct. It was only recently discovered that they are absorbed by the blood; hence the name of glands of internal secretion or endocrines. The thyroid is one of them, and its importance can be realised on seeing men from whom it has been removed owing to certain diseases. They die after exhibiting certain specific symptoms, for which reason an effort is always made nowadays to leave part of the gland; if this is impossible, the patient is fed with the thyroid of a sheep or some other animal. Endocrines always hold a reserve of their secretion, so that their ingestion brings the required supply to the blood.

* * *

The glands that concern us for rejuvenating purposes are the testes and the ovaries. Age is indeed to a great extent due to degeneracy of these glands; if they can be kept active, senility will be avoided, or, at any rate, retarded.

We shall only deal with the testicles here, because their working is much simpler than that of the ovaries, and also because their anatomical and physiological nature is scientifically better known.

The testes are both an endocrine and an exocrine gland; externally they secrete the sperm-cells through the vas deferens and the urethra. A microscopic section of a testicle shows the seminal cells all communicating with a common canal; it also shows in the surrounding tissue a large collection of smaller cells which Steinach has proved to be endocrine. The testicles therefore not only produce sperm-cells but also a substance which enters the circulation.

* * *

Before summing up the practical conclusions of this discovery, we wish to mention a scientist whose work there is a tendency to forget in speaking of rejuvenation. The credit for rejuvenation is chiefly attributable to two men, Steinach and Voronoff; but as early as 1889 the famous French savant Brown-Séquard read a paper on the subject before the Paris Academie des Sciences. Brown-Séquard, then seventy years old, had been experimenting on himself and some of his elderly patients, with a view to preventing the ill-effects of age; he injected an extract of dog's testicles and soon noticed a renewal of muscular, mental and, above all, sexual activity. He was the first to call this process 'rejuvenation', and to him is due the credit of having discovered the method which Steinach later perfected.

Meanwhile, Brown-Séquard met with the fate of most pioneers of epoch-making discoveries: the Academy laughed at him and his discredited process was forgotten.

* * *

The Viennese Professor Steinach based his theory and

method of rejuvenation on Brown-Séquard's work. We shall mainly study the practical results obtained and explain their theory only when necessary to make the process clear.

Steinach performed a series of experiments on rats. These animals were particularly suited to his purpose because their lease of life ranges from twenty-seven to thirty months, so that in about two and a half years it is possible to follow the life of a whole generation from birth until death. Steinach first operated on a male rat which had all the symptoms of senility: fatigue, weakness, baldness, and sexual anæsthesia. He grafted into his subject's abdominal ~uscles testes removed from a young rat, and a surprising result followed: the 'patient', from being near death, became vigorous and full of life, recovered his quick movements and his furry coat, and impregnated a female, who produced a healthy litter.

To test this result, Steinach reversed the process and castrated young rats. They soon showed signs of senile decay: loss of appetite, fatty degeneration, sexual asthenia. When grafted with new testes, they rapidly regained their youth as by a miracle.

These two key-experiments of Steinach's prove that testicle-grafting can rejuvenate the organism. Every other test has confirmed it.

Yet another triumph crowned Steinach's experiments. The average length of life of a rat is twenty-seven to thirty months; that of a grafted rat became extended to thirty-eight or thirty-nine months; rejuvenation carried with it a new lease on life.

The scientist then applied his results to men. But here he met with a material obstacle, that of obtaining the necessary human testes, and had to be content with sound glands removed from hospital patients for specific reasons;

but he was not able in this way to collect enough material to make conclusive experiments.

Voronoff attempted to make good this deficiency by using monkeys' glands instead of those of human beings. In his sensational book, *A Study of Senility and of Rejuvenation by Grafting,* he describes his method, which is illustrated by the following quotation:

'For a long time I had wanted to apply my method to old-age pensioners, in the hope of giving them back enough vitality to enable them to earn their living instead of being a burden to society.

'The Prefect of Algiers acknowledged the social and economic interest of this notion and was the first to help me accomplish my task. The success of my method, applied to a pensioner of the Dookra Home near Algiers and to other old men in Tunis and Alba Homes, was such that its general application could safely be considered.

'My first patient was an Alsatian, George Behr, born at Mülhausen in 1851. Hard work and privations made this seventy-three-year-old man look like eighty. Decrepit and bent, unsteady in gait, with all the external signs symptomatic of exhaustion and stupor, and characteristic emaciation resulting from physiological misery. The graft was performed on March 5th, 1924, at the public hospital of Algiers by Dr. Cochez, assisted by his clinical surgeon, Dr. Piéri, in the presence of the prefect and a number of medical men. I merely supervised the accurate observance of my technique.

'The monkey used for the graft was a tall, tailless specimen of the "Macaque" species, which was used for the first time. Hitherto I had taken glands only from chimpanzees or cynocephalics.

'A year later, on April 7th, 1925, I went to Dookra with the General Secretary of the Algiers Government,

M. Dubief, his Chief of Staff, M. Maury, the Prefects of
Algiers and Constantine, Messrs. Alliez and Lamy-Bois-
rozier, and my two colleagues, Drs. Cochez and Piéri. Our
expectations were more than fulfilled; only a comparison
of photographs taken before and after the graft can convey
an idea of the change in our patient.

'George Behr was truly unrecognisable. From being a
pale and feeble creature with a wondering look and hollow
cheeks, he had become a happy-looking fellow with pink
cheeks, who was in obviously buoyant health. Three
months after being grafted, he obtained a position with
M. Pommereau, the Dookra chemist, who told us that
Behr was spending his days washing bottles, raking the
garden-paths, and looking after the poultry yard and its
inmates, being all the time very happy and contented.
The psychological improvement was also manifest; he
answered questions promptly and brightly, in marked con-
trast to his faulty enunciation and difficulty of expression
before his operation.

'With regard to sexual vigour, he stated that it was
developing satisfactorily after having been non-existent for
years, and that he was experiencing long-forgotten sensations.

'Examination of the scrotum, made by Drs. Cochez,
Piéri, and myself, revealed two large grafted glandular
bodies which could obviously establish not only ultimate
vascular connections and thereby insure their future existence, but also nervous ones, since they were definitely
sensitive to touch.

'The presence of these bodies after a year-old graft
made us feel justified in expecting physiological benefit to
last for a long time.'

Voronoff's procedure in operating is as follows: the
testicle taken from a young monkey is cut into sections,

like an orange; one or more of the sections is then inserted in the patient's gland and stitched*.

*   *   *

Regarding Steinach's experiments, which, as we have seen, consisted in implanting a young testicle in the abdominal muscles of an old subject, the scientist next removed a grafted gland from the rejuvenated animal and examined it through a microscope. He found distinct differences between the grafted gland and a normal one; the former showed a decrease in the tissue which normally produces the sperm-cells, while the ejaculatory ducts had shrunk or even disappeared altogether. In other words, the excretory function of the testicle had atrophied, which is quite intelligible, nature being very prone to do away with useless organisms.

For instance, certain fishing tribes of Southern Guinea who spend most of their life in their canoes, have extremely developed arms and shoulders, while their legs are so unaccustomed to walking that the muscles are semi-atrophied.

The same applies to grafted testes; normally they act as exocrine and endocrine glands; once inserted in a muscle they can only work as endocrines, and the excreting faculty gradually disappears, while the cells of internal secretion increase in size and activity.

These cells being the ones endowed with rejuvenating

* *Editor's Note.*—Although Voronoff's experiments have received much more publicity in the world's Press, and especially in England, than the work of Steinach, it would appear that the former's results are ultimately much less satisfactory. The grafts, being taken from a different species, do not have a long life in the tissues of the new host. Testicular transplantation from another human being is much more satisfactory and lasting. Even with Steinach's method, there is a much greater chance of success if the testicle is taken from a donor whose blood grouping is compatible with that of the host. Compatibility may be determined by appropriate tests for blood grouping.—N. H.

properties, Steinach called the corresponding glandular part of the testes 'the puberty glands'.

In all justice, we must mention here that, just as Steinach's process developed from that of Brown-Séquard's, it was the achievement of two other scientists, Bouin and Ancel, to isolate under the name of 'interstitial glands' Steinach's 'puberty glands' and their function.

* * *

Once science had discovered that the secretions from the puberty glands were the rejuvenating element, the obvious conclusion was that senility arises in consequence of the reduced activity of those glands.

Steinach then propounded the question: Is there a means of stimulating the activity of these glands in aged people without having recourse to testes from another individual?

We have seen how an implanted gland loses its twin function and becomes solely an endocrine. If, then, one can operate in such a way as to block the vas deferens and thus curtail the excretory function, the corresponding glands will atrophy, thereby benefiting the puberty glands. This change of equilibrium will rejuvenate the whole organism through the subsequent fresh supply of certain elements to the blood.

This is the principle on which Steinach founded his rejuvenating method known as vaso-ligature. We remind our readers that the sperm-cells travel from the testes to the prostate along a duct called the vas deferens. Steinach closed the latter by the simple process of ligaturing it close to the testicle; as expected, the production of sperm-cells soon stopped, while the puberty glands became hyperactive.

* * *

Steinach's theory has been confirmed by another famous scientist whose studies bore on the physiological causes of senility. The Czecho-Slovakian doctor Ruzicka has established that the secretions in an old organism are quite distinct from those in a young one; he can actually calculate the age of an individual by examination of his endocrine secretions.

Steinach sent to Ruzicka secretions from young, old and rejuvenated subjects; the Czech doctor found that young and rejuvenated secretions were identical. This conclusion proves definitely that the vaso-ligature can regenerate the whole system and realise the century-old dream of rejuvenation.

* * *

The layman's objection to this method usually takes the form of regarding it as a process similar to castration, that no longer allows intercourse. As a matter of fact, it is nothing of the sort; the sperm-cells have nothing to do with the erection of the penis, as everybody knows who is acquainted with the mechanism of erection, and Steinach's ligature therefore can in no way interfere with it. On the contrary, it will help aged men to have an erection because the secretions of the puberty glands are a nerve tonic and a sexual stimulant.

Another objection is: 'As vaso-ligature entails the disappearance of the sperm-cells, a man will be deprived of the pleasure induced by ejaculation'. This again is a mistake; the seminal fluid issuing from the penis contains only 7 per cent. or 8 per cent. of testicular matter, the rest being supplied by other glands like the seminal vesicle and the prostate, which are unaffected by the ligature.

This operation therefore in no way hinders secretion and ejaculation, while every rejuvenated patient has testified that sexual intercourse has lost none of its pleasures for him.

On the other hand, a man on whom Steinach's double ligature has been performed is unavoidably sterile, since the spermatozoa are produced in the testicles and without them procreation is impossible.

* * *

It is, of course, still too early to pronounce a definite judgment on Voronoff's and Steinach's rejuvenating methods; they are too recent and the number of patients treated too small to allow of any final conclusions. Many hundreds of cases have been done by Dr. Harry Benjamin of New York, Dr. Peter Schmidt of Berlin, Dr. Norman Haire of London, and other surgeons in various parts of the world—vaso-ligature being performed much more often than testicular grafting, on account of the difficulty of obtaining human material for transplantation—and the majority of these authorities report favourable results in a large majority of the cases. They all agree that, if the operation is properly carried out, it cannot produce any ill-effects on the health, even in the small percentage of cases where no apparent benefit results.

We believe that one is justified in saying that a timely rejuvenating operation not only revives a man's virility but also saves him the misery of old age and senile decay.

As regards longevity, it should be noted that the number of people who die nowadays of old age is negligible. If the rejuvenated individual is suffering from cancer, heart disease, or some organic disorder, the process cannot help him.

A rejuvenating operation will not prolong the life of an organism debilitated by the excessive use of alcohol, nicotine or narcotics. Senile decay alone can be overcome, and death from this cause is of such rare occurrence that the value of rejuvenation in terms of longevity is negligible.

* * *

As regards women, science has unfortunately not yet found such an easy method as the vaso-ligature, because the ovarian function is too complex to be tampered with. Voronoff has, however, practised with more or less success the graft of monkeys' ovaries. Steinach applies an electrical method which does not require a surgical operation and is often very satisfactory.

An adjunct to both methods of rejuvenation is plastic surgery, which endeavours to remove the external signs of age (wrinkles, crow's-feet, sagging chin, etc.). This operation, however, is not truly a rejuvenating process, since it merely hides age behind an artificially youthful face.

BOOK V

SEXUAL ABERRATIONS

BOOK V

CHAPTER XXXI

DEVIATIONS OF AIM

Distinction between deviation of aim and of object. Voyeurism the most innocent of all aberrations. Satyrs of public gardens, girls' schools and churches. The treatment of exhibitionism. Definition of sadism and masochism. The close relation between these two aberrations. Strong emotion and physical violence. An historical case of masochism. J. J. Rousseau. The strange desire of a masochist.

'THE pathology of love is a hell the gates of which should never be opened', writes Rémy de Gourmont in his *Physique de l'Amour.*

But the celebrated author of the *Livre des Masques* only expresses in a striking manner one of the most common-place opinions. For many centuries, the average man professed that opinion, and we speak not only of the laity, but also of recognised ethical authorities and of physicians whose duty it should have been to take an interest in these problems which had been shrouded for far too long in darkness. We may even say that those who regarded sexual aberrations as manifestations of incurable madness were among the most enlightened, for others considered these phenomena criminal acts, which should be mercilessly punished. In fact, the most severe penalties were inflicted on those who were sexually abnormal, and if the severity of the punishment became somewhat moderated after the Middle Ages, when the *ultima ratio* was the stake, the principle of penalising the sufferers remained the same.

[405]

Millions and millions of sick people lived in anguish, being a prey to the most horrible torments, and their life one long martyrdom.

Anyone who made fun of an abnormal man, a hunchback for example, would have had the whole world against him. But for the humiliation of certain sexual perverts, no more responsible for their abnormal condition than was the hunchback, every kind of infamous treatment was permitted, for these individuals were regarded as outcasts of society.

It is only fairly recently that the medical profession has discovered the truth of that illuminating statement of Stekel: 'Only the normal man is capable of fully enjoying his sexual faculties'. This sentence, in fact, gives us the key to the problem of inversion and other sexual abnormalities.

When we ask ourselves the reason for the profound contempt with which society even to-day treats these unfortunate people, we find only one plausible answer: ignorance. Ignorance in the first place of the masses, and then the ignorance, or more correctly speaking, the indifference of certain specialists who do nothing to destroy these vicious superstitions which cause such untold suffering. 'It is knowledge which most men lack', said Magnus Hirschfeld, and this statement is particularly applicable to the sexual problem.

At the beginning of the chapters we are about to devote to sexual perversions, it is important to make a clear distinction between perversion and perversity, which, unfortunately, are too often confused in the minds of the masses. No one has defined the difference between these two phenomena with greater precision than Dr. A. Hesnard, formerly professor of psychology at the naval school of medicine in Bordeaux, and neuro-psychiatrist to the hospitals, in his *Traité de sexologie normale et pathologique* (Payot, 1933), a work from which, in the following pages, we shall often have occasion to quote. This is what Dr. Hesnard has to say on this question:

'Perversion is a deviation of tendency in a normal sexual impulse, and can neither afford the individual any malignant pleasure nor appeal in any way to his desire for that which is forbidden; whereas perversity is a more or less abnormal quality in his character which impels him to do evil for its own sake, and to perform or wish to perform certain acts simply because they are forbidden. If the two are combined (in cases of mental derangement, abnormality, alcoholism, etc.), it is necessary to describe each one separately.'

Sexual abnormalities are legion; numerous varieties and combinations of all kinds are to be found. For this reason, their classification is an extremely delicate matter. Many learned men, not the least of whom are Magnus Hirschfeld, Havelock Ellis, Stekel, etc., have undertaken to classify them according to their nature. In the following pages, we shall adopt the classification of Dr. Hesnard, which, though at first sight it may seem somewhat schematic, has the advantage of being simple, logical and clear—good reasons for following it in a work which is intended as much for the use of the general public as for that of specialists.

Dr. Hesnard first of all makes a distinction between deviations of aim and deviations of object. The former include all pathological states characterised by the fact that the individual while seeking a normal object (a man a woman, or a woman a man) has only repugnance or indifference for the sexual act. He seeks to replace it by one of its derivatives, or rather by one of its constituent acts. For example, a male exhibitionist will find pleasure with a normal female partner, but he will do so not during

[407]

the normal sexual act, but during one of its derivatives. It is the same with sadists and masochists: the object remains the same, but the aim differs essentially from the normal. On the other hand, in deviations of object, the individual seeks the normal sexual aim, but in conjunction with an object which normally would not produce excitement. As examples, we may mention homosexuality and zoophilia.

We shall now examine in detail perversions of aim and perversions of object in their various manifestations, taking each one in its turn.

* * *

One of the most frequent abnormalities is undoubtedly *voyeurism*, also known as *scoptophilia* or *mixoscopia*. The individual who is subject to it is nearly always incapable of performing the sexual act—old men who are impotent or young men suffering from morbid shyness form the majority of cases—and finds satisfaction in watching it being performed by others. In many cases, however, it is not necessary to see the act itself performed, at least not under normal conditions. For some patients the sight of the complete act is indispensable in order to produce satisfaction, for others the sight of the genital organs of a member of the opposite sex is sufficient. There are some men who are satisfied by the simple fact of seeing a woman clambering up a steep place or balancing herself in an armchair in a provocative position. Others find pleasure in witnessing the copulation of animals, still others in watching acts of defecation or micturition.

To the general public, voyeurism seems the most innocent of all abnormalities. This is to some extent consistent with reality, because it is very difficult to draw the line of demarcation between normality and the first symptoms of the morbid state. That is the reason one of the greatest experts in sexual matters, Havelock Ellis, was led to write the following words:

'To a certain extent, this tendency (voyeurism) is absolutely normal; that manifestation of it should be considered shameful is due simply to the rigid secrecy which convention attaches to the naked body. Many respectable men have, during their youth, sought secret opportunities to surprise women in their bedrooms, and more than one honourable woman has looked through the keyhole of a man's bedroom, though she would not, to-day, be prepared to admit it. It is certainly a common habit for landladies and servants to put their eyes to the key-holes of rooms where there were couples they suspected of being in love. . . . These manifestations have sometimes attracted the attention of the police, notably in Paris. Women whom I know have discovered that men were looking at them through the openings in the roof of the toilets in the Tuileries gardens.'

Voyeurism, moreover, is one of the perversions most easily exploited by directors of the more luxurious *maisons closes* where one is regaled with love-scenes which are partly cinematographic and partly real, reflected in mirrors. The interior of these special establishments, provided with observation posts, has been too often described in sensational novels for us to enlarge any more upon the subject here. The fact remains that voyeurism has given rise to a whole industry of obscene productions of the most varied kinds, bringing in large profits to those concerned.

Let us repeat that in most cases voyeurism simply indicates impotence or a certain sexual weakness. It may, however, have a profound effect on the actions of the sufferer, as is shown by the following observation of Magnus Hirschfeld:

'Eric W——, formerly an army officer, now thirty-eight years of age, had married, three years earlier, a woman fifteen years older than himself, who before her marriage had been a prostitute. He did so against the wishes of his parents, and was obliged, on account of the marriage, to give up the military profession, to which he was so greatly attached, having sprung from a line of army officers extending through several generations.

'He was questioned, one day, about his motives in marrying, in such circumstances, a woman so much his senior and lacking not only charm but all spiritual and moral qualities.

'He replied that he had noticed this prostitute long before he had made her acquaintance and that he had gradually become charmed through observing the strangeness of her walk and the movement of her arms.

'He had then followed her, for hours on end, through the streets where she practised her deplorable profession, never losing sight of her different movements. Finally these had excited him to such an extent as to produce an orgasm.

'From that moment, nothing provided him with greater sexual excitement than the movements of this woman, or the thought of them. But soon, these phantasies were not sufficient: he felt the imperious need to have these movements continually before his eyes, since they alone could produce sexual excitement in him. This fetichist, when questioned by us about his sexual relations with his wife, told us that the latter had to walk up and down the room until his sexual feelings were sufficiently roused for him to be able to possess her. The strangest part of the story is that before meeting this woman the officer had never experienced anything unusual. On the contrary, he had always been capable of performing the sexual act in a perfectly normal way. It was only after watching the prostitute that he felt himself suddenly attracted by the movements of her legs and her arms.

'As he had always been attracted by women older than he himself, he assured us that he had never even looked at his wife's face, during the first few weeks; his love having been awakened and excited merely by these movements, her face had little importance for him; it was only her walk that mattered.'

It is impossible to adopt any guiding principle for the treatment of voyeurism. Since the same reactions are produced as a rule in different patients by various causes, the first task of the physician is to discover that cause.

* * *

Garnier, who was one of the first to devote his attention to the study of *exhibitionism*, gives the following definition of it:

'Exhibitionism is a sexual aberration, obsessive and impulsive, characterised by the irresistible need to display in public, and generally under certain conditions of time and place, the genital organs in a state of flaccidity, quite apart from any voluptuous or provocative manipulation; the act is induced by sexual desire, and its performance puts an end to an agonising struggle and terminates the attack.'

The observations of several experts, however, cast some doubt upon the impulsive nature of exhibitionism as defined by Garnier. Thus, Dr. Hesnard rightly remarks that the number of non-impulsive exhibitionists, 'that is to say, perfectly capable of resisting, when necessary, their tendency towards what is forbidden, and at other times knowingly giving way to it with all the refinements indicative of a deliberate and reasoned voluptuousness', is much greater than that of individuals who practise exhibitionism in a way that shows it to be more or less involuntary and irresistible.

[411]

That is why Dr. Hesnard defines exhibitionism as follows: ' It is a perverse tendency, characterised by an effort to obtain erotic enjoyment by displaying, in a more or less indecent manner, to one or more witnesses, the sexual organs or parts of the body participating in their traditionally shameful character. The combination of shame and visual pleasure is characteristic of this form of sexual aberration, the aim being rarely to produce shame in the partner, but nearly always in the subject himself.'

Havelock Ellis, however, gives a much more summary definition of this perversion. Exhibitionism, according to him, is an impulse to expose a part of the body, especially the genital region, for a sexual reason, either conscious or unconscious.

We have given all the preceding definitions because, in this case, it is important to be precise concerning the nature of this perversion. In fact, here, perhaps more than in the case of other forms of perversion, the dividing line between the normal and the abnormal is very indefinite, and some authors go so far as to see signs of exhibitionism in the obscene jokes which men and women make with members of the opposite sex. Obviously, in this case, we are concerned with a purely psychological phenomenon, but one which is nevertheless sometimes more or less closely related to that of exhibitionism proper.

Havelock Ellis concludes also that exhibitionism, up to a certain point, may be a perfectly normal phenomenon; it is usually controlled, and manifests itself merely by a certain pride in the possession of fully developed masculine or feminine attributes.

We know that the great majority of exhibitionists belong to the male sex, and that they expose the penis; women, according to Douglas Bryan, regard the whole body as a kind of penis to be exposed.

But it must not be supposed that among men it is always the penis that is the object of exhibition. Certain individuals obtain pleasure, doubtlessly a less morbid pleasure but none the less evident, by exhibiting other parts of their bodies, the chest, the abdomen, or the legs. There are all possible degrees in this perverse pleasure, which must not be confused with the healthy pleasure of the nudist, who enjoys the good things of nature, air, water and sunshine, without experiencing any shame or any perverse satisfaction in displaying his genital organs to equally nude individuals of either sex who surround him. The nudist professes an indifference to nakedness which we scarcely ever find anywhere else except among primitive people or young children. The exhibitionist, on the other hand, experiences sexual excitement in displaying his nakedness, the result very often of his prudish upbringing. It is for this reason that women who have received a puritanical education lapse sometimes into exhibitionism of the entire body or of the breasts, these latter corresponding in some way to phallic exhibitionism in a man.

As we have just seen, the classical form of exhibitionism consists in completely uncovering the male member. According to the case in question and the circumstances, the member may be erect or flaccid. In former times, it was generally believed that all exhibitionists, on exposing the penis, indulged in masturbation. To-day we know that this is not always the case, and that even when an individual does behave in this way, his act rarely results in a complete emission.

In other cases, which form the majority, it is only when they have fled from the scene of their exploits and returned to their homes that exhibitionists, trying to recall what has just taken place, indulge in masturbation; a certain percentage even indulge immediately in normal copulation.

Garnier had already noted how set exhibitionists were in their habits, and how regular as to time and place in their practices. The observation is perfectly correct. Certain districts have their exhibitionists, their satyr of the public gardens or of the girls' high school. Dr. Abraham remarked that women often tell each other that the exhibitionist of the district performs at such and such a place.

Public gardens and girls' high schools, however, are not the only places that exhibitionists like to frequent. Many of them are not contented with such a commonplace sphere, and choose churches as the scene of their exploits, especially at moments when few worshippers are present. The general public readily believes these acts to be inspired by sacrilegious motives, and is all the more severe in its condemnation of the individuals guilty of them. It is easy to understand how painful it must be for a woman, absorbed in her devotions, suddenly to be a witness of so unseemly a spectacle, but we realise that the aim sought by the exhibitionist is not exactly that of sacrilege.

Very characteristic, in this connection, is the confession made to Garnier by one of his patients, who was a frequenter of churches.

'Why do I like to go to churches? I cannot say. But I know that it is only there that my act takes on its full importance. The woman is in an attitude of devotion and she must see that such an act, in such a place, is not a joke, indication of bad taste, or obscenity; if I go there, it is not for fun; it is far more serious than that. I watch the effect produced on the faces of the women to whom I expose my organs. I hope to see them express profound joy; I really wish to hear them exclaim: "How impressive is nature when one sees it in these circumstances".'

In commenting on this case, Havelock Ellis remarks that we here find a trace of the same sentiment which, formerly, inspired the cult of the phallus. However that may be, it is certain that the exhibitionist seeks to arouse admiration and joy in his female spectators, and would rather see their flattering smiles than their indignation or fright.

In Rousseau's *Confessions* there is a fine description of the psychology of the exhibitionist:

'My blood being all afire, my mind was continually preoccupied with women and girls. But shame came in the course of the years: and increased my natural shyness to such an extent that I could not overcome it, and never, either at that time or since then, have I been able to make a lascivious suggestion unless she to whom I made it had in some way forced me by her advances to do so.

'My restlessness increased to such a degree that, being unable to control my desires, I stimulated them by the most extravagant methods. I used to seek out dark lanes, remote places, where I could expose myself at a distance to members of the opposite sex in the way in which I would have liked to be near them. What they saw was not something obscene—that idea did not occur to me—but something ridiculous. The pleasure I derived from displaying it to them is indescribable.

'One day, when the girls came to the fountain, I offered them a sight which was more ridiculous than seductive. The more serious of them pretended not to see anything. Others began to laugh. Still others considered themselves insulted and made a fuss. This adventure, while not having the results it might have had, sufficed, none the less, to make me prudent for a long time.'

Fear of the consequences which his reprehensible act may bring about only adds to the excitement of the exhibitionist. His pleasure is so much the more intense when the time and the place are such as to expose him to greater risk. He knows, however, that conventional morality disapproves of such conduct, and that once in the hands of the police, he may have to pay dearly for his voluptuous thrill. His perverse tendency is stronger than his reason. The danger which he fears has no effect other than that of inflaming his imagination.

In any case, we may say that there is no form of sexual perversion that renders the patient more unhappy than exhibitionism. This is, however, partly explained by the fact that it is the form most frequently detected by the law. Norwood Heast found that of the 291 sexual delinquents confined in Brixton prison, 101 were exhibitionists under preventive arrest or condemned for indecent behaviour. To show what tragic conflict exhibitionism may produce in the mind of the patient, we quote the following authentic letter, sent by one:

'I am an unfortunate creature who implores your help. In everyday life, I am a normal man who does his work (that of a bank clerk) in an irreproachable manner. For two or three months all goes well, but then I am suddenly attacked by a kind of anxiety which impels me to spend hours on end walking about the streets. I know that is far from being a good sign. Once, when I felt an attack coming on, I took refuge in a mental hospital, thinking in that way to escape the inevitable. Alas, at nine o'clock in the evening the impulse was too strong for me. I was quite lucid, but that man who clambered up the railings and jumped down on the outside was not myself. I was impelled by an invisible force which I could not resist. Out of breath, I ran as far as the suburbs. There, in a deserted street, I saw in the distance a young girl approaching. I hid myself and—I know the rest from the police report—so soon as I found myself near her, I opened my trousers, uncovered my genital parts, and began to masturbate. I remember, vaguely, that her wide open eyes and her terrified look excited me to such an extent that I immediately had an ejaculation. At once I regained possession of myself and I tried to run away, but fell into the hands of the police.

'I beg of you, Doctor, to tell me if I am mad, if I ought to be shut up in a lunatic asylum, since I cannot be responsible for my actions. I beg of you, also, to explain to the judges that I am not vicious, as they say, but an unfortunate creature who is suffering, and who has been severely punished by nature.'

Here is another case of exhibitionism quoted by Dr. Morin, and showing to what sad vagaries this detestable perversion may bring its victim:

'He was a salesman working for a rubber company. Some fifty years of age, of good presence, with the manners of a good employee who takes his business seriously, his outward appearance was that of an impeccable and even austere official. Having taken an active interest in organisations concerned with adult education and evening classes, an academic distinction had been conferred on him, and while doing his rounds he wore his violet ribbon.

'But when he visited the company's customers, the same almost ritual ceremony would invariably take place.

'He would use choice terms to extol the merits of his wares, going into details about the matchless quality of his rubber. Everything would go on normally and correctly, until suddenly, when he came to recommend a certain tube for kitchen taps, his eyes would begin to water, his eyelids would flicker and his cheeks grow red. He would begin to stammer and his voice, which was usually grave and sedate, would become vulgar and coarse. One could see from his desperate condition that he was struggling with savage energy against a morbid obsession which continued

[417]

to gain power over his brain and was getting the better of him, sweeping aside all his scruples and breaking up his veneer of respectability. A kind of sudden moral collapse in this poor human puppet indicated the triumph of his instinct. Piteously, he would look into the face of his terrified customer, undo his clothes, and concerning the rubber tube, would make a most unexpected and repugnant comparison.'

On the question of the extent to which individuals afflicted with exhibitionism may be regarded as diseased, Magnus Hirschfeld considers that it is nearly always due to the presence of morbid factors, with consequent disturbance of balance. According to Kosel, Schiffer declared that among 75 exhibitionists 18 were epileptics, 13 individuals subject to hallucinations, 10 mentally deranged, 8 neurasthenics or drunkards, and 7 feeble-minded. Of 85 cases, only 11 were women.

Others, however, are much less convinced on the question of mental derangement. Thus, Dr. Hesnard, whose opinion we are inclined to accept, states:

'On reading authors who have made a study of exhibitionism, one gains the impression that we are concerned with a phenomenon that is frankly and invariably morbid. This is not our opinion. From our experience, we are led to conclude that many individuals, scarcely in any way unbalanced or neuropathic (at any rate, classed from a medico-legal standpoint, among those entirely responsible), seek pleasure in self-exposure. The "satyrs" who haunt our public gardens are legion, and we are of the opinion that a considerable number of them are to be regarded as normal from the standpoint of psychiatry. Let us add that in popular or village gatherings where the social censure of everything relating to sex is less severe, the sight of a young man exhibiting himself, to the accompaniment of coarse jokes, before a group of girls, is a matter of common occurrence.

'We shall complete our survey of this little known branch of psychology by saying that the exhibitionistic tendency implies a curious and subtle mixture of sexual pride and shame, of virile protest and sexual fright, elements found in various combinations according to the case in question. There is both erotic vanity and self-satisfied narcissism in this strange behaviour. But there is also anxiety, fear of action, and defiance reacting to a threat.'

There remain still two questions to be examined, that of responsibility before the law and that of the treatment of such a disorder.

Most sexologists, while admitting the necessity of treating exhibitionists, are nevertheless of the opinion that society should institute penal laws against individuals convicted of having outraged public morality. Thus, Wulffen openly demands imprisonment for exhibitionists; Havelock Ellis, in a very broad-minded way, also maintains that under present day social conditions the conduct of these patients, even though it may be the outcome of a more or less natural cause, cannot be tolerated. He gives as his reason that the sight offered by the exhibitionist may provoke serious nervous or hysterical symptoms in the innocent young girl who witnesses it. On these grounds the intervention of the police is desirable.

As for the treatment of the disorder, it has been studied in detail by psycho-analysts. These trace the origin of exhibitionism to the castration complex. This complex, which is rather common, is due to the male child's fear of being deprived of his sexual organ. The fear of castration may degenerate into a veritable obsession, which will manifest itself later on. The sexual enjoyment of the exhibitionist would then be nothing more than a sort of protest against this primitive anxiety, and nothing except an analysis would be capable of bringing about a cure.

Havelock Ellis, in his *Précis of Sexual Psychology,* indicates another treatment. We quote *in extenso* the passage which refers to it:

' As for therapeutic treatment, I would like to say that it would have a chance of being efficacious if it were combined with a sun-bathing camp in accordance with the nudist system, which is now beginning to be recognised and generally adopted. If the exhibitionist is often nothing more than a narcissist of an unusually pronounced type showing evidence of impulses which are not necessarily anti-social, and which, under certain conditions, society could recognise, then to give him an opportunity of expressing them legitimately would be to give him a new capacity for self-control. An exhibitionist who is encouraged to practise nudity in the midst of men and women who, being themselves completely nude, accept this as a natural thing, is in a position to satisfy his narcissistic desires, in so far as they are innocent, and to deprive them of their morbid intensity. He will know that if these impulses cannot be confined within innocent limits, he will be deprived of the advantage that has been granted to him. Thus, a healthy and socially admissible expression would be found for an impulse which would otherwise isolate and degrade the person subject to it.

' The first advice to give an exhibitionist who has not yet attracted the attention of the police is that he should never go out alone. Hirschfeld, who recognises the importance of this rule, remarks that the advice is usually taken in good part, because the exhibitionist lives in terror of his own impulses. If he has been arrested and brought before a judge, the most humane method and the most reasonable, for a first offence, is to release him with a warning that it is only on condition that he obtains medical advice. In several large towns there are now special clinics in which police physicians and social agents are placed at the disposal of judges for a very low fee, and they should be made use of much more frequently. For the second offence, it would be necessary to inflict a term of compulsory seclusion of at least one month in an establishment for examination and treatment. This solution is in accordance with the opinion of Forel, who says that exhibitionists are not dangerous and (except when they are feeble-minded) should be detained only in a clinic for mental disorders, and then only for a short period.'

*   *   *

When the sexual element is accompanied by the element of pain, either active or passive, we have the phenomena known as *sadism* and *masochism*.

In a remarkable book, from which we have several times had occasion to quote in the course of this study, Dr. Hesnard gives the following definition of sado-masochism:

'A sexual perversion characterised by the pursuit of erotic enjoyment obtained by the idea of violence, not necessarily directed to the sexual organs, but either exercised on the object (sadism), or provoked on the subject himself from the object (masochism).'

The terms sadism and masochism were created by Dr. Krafft-Ebing. The former is derived from the Marquis de Sade (1740-1814), the author of numerous works (one of them *Justine and Juliet*) which were celebrated for the accounts of amorous violence they contain. Jules Janin characterises in striking terms the work of the father of sadism:

'It describes bleeding corpses, children wrenched from

[421]

the arms of their mothers, young women whose throats were cut at the end of an orgy; cups filled with blood and wine, unheard-of tortures. Boilers are heated, wooden horses are erected, men have their skin, all steaming, stripped from them; they shout, they swear, they blaspheme, they bite themselves, they wrench their hearts out of their chests: and that throughout twelve or fifteen endless volumes and on every page, in every line, always. Oh what an indefatigable wretch! In his first book, *Justine*, he shows us a poor girl, at bay, lost, ruined, overcome by blows, led by monsters through one underground passage after another, from one cemetery to another, beaten, stifled, withered, crushed. . . . When the author has finished with crime, when he has exhausted the list of incest and monstrosities, when he stands panting over the corpses that he has stabbed and violated, when there is no longer a church that he has not desecrated, not a child that he has not sacrificed to his rage, not a moral thought over which he has not cast the filth of his ideas and his speech, that man finally stops and looks at himself; he smiles at himself and is not afraid of himself.'

Masochism takes its name from the German writer Sacher-Masoch (1835-1895), author of *Venus in a Fur-coat*, which describes the love-affair of a violent and authoritative woman and a man who finds pleasure in allowing himself to be dominated by her. It should be noted here, for the sake of exactitude, that Sacher-Masoch always protested violently against his being regarded as a 'masochist', but neither he nor his son has succeeded in eliminating from scientific language that term, which in a few years has become very popular.

The uninitiated might be tempted to believe that there is an irreconcilable antagonism between sadism and masochism. This is not so, and for that reason many authorities include both two morbid phenomena under the common term *algolagnia*, invented by the great specialist Schrenck-Notzing.

We shall therefore endeavour to show the similarities existing between sadism and masochism, in spite of their apparent difference. In the first place, let us note that these two phenomena often co-exist in the same person. In this connection, let us quote a clinical observation by Dr. Abraham:

'A.B. . . . 35 years of age, a manual labourer, likes to be beaten and chained up by his wife, and to surrender himself entirely to her. She satisfies her husband's desires only to a very limited extent, so that their sexual relationship does not permit a full expression of the man's feelings. For this reason, the man indulges in various acts of auto-sadism, notably by wounding himself with a knife, in order to produce a seminal emission. These wounds are made on the buttocks. He also frequently feels a desire to perform sadistic acts on his wife. From time to time, according to his means, he also visits prostitutes and indulges in flagellation. The two perversions never coincide, so that his desires are sometimes sadistic, at other times, masochistic.'

We may even say that it is comparatively rare to find either sadism or masochism in a pure form. Numerous masochist documents that we have consulted have contained sadistic elements, and the works of sadist authors, not excepting those of the Marquis de Sade, contain masochistic elements.

That is why, according to Freud's definition, masochism is a kind of sadism ' turned against oneself ', while sadism is a kind of masochism ' turned against others '. The definition is ingenious, and is not to be regarded as a mere fancy.

Until recently, some regarded sadism as essentially active and masculine, and masochism as essentially passive and feminine. Numerous observations, however, have established the fact that there exist a great many masochists virile in appearance and character, and sadists of effeminate appearance and timid manners.

Faced with the complex nature of the phenomenon, and in order to avoid the difficulties of a special definition of sadism and of masochism, Magnus Hirschfeld has sought to include certain aspects of the two morbid manifestations under the general term of *metatropism*. By this, he means a sort of reversion or exchange of sexual attitude. 'Thus sadism in a man would be simply an accentuation of the normal male sexual attitude, and masochism in a woman would be simply an accentuation of the normal female sexual attitude; but sadism and masochism must be regarded as totally different conditions according to whether they appear in a man or in a woman. Masculine sadism and feminine masochism are then, for Hirschfeld, nothing more than hyperæsthetic or erotomaniacal excesses of the normal sexual impulse, while in the opposite sex they become completely metatropic deviations of the normal state.'

However that may be, the author of *Homosexuality* has not been able to impose his very interesting conceptions on any except his pupils.

In sadism as well as in masochism, the normal genital organs do not usually function. The sexual act itself is replaced by an act of violence, either real or symbolic. Certain authors emphasise that this is, apparently at least, a chaste perversion. That, however, is only an illusion, for it is only in exceptional cases that, under favourable conditions, erection or other signs of sexual excitement are lacking. Dr. Hesnard notes that in most cases, sadists and masochists 'make use of their capacity to become excited by suffering, whether actual or symbolic, active or passive, in order to find a means of producing an orgasm, which in fact then takes place, or is at least facilitated by auto-erotic manœuvres, sometimes by normal sexual intercourse—although perverts of this type are most often impotent in this respect'.

Very often, the uninitiated are surprised to find that in both cases, and especially in masochism, there is a correlation between pain and pleasure. The explanation is simple, for what constitutes the pleasure is not so much the pain as the emotion provoked by it. Moreover, as Havelock Ellis rightly points out, sadists and masochists show evidence of sexual deficiency, and they therefore require stronger stimulation than the normal to provoke sexual emotion in them. Certain sensations or violent emotions, such as anxiety or grief, are capable of stimulating their sexual activity.

On the other hand, it must not be forgotten that, like most abnormalities, algolagnia, that is to say, sado-masochism, has its roots in normal sexual life. Normal sexual life presents certain aspects in which there are elements of pain, experienced by the subject or provoked by him in the partner. Let us note in this respect how certain animals 'make love', the female witnessing the struggle of the males; and, in human beings, the excitement produced in the woman by certain pains inflicted by the partner (biting, etc.). The sexual act itself also possesses a certain violence of character, whether we are concerned with the desire of the male to penetrate as deeply as possible into the female, or with the desire of the female to have the male penetrate into her as deeply as possible even if that penetration should imply suffering. It follows that in certain cases, where, for various reasons, this penetration cannot take place, the desires associated with it may be transferred to the extra-genital sphere, psychological or physical.

It happens, as a matter of fact, that sadism has a purely psychological character—masochism also—and belongs to a sphere which apparently has no connection with sexuality. Some sadists find a violent pleasure in tormenting those about them, and certain masochists unconsciously go out of their way to frustrate their own desires, in order to cause themselves suffering. There are some who, so to speak, force their partner to deceive them, in order that they may enjoy their own misfortune.

The cruelty of sadists has often been emphasised. Undoubtedly, their acts may appear extremely cruel, but it must not be thought that they are committed through a thirst for cruelty. It happens quite frequently that a perfectly normal lover inflicts pain on the woman he loves and anxiously watches the effect produced. In this case, he desires, as Havelock Ellis remarks, that the woman should feel the pain as pleasure. The sadist, in fact, merely pushes the same experience too far *mutatis mutandis*; for instance, he pricks a girl's skin with pins, all the time requiring her to keep smiling. He means to excite the feelings of his victim by provoking a strong emotion in her, and according to Havelock Ellis, the most effective method he knows of is to inflict pain on her. In the case of the girl whom the sadist pricks with pins while obliging her to smile, there is no search for cruelty for its own sake. Even when sadists go so far as to kill their victims, they are not dominated by the desire to produce death nearly so much as by the desire to shed blood, an excitant known all the world over.

It is for this reason, according to Liepmann, that the wounds made by sadists are always situated in those parts of the body where the hæmorrhage is most violent.

The statement holds good, in the reverse sense, for masochists, who for their part have no wish to submit to cruelty. But the masochist who finds no pleasure in the performance of coitus seeks a sort of compensation in the ill-treatment which he has had inflicted upon himself. These injuries may vary from mere verbal insults to the most painful humiliations. He does the most repugnant work, has himself beaten, bound, trampled upon, etc.

Let us now consider some typical manifestations of sadism. It may at first express itself in an essentially innocuous form, and the person addicted to it may be quite unconscious of what his real tendencies are. In this category are to be placed people who seek strong emotion by frequenting the Grand Guignol, boxing rings, bull fights, and even dangerous circus performances.

Sadism finds a much clearer expression in certain forms of corporal punishment, and especially in flogging. It is known that in Greco-Roman times, slaves were severely beaten with rods, and this punishment was not always disinterested. In Sparta, on the occasion of certain feasts, young men had to undergo trials of endurance, by being thrashed to such an extent that many of them succumbed. We shall say nothing of the vogue of flogging which flourished during the Middle Ages, as it is well known to all. Let us remember that corporal punishment often plays a large part in education—for instance, in the schools of Great Britain—and certain educators take an excessive pleasure in this, giving a somewhat original interpretation to the old saying: 'He who loves well, punishes well'. This mania for flogging sometimes becomes quite revolting, as is shown by the following letter:

'Dear Doctor,—Allow me to explain my case to you, and to ask your advice. About ten years ago I married a widow who brought two little girls to my home, aged respectively four and five years. We get along very well together, and the only cause of contention between us is the upbringing of the children. My wife is very indulgent towards them, while I believe in being severe in such matters. When one of the children has done something wrong, I have always insisted on correcting her myself. Up to the present I have been able to do this, but now that my step-daughters are fourteen and fifteen years old, they refuse to allow themselves to be beaten, and take refuge by their mother's side, so that our household is now not so harmonious as previously. I often quarrel with my wife about this matter, and that has led me to appeal to you, to ask if, in my capacity as educator, I have not the right to correct my step-daughters.

'In order that you may the better be able to judge matters, I shall describe my methods in detail. When one of the girls has done wrong, I immediately warn her that she will be beaten. She begins to cry, and tries to escape, but I have previously taken the precaution of closing the door, and as I am the stronger I am not long in getting the better of her. I insist that her sister shall witness the scene, for I consider that example plays a large part in education. I lay the guilty one on the sofa, with her head under my left knee, while I hold her legs with my right foot, and her hands with my left hand. Previously, I have pulled down her drawers and rolled up her petticoat. I attach great importance to letting the blows fall on the buttocks, as in this way they are sure to be efficacious without causing an accident. If the offence has not been too serious, I am satisfied with ten fairly hard strokes, making the buttocks red. Naturally, I avoid making them bleed. The child cries unceasingly during this scene, but I do not let that hinder me, and I continue to strike with half a minute's interval between each blow. I choose, beforehand, the place where the blow is to take effect. After the sixth blow, I urge my step-daughter to confess her fault and to ask my pardon. She knows very well that if she refuses the blows will be redoubled. It is no use her struggling, for I hold her firmly. She moves the buttocks, trying to avoid the blows, but I have had much experience and I never miss my aim. After the ninth blow, I pause once more, in order to give my step-daughter a chance to repent. She then says: "Dear father, I shall not do that again. I thank you for having punished me and I beg of you not to beat me any more, for I am suffering terribly". When she has uttered these words, she receives the last blow, the hardest of all. Her buttocks are marked with stripes, but never wounded. Then I leave her alone. She arranges her clothes, pulls up her drawers and wipes her eyes. I open the door. The correction is finished.

'Do you believe, Doctor, that this method is injurious to the children and that I am not justified in making use of it to prevent my step-daughters behaving badly? Of course, sex can have nothing to do with it, because I insist that the sister should witness the scene.

'I remain, dear Doctor, etc. . . .'

This is a case of unconscious sadism. Another one, quoted by Dr. Chapotin, is of the same kind.

'A maniac', writes Dr. Chapotin, 'assiduously frequented a little café where the drinks were abominable and the seats deplorably hard. He went there simply because he took pleasure in listening to the cashier, a very ugly woman, afflicted with a coarse voice, insulting and ill-treating a simple-minded waiter; by repeating his orders, he could manage to get the waiter into trouble. Then, once the tirade had broken out, he would quit the establishment, feeling greatly relieved.'

Let us now examine the case of sadists who abandon themselves to their passion during amorous scenes. These cases are much more frequent than is generally supposed, and similar practices existed even in ancient times. Thus Lucian makes one of his characters say: 'He who has not rained blows upon his mistress, who has not torn out her hair and rent her clothes, is not yet in love'. Amorous sadists of this kind may frequently be met with nowadays in brothels where, for a consideration, they are given the right to indulge in acts of violence on the prostitute. These disciples of the Marquis de Sade bite, crush and gash the bodies of their victims or beat them with horse-whips in order to draw blood.

There also exist female sadists who make fierce attacks, especially on the genital organs of their partners. Male sadists, on the contrary, nearly always spare the sexual organs of women, but some of them attack the breasts. This motif is to be found in many works of art and occurs frequently in sadist drawings.

Huysmans gives us the following description of a mystico-sadist love scene, of which Saint Lidvine de Schiedam was the victim:

'Towards the end of her fifteenth year, the amorous madness of her husband descended upon her like an eagle of love. That delicate and charming flesh with which he had clothed her, suddenly seemed to annoy him, and he cut it, he opened it on all sides in order better to seize the soul. He magnified this poor body, he gave it the fearful capacity of absorbing all the evils of the earth. . . . She was, in fact, a fruit of suffering that God pressed and crushed until the last drop of juice had been drained from it.'

Let us note, furthermore, that sadist elements may enter into certain ritual crimes, as well as into certain murders apparently committed for political reasons.

Here, we come to the case of sadistic murderers analysed at length in medico-legal works. It appears that certain historical personages, Heliogabalus, Caracalla, Nero and Ivan the Terrible, are to be classed in this category. In another sphere, and nearer home, let us recall the case of Vacher, of the Vampire of Düsseldorf, or of Matuska, who was responsible for the terrible Bia-Torbagy railway accident, which cost ten human lives, a terrible spectacle over which the criminal gloated in voluptuous pleasure.

*　　*　　*

Masochists are perhaps more numerous than sadists, and from a medical point of view they offer less variety. Masochism, as Havelock Ellis states, is met with chiefly in men, partly because in women a certain degree of sexual subjection may be considered natural—witness, for instance, the relations between women of the streets and their ponces—and also because masochism springs chiefly from an effort to replace or to stimulate deficient sexual vigour in the male.

The form of masochism most frequently met with—so frequently that it is not a question of masochism proper, of the phenomenon regarded as a perversion—is that found in men whose aspiration it is to be dominated by more virile women. We may mention, for instance, the historical cases of Musset and Chopin.

As for Jean-Jacques Rousseau, he was familiar from his childhood with the perverse pleasure of the masochists and he confesses it in his works. He allowed himself to be flogged unmercifully by Mademoiselle Lambercier, and this practice left an indelible impression on his emotional make-up. All through life, love and humiliation were associated in his thought.

'To be at the knees of an imperious mistress,' he cries, 'to obey her orders, to have to ask her pardon, were for me very sweet pleasures, and the more my lively imagination inflamed my blood, the more I resembled a lover in his transports.'

With other individuals, the need to have physical suffering

[431]

inflicted on them exists, but they are so ashamed of their aberration that they do not dare to ask their partner to conform to it, and consequently their tendencies remain more or less unsatisfied. Some of these sufferers go to brothels in order to be pinched or whipped by girls, but owing to lack of enthusiasm on the part of their tormentors, they frequently prefer to give up these attempts and take refuge in masturbation. According to Dr. Hesnard, the perverse masochists are those who indulge in erotic practices which aim at arousing excitement with a partner—stimulation of the senses, usually auto-erotic, although some can, on rare occasions, accomplish the sexual act—by allowing themselves to be flogged and pricked, by having the breasts pinched, the neck or waist crushed, or still more humiliated by being literally polluted by another person. Some indulge in the same practices when alone, evoking any partners whatsoever, more or less imaginary and complicated by a fetichist staging—prison or dungeon scenes, with chains and instruments of torture, scenes of barbarity, especially in convents, etc.; the phantasy of the page beaten by a pretty girl, humiliating himself before her, even going so far as to drink her urine ('pagism', according to Krafft-Ebing). These practices take place in the home of the patient, who is, moreover, frequently a collector of drawings or photographs of torments or floggings, or is himself able to draw; or they may take place in brothels where grotesque accessories of this nature are at his disposal. We know of some masochists who, being of a thorough-going type, have in their homes quite an arsenal of pincers, pressing machines, ropes, rods, nails, pins to be heated before use, etc. Others limit their *mise en scène* to more subtle practices in which they are threatened by the partner, lie at her feet, undertake the most menial and humiliating tasks for her sake, even going so far as to be ridden like a horse (the '*equus eroticus*'

[432]

of Krafft-Ebing), or they impersonate, either in dreams or in reality, the horse equipped with a halter, harnessed and whipped.

Dr. Chapotin quotes the case of a retired commandant, a one-time bon-vivant, whose instinct showed a most curious aberration:

'He, in whose arms a great many women had lain voluptuously, was no longer able to accomplish the sexual act except by wandering through the workmen's quarters in Paris, and soliciting a female greengrocer, who was returning to her lodgings behind the empty cart which she had been pushing all day. He persuaded this woman, not without many unsuccessful attempts, as we may well suppose, to accompany him to a room in a hotel. There, laying her on the bed, he sucked one of the toes of her left foot. . . .'*

Usually, the ambition of the male masochist is to play the part of a woman's slave, and as not all of them find it convenient to frequent brothels, there frequently appear amongst the advertisements in certain 'special' journals applications for a 'severe governess', an 'energetic masseuse', an 'elegant woman of an energetic character, acquainted with English methods of education for boys of a mature age', etc., etc. These are the advertisements of

---

* *Editor's Note.*—Lest it should be thought that this story is exaggerated or apocryphal, it may be well to mention an even more remarkable case which came under my notice lately in London. A highly respectable professional gentleman, aged sixty-odd, was in the habit of haunting the neighbourhood of a large military barracks near Regent's Park. He would pick up a soldier and take him home. He would ask the soldier to take off his boots and socks, and if the socks were sufficiently dirty and malodorous, the old gentleman would chew them and have an orgasm. In this case the soldier was rewarded to the extent of one pound. But if the socks were too clean, the soldier only received ten shillings, together with a promise of another pound if he would wear a pair of socks continuously for at least a week and come back with them at an appointed date. In this case two abnormalities were present—not only masochism, but also homosexuality.—N. H.

masochists in quest of partners. These quests, however, are not always easy, and this preoccupation with the 'severe mistress' may degenerate into an obsession. We reproduce below a very long letter received by Dr. Abraham, one which constitutes a real human document, and gives more insight into the mental state of these unfortunate people than all the medical statements:

'My dear Doctor,

'Please excuse me if I appeal to you, in the absence of Dr. Magnus Hirschfeld, about a very painful matter. My sexual condition has become such as to cause me the greatest perplexity. I did write to your colleague about this matter, but the correspondence demanded great caution on account of my being married. It was not possible for me to ask your colleague to explain his opinion in writing, for his letter might easily have been intercepted. Since then, however, my condition has become so much more serious that I do not know how to escape from this dilemma. My predisposition to masochism has become so accentuated that now I stop at nothing. My wife—a gentle and loving creature—would not be able to understand this condition, about which I have only hinted to her in the most delicate fashion. In any case, she would not possess the understanding necessary for my salvation. Do not believe, my dear Doctor, after reading this letter from beginning to end, that you are dealing with a madman. . . .

'As I have just said, I cannot expect any direct help from you. Moreover, I am resolved to deny, if need be, having ever had anything to do with you. But, perhaps you could help me in an indirect way, without allowing any shadow of suspicion to fall upon you. My craving is to be enslaved, completely and permanently, in the most extreme way. I want someone with connections abroad, who would be able to take me away. This person should be one who would take pleasure in reducing her victim to a state of blind obedience by all the means at her disposal. Thus she ought to be able to regard it merely as a matter of business to sell me as a slave to some person whom she knows abroad. I refer to my two last letters. I have lost all my fortune and consequently could not contribute any sum towards that transaction. The person concerned could dispose of me at her will, in the way which seemed most advantageous to her. She could lend me or hire me out for any kind of work whatsoever. She could sell me like an animal under the most severe and the most cruel conditions. I would be devoted to her unconditionally, as long as I lived. I renounce, therefore, all the rights of a human being. I retain only duties. All this could not be done in Germany. But it would, I think, be possible in a secluded place abroad. I would personally prefer to be forced to do unpleasant work in the house, in a yard or in a garden. My maintenance would cost my mistress hardly anything, because I could be clothed and fed in the simplest way. I imagine, for example, a solitary farm in the forests of Bohemia, inhabited by two ladies and a robust and taciturn maidservant. There I could be driven to work under the threat of the lash, without being able to count on any sort of mercy. Nobody would know of my existence. The women in question would have every means of making my escape impossible. Such a situation cannot be found easily. I have thought of having myself kidnapped, and, personally, I would do whatever I could to expedite the plan. It should not be difficult to carry out. At present, I am travelling in remote parts of the province of P—— as representative of a business concern in our town. The person in question should communicate with me as soon as possible. The password should be "Prometheus". For instance, a fairly short, typewritten letter could be sent to me as follows:

'"Dear Sir,

'"I am in receipt of your proposal concerning 'Prometheus, Limited', and I am prepared to accept your conditions. Kindly be present at such and such a time and at such and such a date at the gate of X station in order to continue negotiations."

'This communication could be signed illegibly. I would be at the appointed place and the lady could inform me of her plan and let me know where I should meet her again, in order to be taken immediately by car to my destination. Please understand that there can be no question of treachery or blackmail, because it is to my interest, on account of my condition, to contribute towards the success of the enterprise. So soon as I have either heard or read the word "Prometheus" I shall know that the hour of my destiny has struck and that there is to be no turning back. During my kidnapping a man might be employed to master me. I would personally offer to have my hands and feet fettered. Evidently, it would be preferable to do this during the night. I could be summoned to a place, arranged in advance, on a road where a car would be waiting for me. Nobody would know what had happened to me, and as soon as my disappearance was discovered, I would be well guarded on this side of the frontier. After some years, when the affair is forgotten, I could be taken abroad. I have told you that I am poor, and that I could in no way contribute towards this plan. But I believe that the lady in question could make quite a lot of money out of it. I know that in time I would succumb to this régime, but that does not frighten me. I would have accomplished my destiny, for I have no hold on life and wish to die. . . .'

As to the treatment of sado-masochism, obviously it is difficult and varies according to the case. The physician treating it has at his disposal a large variety of therapeutic measures, ranging from persuasion to castration, and including psycho-analysis. In certain countries, castration is performed in cases which resist all the other treatment. Obviously, this procedure cannot be classed with the usual methods.

CHAPTER XXXII

DEVIATIONS OF OBJECT

*The love which does not dare to speak its name. Prestige of homo-
sexuality in antiquity. A characteristic poem of Shakespeare. Is
homosexuality congenital or acquired? The treatment of sexual inversion. Some curious examples of transvestism. Narcissism or automonosexualism. 'Bilitis has paid Bilitis.' Infantilism and gerontophilia. Necrophilia, the most repulsive aberration. The innumerable
variations of fetichism. Stories about shoes. Man and beast: love affairs
of zoophiles.*

In the preceding chapter, we made a survey of the principal
deviations of aim: voyeurism, exhibitionism and sado-
masochism. We shall now begin the study of deviations of
object, those perversions in which, generally speaking, the
aim pursued by the individual is the same as that sought
by the normal subject, but in which the object is abnormal.

Of all deviations of object, the most widespread is
unquestionably the 'love which dares not tell its name',
homosexuality, as opposed to heterosexuality or love
between individuals of different sexes.

Magnus Hirschfeld defines homosexuality as the sexual
tendency experienced by certain men for other men and by
certain women for other women. In German scientific
works, the term uranism, which indicates the same phenomenon, is often used as an alternative.

While on the question of definitions, it should be noted
that among the general public some confusion generally

exists between pederasty and homosexuality. It is not correct to identify these two phenomena, pederasty being merely one variety of homosexuality.

To describe women afflicted by this abnormality, the terms lesbian and tribade are used.

We have now to define *bisexuality*, which differs from homosexuality in that the bisexualist is attracted by individuals of either sex, and in that, as Hirschfeld remarks, the attraction exerted by his own sex has not a counterpart in the repulsion inspired by the other sex, as is the case with homosexuals. Obviously, a bisexual person may have more heterosexual tendencies than homosexual ones, or vice versa.

For a long time, it was generally believed that homosexuality was a phenomenon confined to the human species, but the observations of many experts have proved that this is not the case. Even Aristotle observed homosexual tendencies among certain pigeons. Coming nearer home, Hamilton has stated that certain male monkeys may pass through homosexual periods, and Zuckerman has also noticed homosexual practices in baboons and chimpanzees. Steinach has observed the same phenomenon in cockchafers, and Hirschfeld in silkworms.

In the human species, homosexuality has been observed since the most remote times. Thus at the time of the Egyptians, Horus and Set were homosexual deities; we also find traces of these practices among other Oriental peoples. In Greece, Aristotle speaks of the love of young boys, and other philosophers go so far as to place this love on a higher plane than normal love.

We quote a long extract from Plato, which throws light on the customs of ancient Greece:

'It is very unjust that they (homosexuals) should be accused of immodesty, for it is not through lack of modesty that they act in this way; it is because they have a strong

soul, manly courage, and a virile character, that they seek
their own kind; and this is proved by the fact that with age
they seem to be more efficient than the others as servants of
the state. When they in their turn become men, they love
young men; and if they marry, if they have children, it is
not because nature urges them to do so, but because the
law forces them to do so. What they like is to spend their
lives with each other in celibacy.

'To me, it seemed impossible to resist Socrates. At first,
thinking him envious of my beauty, I congratulated myself
on that good fortune; I believed I had found a wonderful
way of succeeding, for I thought that by showing some
consideration for his desires, I should get him to communicate all his knowledge to me. I decided to attack him
vigorously. Having once begun, I did not want to give up
before knowing on how much I could count. I invited him to
supper, like those lovers who lay a trap for their beloved;
at first he refused, but eventually he consented. He came,
but immediately after the meal he wished to go away. A sort
of modesty prevented me from retaining him. But another
time I laid another trap for him, and after supper I continued
our conversation long into the night; and when he wanted
to go away, I obliged him to stay, on the pretext that it was
too late. He therefore lay down on the couch where he had
had his supper; this bed was very near my own, and we
were alone in the house.

'So far, there is nothing that I cannot say before anybody.
As for what follows, you would not hear it from me if it
were not that wine, as the proverb says, either with or
without youth, always speaks the truth, and if, furthermore,
it did not seem unjust to me, to hide an admirable quality
of Socrates, after having sung his praises.

'When, then, my friends, the lamp was extinguished and
the slaves had retired, I considered there was no need to

proceed in a roundabout way with Socrates, and that I ought to express my thoughts to him frankly. I therefore touched him and said: "Socrates, art thou not yet asleep?" "Not yet", he answered. "Well, then, dost thou know what I think?" "What then?" "I think", continued I, "that thou art the only lover worthy of me, and it seems to me that thou dost not dare to let me know thy feelings. As for me, I should consider myself very unreasonable if I did not seek to please thee on this occasion as on all others, when I could render thee a service, either by myself or through one of my friends."

'So saying, I believed him to have been struck by the shaft I had aimed at him. Without giving him time to add a word, I arose, wrapped in this cloak which you see, for it was winter, and lay down under the old mantle of that man, and throwing my arms about this divine and wonderful person, I spent the whole night with him.'

We also have evidence of the homosexual customs of certain of the inhabitants of Carthage, a town where this practice was generally permitted and even cultivated. After the Punic wars, many of the Romans also became addicted to such habits; some moralists believed Carthage to be responsible for this state of affairs. It has been said that Julius Cæsar himself was an invert; at all events, many of the Roman emperors had definitely homosexual tendencies. There was the case of Nero and that of Galba.

Homosexuality survived the triumph of the Christian church, and we know that it was in vogue even in certain monasteries. Everybody knows of the famous lawsuit brought against the Templars under Philippe le Bel. Later on, certain monarchs, such as Henri III and Rudolf II of Habsburg, made no secret of their peculiar tastes.

The Renaissance witnessed the development of homosexual customs, among the most famous of the inverts being

Michel Angelo; later, the English dramatists Marlow and Shakespeare, who in the following famous poem frankly reveals his inclination:

A woman's face with Nature's own hand painted
Hast thou, the master-mistress of my passion;
A woman's gentle heart, but not acquainted
With shifting change, as is false woman's fashion;
An eye more bright than theirs, less false in rolling,
Guilding the object whereupon it gazeth;
A man in hue, all 'hues' in his controlling,
Which steals men's eyes and women's souls amazeth.
And for a woman wert thou first created;
Till Nature, as she wrought thee, fell a-doting,
And by addition me of thee defeated,
By adding one thing to my purpose nothing.
    But since she picked thee out for women's pleasure,
    Mine be thy love and thy love's use their treasure.

Examples of this kind could be multiplied *ad infinitum*. We shall mention only those of Hans Andersen, Walt Whitman and Verlaine.

*   *   *

The great problem put before the sexologists who study the problems of homosexuality is to know whether this phenomenon is congenital or acquired. Until the time of Krafft-Ebing, the medical profession regarded it as an acquired vice, the result of either heterosexual excesses or over-indulgence in masturbation.

Since the publication of the works of the learned professor, it is known that homosexuality may be congenital; it remains to be seen to what extent.

Magnus Hirschfeld and his pupils go so far as to maintain that homosexuality always contains a congenital element, even though the manifestation of this tendency is not revealed until later on.

Thus Magnus Hirschfeld is led to write as follows:

'The complete fusion of homosexuality with the whole personality of the homosexual or of the lesbian tends to prove that homosexuality is innate in the individual, and not acquired by him during his life. If homosexuality were acquired in the course of time, as a result of some external circumstance, it could disappear later on, as a result of some other event; now this is not the case; this appearance and this disappearance are contrary to all the observations that have been made during many years.

'It is an established fact that energetic homosexuals and strong-willed lesbians, being ardently desirous of changing the direction of their sexual impulse in order to become normal, have struggled in vain against the tendency with which they are possessed.'

Certain authors, notably Ivan Bloch, recognise the existence of innate homosexuality in certain cases, while pointing out that there exist temporary inverts, especially among sailors and pupils in boarding schools, who indulge in these practices only when they cannot find partners of the opposite sex. Others may be led to such practice by the influence of real homosexuals. These, however, take advantage of the first opportunity to give up homosexuality and become once more heterosexual*.

Further, Professor Bloch and those who share his opinion distinguish between two classes of inverts: congenital inverts and occasional inverts whom they describe as pseudo-inverts.

---

* *Editor's Note.*—This is not in accordance with my experience. I have found that many men go through homosexual experiences during adolescence, and then abandon them and become completely heterosexual. But where homosexual activities have been learned in adult life, as in the army and the navy, it is rare for the individual to abandon them altogether, even when opportunities for heterosexual satisfaction are freely available.—N. H.

For certain disciples of the school of psycho-analysis, homosexuality is always acquired. Professor Sigmund Freud, while not entirely concurring in this opinion, nevertheless admits that homosexuality is to a very great extent an acquired character. That is why he writes as follows:

'If psycho-analysis has not yet been able clearly to explain the origins of inversion, it has, at least, discovered the psychological mechanism of its first appearance and presented the question in many different aspects.

'In all the cases which have been under observation, we have been able to note that those who are, later on, to be inverts, pass through a short period during which their sexual instinct is intensely concentrated on a woman (usually on the mother), and that after having passed through this stage, they identify themselves with the woman and become their own sexual object—that is to say, starting from narcissism, they seek adolescents who resemble themselves and whom they wish to love as their mother has loved them*.

'We have also frequently noted that so-called inverts were by no means indifferent to the charms of a woman, but that they transferred the excitement produced by the sight of a member of the opposite sex to the male object. Thus, throughout their lives, they merely repeated the mechanism which was at the origin of their inversion. The obsession which urged them towards a man was conditioned by the constant flight from a woman.'

The number of homosexuals in the world is very considerable. It is extremely difficult to give exact figures in this connection, since homosexuals take great care to hide their tendencies. We may admit, however, that a figure between

* *Editor's Note.*—This is by no means universally valid. A great many male inverts never feel any attraction for adolescents at all, but are, from the beginning, attracted only by virile adult men of strongly masculine type.—N. H.

one and three per cent., especially in large towns, seems probable. It should be noted that the percentage of homosexuals varies considerably in the different professions.

To explain the phenomenon of homosexuality, various writers maintain that every one of us possesses in himself a blend of male elements and female elements. A male homosexual is simply a man possessing a greater percentage of female elements, and a female homosexual a woman possessing a greater percentage of male elements. Havelock Ellis, however, rightly remarks that this is too schematic a conception, and one which does not take into account all the phenomena coming into play. For, apart from the occasional homosexuals of whom Ivan Bloch speaks, and who, in the final analysis, should be classed with normal individuals, it seems justifiable to regard homosexuality as a congenital tendency, as an anomaly based on congenital conditions, 'so that an invert may be just as healthy as a person who is colour-blind. Congenital sexual inversion is therefore of the same order as a biological variation. It is a variation due undoubtedly to imperfect sexual differentiation, but one which often has no definite connection with any morbid condition in the individual himself'.

And Havelock Ellis remarks that this conception of sexual inversion now tends to prevail, and that it has recently gained in favour.

As to the origins of homosexuality, we have no space for a detailed examination of the as yet little known laws of heredity. Most medical men agree that it is at about the age of puberty that homosexual tendencies are generally observed for the first time*. It often happens, however, that

* *Editor's Note.*—This does not accord with my experience. In investigating the histories of homosexual patients I have very frequently been struck with the fact that their homosexual tendency has been clearly manifest at a very early age, some at five years and many others at ages between five and puberty.—N. H.

[445]

a future invert has erotic dreams of a definitely heterosexual character.

In his *Manual of Sexology*, Magnus Hirschfeld publishes statistics concerning five hundred homosexuals who were interrogated concerning the first manifestation of their tendency.   Here is the result of the enquiry:

3 at 4 years	4 at 8-9 years	68 at 14 years
5 at 6 years	22 at 9 years	68 at 15 years
5 at 5-6 years	6 at 9-10 years	25 at 16 years
14 at 6 years	40 at 10 years	14 at 17 years
4 at 6-7 years	32 at 11 years	18 at 18 years
15 at 7 years	54 at 12 years	4 at 19 years
6 at 7-8 years	43 at 13 years	6 at 20 years
18 at 8 years		

I.e. 70 cases from 4 to 8 years. | 201 cases from 8 to 13 years. 54.4 per cent. | 183 cases from 14 to 20 years. 36.6 per cent.

The remaining 8 per cent. are divided as follows: five persons from the earliest age; 16 persons very early, and 25 persons unable to supply any answer.

As to the behaviour of homosexuals in love matters, according to the observations of Havelock Ellis:

20 per cent. abstain from all sexual intercourse:

from 30 to 35 per cent. are content with close physical contact or with mutual masturbation;

from 50 to 55 per cent. go as far as intercrural connection* or occasionally fellatio†.

The percentage of those who practise pederasty‡ does not seem to be very high. Hirschfeld places it at 8 per cent. and

* Friction of the penis between the thighs of the partner.
† Insertion of the penis in the mouth of the partner.
‡ Insertion of the penis in the anus of the partner.

Havelock Ellis at 15 per cent. It may be stated that, contrary to general opinion, physical possession in the form of anal penetration is not desired by the great majority of inverts.

Dr. Bouardel reports a case in which he was interested in his capacity as an expert. The accused was a hospital officer. On market day, he used to entice into his room any adolescents who happened for the moment to be in the village, and the following scene would take place:

'The boy was made to lie down in a horizontal position; a lamp glass was then attached to his penis, in which the operator by means of a pneumatic machine would produce a vacuum. This naturally gave rise to a local congestion in the visitor. So soon as this was obtained, the hospital officer would remove the glass and perform, on his client, an act which is not legal, even between married people. Each client paid the sum of one franc. There were eight or ten of them every time.' (Chapotin, *Les défaitistes de l'Amour.*)

An interesting observation concerning homosexual habits is supplied by Dr. Garnier. One day, on a public promenade, he noticed two little boys, precocious inverts, practising the following trick:

'Some distance away from their nurses, they indulged in suction, while pretending to play the game known as "hot hands". The one, seated upon a chair, placed the head of the other between his legs, covering it carefully with his apron. The game was to tell with which hand the tap on the back was given.' The doctor, being struck by the slowness and the irregularity of their play, suddenly raised the apron and discovered the artifice.

There is often a tendency to consider inverts of the male sex as necessarily effeminate. This is perhaps true of a large number of them, who, in addition to presenting an appearance of marked femininity, possess certain feminine psychological characteristics, such as frivolous vanity, love of adornment, and mincing manners. But this does not by any means apply to all inverts. Male homosexuals can no more be compared with effeminate male prostitutes than can female prostitutes be regarded as representatives of their sex. There exist homosexuals with a manly appearance and even an essentially masculine character. But the effeminate type is much more striking and is therefore regarded as typical. Some cultivate manliness—frequently to compensate for their feeling of impaired virility, as Dr. Hesnard rightly remarks—while others look for manliness in their partners.

As for female homosexuals, they may also be classed in two categories. Many of them show a distinctly mannish character, sometimes only on the psychological plane, but sometimes on the physical also. Those in the other category, however, are essentially feminine in their appearance, and the most perspicacious observer would not be able to detect their peculiar tendencies. Dr. Hesnard says that women belonging to the first category seek to emulate the opposite sex, while those of the second category are content with their own sex, though they make no use of it except with regard to other women. In a similar way, male inverts, amongst whom the distinction is less pronounced, may show evidence of a desire to be women, while others, ' those who remain men in their sexual attitude, make use of their masculine tendencies to desire men, being by their infantile conflict cut off from women '.

The question of homosexuality deserves a much more profound study than is possible within the limits of this book. We refer those of our readers who may be particularly interested in it to the book of Drs. Magnus Hirschfeld, Felix Abraham and Pierre Vachet, and to the work of Dr.

Maranon, *The Evolution of Sexuality and of Intersexual States,* to those of Havelock Ellis, and finally to Dr. Hesnard's excellent book, the exact and conscientious documentation of which has been of great help to us.

Concerning the controversial problem of the treatment of sexual inversion, it must be admitted that, properly speaking, there exists no remedy capable of transforming an invert into a person of normal sexuality. Surgical intervention may prove efficacious in certain cases and, for the rest, for certain phenomena associated with homosexuality, such as neurotic depression, a dietary régime allied with a system of re-education may be carried out with success.

As to curative treatment, some, following the footsteps of Dr. Schrenck-Notzing, have advocated hypnotic suggestion. It appears, however, that this method has not proved efficacious, and has failed to give the results which its inventors expected.

The psycho-analytic method has also found fervent partisans among psychiatrists. At one time, it was applied with great enthusiasm; nevertheless, the great majority of specialists maintain that it cannot give any appreciable results.

Albert Moll has proposed treatment by association, borrowing the expression of Havelock Ellis, which consists in finding a compromise by means of which the desires of the invert are directed towards the normal sexual act. Thus the patient whose leanings are towards young lads would be directed towards women with mannish ways.

In this connection, Havelock Ellis quotes the case of one of his patients who was desirous of returning to a normal life, and who one day, in Malta, met an Italian girl who invited him to her house. Here is the confession of the patient:

‘ She was slim like a boy, she had the figure of a lad, and

hardly any breasts at all. I went to the rendezvous in her apartment, and found her dressed in a man's pyjamas. I felt definitely attracted, and yet I was incapable of playing the part of a man. I left her, but without my usual feeling of repulsion: on my return the following evening, I was over-joyed to find that the result was satisfactory. I saw that girl again several times before leaving Malta, but although attracted by her, I never really enjoyed the act, and as soon as it was over, I wanted to turn my back on her. Since then, I have had relations with about a dozen girls. But it is always an effort, and it leaves me with a feeling of repulsion. I have arrived at the conclusion that normal sexual relations are for me nothing more than an expensive and dangerous form of masturbation.'

Is that, then, to be considered an excellent therapeutic result? It is clear that there is every reason to be suspicious of marriage as a remedy for homosexual tendencies. In fact, there is little chance of this being the means by which a homosexual may rid himself of his tendencies towards inversion. On the contrary, it may still further accentuate his tendency. At the same time, reasonable people would hesitate to go so far as to declare categorically that indivi-duals with homosexual tendencies should never marry. In fact, in certain cases, after medical advice has been sought, and once the other party has been frankly informed of the state of affairs, it is possible that marriage will not be inadvisable, although there will always be the danger that the invert will regard the sexual act with his partner as a kind of masturbation in the vagina.

Havelock Ellis concludes that the best course of action for the congenital invert under present-day social conditions 'is to retain his particular ideal and his instincts, but to give up all hope of obtaining satisfaction of his abnormal desires, or of becoming normal, even if such a course inevitably forces him from time to time to seek an auto-erotic form of relief, however unsatisfactory that may be '.*

* * *

We cannot end this study of homosexuality without making some mention of *transvestism*, even though that may not be a perversion of object, in the exact sense. The patient who is afflicted by it identifies himself with the opposite sex just as much in his manner of dressing as in his ideals in general. He does not, however, necessarily have homosexual tendencies.

Transvestism is the term used by Magnus Hirschfeld; others, following Havelock Ellis, call it *eonism*, from the name of its prototype, the Chevalier d'Eon.

This was a historical personage, like the Marquis de Sade. He died in London at the age of 83, after spending 49 years of his life as a man and 34 years as a woman. For many years his real sex was unknown, and this was a favourite topic of conversation in society. It is said that bets on this subject

---

* *Editor's Note.*—There is, as yet, no general agreement as to the causation of homosexuality. At the one extreme there are those who consider that it is always due to the psychological effect of a wrong environment, but if one accepts this view it is difficult to understand why some persons subjected to a particular set of environmental influences become homosexual, and others subjected to the same set of influences do not. One is forced to the conclusion that there must be a predisposition in some persons and not in others. Such a predisposition could presumably, in the last analysis, be reduced to physical factors, possibly connected with the ductless glands.

At the other extreme there are those who consider that the psychological and environmental factor is negligible, and that homosexuality is inborn. This school frequently points to physical characters, such as wide hips and knock-knees in male homosexuals, or narrow hips and other male characters in female homosexuals. At first sight this argument would seem conclusive, but we are faced with the difficulty of explaining the large numbers of men with feminine physical characters, and women with male physical characters, who are nevertheless not at all homosexual, as well as large numbers of profoundly homosexual men and women who present no physical characters suggestive of the opposite sex.—N. H.

amounted at the time of his death to £200,000 in England and £80,000 in France. A post-mortem examination finally revealed the fact that he was, in fact, a man.

Transvestism is a very frequent phenomenon, almost as frequent as homosexuality. Persons who have such a tendency usually conceal it very cleverly, so that their nearest relatives are often unaware of it. Moreover, they may lead an absolutely normal sexual life, though, as Havelock Ellis remarks, their sexual vigour is often below the average.

The way in which transvestism is brought about raises the same problem as that of the origin of homosexuality. Some insist on its acquired character in the majority of cases, and believe that a too close attachment to the person of the mother often has something to do with the evolution of this tendency. On the other hand, Magnus Hirschfeld and his followers maintain that transvestism is not an acquired tendency, but that it is innate and simply becomes stronger as the subject advances in age. At all events, an apparently chance occurrence may suddenly cause it to attain complete development.

Magnus Hirschfeld distinguishes ten categories of transvestists: the complete transvestist, the extreme transvestist (who wants to change his sex), the partial transvestist (who is content to wear silk stockings and underwear, in the case of a man, and a man's underwear in the case of a woman), the transvestist in name (who adopts a Christian name belonging to the opposite sex, like George Sand, for instance), the constant transvestist (who remains so all his life), the periodical transvestist, the narcissistic transvestist, the metatropic transvestist (seeking the love of mannish women in the case of a man and that of effeminate men in the case of a woman), the bisexual transvestist, and finally the homosexual transvestist.

To show to what an extent this tendency may enslave an
individual, we shall quote a clinical case described by Dr.
Hirschfeld:

'Rudolf ("Dora R——"), forty years old. Different
simple occupations; latterly employed as cook in a big
Berlin restaurant. The patient was born in the Erzgebirge of
healthy parents, who have several other children, all equally
healthy in body and mind, that is, if the indications given by
R—— are correct. Until his sixth year, R—— was not in
any way distinguishable from the other children. He had the
usual children's ailments, was docile and easy to educate.
The child was remarkable only for his calm and reserve; he
played alone and never troubled either adults or his playmates. It was only when his parents wished to replace the
girl's dress which is customary with very young children by
a boy's suit that the child became recalcitrant and fought
with all his strength against having his clothes changed. He
still wanted to wear a dress; nevertheless, the parents
insisted that the child, who was perfectly masculine in
physical form, should wear trousers. It was during his sixth
year that the conduct of the boy first became strange: he
tried to ligature his penis with a piece of string. He said
he considered his sexual organ superfluous, and wanted to
get rid of it in this way. He was discovered in time to
prevent more serious consequences, such as suppuration or
necrosis.

'However, in the course of the following years, it became
still more evident that the boy was adopting girlish ways.
He would secretly dress himself in the clothes of his sisters,
and nothing gave him more pleasure than to walk about in
this attire. Outwardly, he was not in any way different
from his comrades of the same social class. He finished
schooling with success, after acquiring a good general
knowledge. Having begun work at the age of fourteen

[453]

years, he was skilled, well thought of, and in public his conduct was perfectly correct. His sexual development was normal. But it soon became evident that his tendencies were of a homosexual nature. His mania for dressing like a woman became intensified in the course of time. On account of this, he left his home district and established himself in a large town, where he could give full freedom to his tendencies. There he managed to live the life of a woman, beginning at the age of about 26-27 years. As is often the case with transvestists, this external resemblance to the female sex gradually became insufficient for him, and his one desire was to transform his body in the same way. In this he was aided by his primary constitution, which was of the androgynous type, that is to say, in him the chest, the lower abdomen and the buttocks as well as the arms and the legs were definitely feminine in form. This development of the body took place during and after puberty. He took the first step towards changing his sex in 1921, when he had himself castrated. As a result his sexual instinct was enfeebled, but the homosexual tendency, as well as his own feelings, remained the same. This step, however, was not sufficient for him, and he tried to obtain a still greater degree of femininity in his sexual parts. Finally, in 1930, the operation which he himself had attempted at the age of six was performed upon him, viz., the removal of his penis, and six months afterwards the transformation was completed by the grafting of an artificial vagina.

'We see, then, in this case a tendency first evincing itself at the age of six, and persisting throughout life, in such a way that nothing can obstruct its development or its intensity. On the contrary, it becomes stronger and stronger, and the consequences are more and more profound. In no other case is the goal pursued with such intensity of effort and so indefatigably, until definite success is attained.'

Usually, the wearing of a garment belonging to the opposite sex does not imply any serious inconvenience, either for the patient or for his neighbours. It happens sometimes, however, that serious embarrassment may be brought about, as in the case of the transvestist sailor mentioned by Magnus Hirschfeld. This individual, having been mobilised during the war, took advantage of his periods of leave on land to dress up as a woman. His suspicious manners attracted the attention of the authorities, who took him for a spy. He would have been shot immediately if his case had not been known to Magnus Hirschfeld, who intervened just in time. Other transvestists, arrested on both sides, were executed without mercy.

The case of transvestists who go so far as to demand a new civil status, or ask the doctor to change their sex, would require a special study which we cannot undertake here*.

*   *   *

Narcissism, from the name of the legendary Greek hero

* *Editor's Note.*—Transvestism is much commoner than is generally realised. Quite a large number of persons seize every opportunity of going to a fancy dress ball in the clothes of the opposite sex. Many of these individuals themselves are not fully conscious that there is a sexual element in the pleasure that they get from 'dressing up'. Cases frequently come before the Courts of men, arrested for various offences, who were found to be dressed as women, and less frequently of women dressed as men. In England, the judicial and legal authorities usually seem to be ignorant of, or at least make no reference to, the fact that there is a sexual element in these cases. Considerable public interest was aroused by the cases of a man named Augustus Hull and a woman known as 'Captain Barker' in this country within the last few years. The most notorious case in recent years of an individual submitting to surgical operations in order to bring about an approximation to the other sex is that of the Danish painter, Einar Wegener, who had his genital organs removed, ovaries transplanted into him, and attempts made to furnish him with an artificial vagina. He died as a result of the series of operations, but before his death his marriage was annulled by the Danish authorities, who issued him a new birth certificate as a female, in the name of Lili Elbe. The case is discussed at length in a book entitled *Man into Woman* published by Jarrolds, London, 1933.— N. H.

who fell in love with his own image which he saw reflected in the waters of a river, is another form of perversion of object. This anomaly has, moreover, been given a different name by experts who have paid special attention to it; thus Magnus Hirschfeld calls it *automonosexualism*, and Latamendi, of Madrid, *autoerasty*. The automonosexuals, who in the terminology of Hirschfeld are called *autists* for short, are individuals sexually attracted by their own bodies. 'Narcissism', says Dr. Hesnard, 'consists essentially and primitively in the fact that the individual in question—a child, an adolescent or an adult—experiences a special attraction of a sexual nature for his own being, and especially for his own body, for his own image and also for his own intellect.'

For a long time the phenomenon of masturbation has been confused with that of narcissism. There is, however, a fairly distinct difference between them. The latter may be combined with the former, but the former does not necessarily imply the latter. The adolescent addicted to masturbation has resource to this procedure merely as a last resort, because he has no partner, while the active narcissist does not in any way feel the need of sharing his emotions. The former finds in himself the instrument of his satisfaction, while the second sees in his own body the object of his desires. The former loves only his pleasure, while the latter is in love with himself. Besides, narcissists are not always masturbators; the most innocent forms of play, superficial caresses, or merely the contemplation of their own bodies in the mirror, may be quite sufficient for them.

In the earlier parts of this book we referred to the theory of Freud, according to which every human being, during his childhood, passes through a period of auto-erotism. This need, therefore, would appear to be an innate factor in man, simply modified by external events, and directed towards the outer world. Philosophers of love have often expressed the idea that what one really loves is oneself, and that it is vanity and pride in one's own body that incites one to seek an admirer. The wish to inspire love would therefore be nothing more than an egoistic ideal tending in some way to consecrate one's own worth. Here is a striking passage on the subject from Rémy de Gourmont:

'. . . What we see clearly and deliciously as in a mirror, is ourselves, remoulded and made more beautiful by love. It follows that when we think we love another being, it is ourselves that we love, and as that other one is subject to the same illusion with regard to us, the two lovers are under the impression that they are giving themselves and taking each other, whereas they are merely taking themselves and giving themselves to their own egoism. . . . From the purely idealistic point of view narcissism would be the supreme formula of love. . . .'

It is, above all, sensitive people, æsthetes, and especially women, who show narcissistic tendencies. Sexologists often quote a passage from a short story by the Spanish writer Valera, who makes one of his heroines utter the following words as she comes from her bath:

'At this time, I feel myself urged towards childish acts, either innocent or vicious, I know not which; I only know that I like to look at myself, to contemplate myself and to admire my own beauty in a disinterested way. For me, it is not a question of vulgar sensuality, but of æsthetic and platonic visions. I behave like a narcissist; I place my lips on the cold surface of my mirror and I kiss my own image.'

Women conscious of their beauty have always been pleased to contemplate their own image, and the mirror plays an enormous part in their life. When they are tired of their nakedness, they deck themselves out in beautiful silks and practise making seductive poses for the pleasure of

[457]

their own eyes. They require no witness. The company of their own reflection is for them a sufficient and an inexhaustible source of joy. Photography is another source of pleasure to them. They spend hours admiring portraits of themselves, preferably those in the nude, which they conscientiously collect. Those of a more daring nature are not content with this visual pleasure, and indulge in passionate caresses, inspired by the love of their own bodies. Pierre Louys, the writer of love romances, gives a description in his *Chansons de Bilitis* of a courtesan in love with herself. She tells how she adores her breasts, how she is never tired of caressing them, and she addresses to them the following loving and ardent words:

'Flowers of flesh, O, my breasts! How rich you are in voluptuousness! My breasts in my hands, what softness is yours, what mellow warmth and what youthful perfumes!

'Formerly, you were icy cold like the breast of a statue and hard like insensate blocks of marble. Since you have become supple, I have cherished you all the more, you whom I loved even formerly. Your full and rounded form is the glory of my brown body. Whether I imprison you in golden network, or whether I release you all naked, it is your splendour that goes before me.

'Be happy, then, this night. If my fingers are to caress, only you shall know it until to-morrow morning; for to-night, Bilitis has paid Bilitis.'

Men also, though less frequently, may start by practising *faute-de-mieux* masturbation and come to find complete satisfaction in their auto-erotic practices, and thus become narcissists in the full sense of the word. They are usually timid persons, lacking in daring and the spirit of conquest, and the perversion saves them the trouble of finding a partner. But the æsthetic sense continues to play its part, and it is a rather rare thing to find narcissists in

[458]

individuals who are not favoured by nature. Among actors and singers, narcissism is very common, though not always exclusive. Being spoilt by success and by applause, they finally come to see in themselves an object worthy of exceptional love, and while retaining a healthy sexuality, they fall into narcissistic excesses which are psychological rather than sexual. Magnus Hirschfeld had under observation a man so in love with his own beauty that narcissism had, in his case, supplanted every other form of love. We ourselves are in possession of numerous photographs of a man with a big reputation, who is not attracted sexually towards either women or men; he has never had any form of intercourse with another human being. It is in calmly contemplating his own naked body—which, by the way, is beautifully modelled—photographed in various artistic poses, and surrounded by beautiful objects, lying, for instance, on fine skins, that he finds the desired erotic excitement.

A somewhat special form of narcissism is that which consists in finding pleasure in looking at one's own reflection during normal sexual intercourse. This is not pure auto-eroticism, but a kind of voyeurism applied to oneself. The aberration is more frequent than is usually supposed, and the proprietors of brothels are fully aware of the fact, for nearly every large establishment of this kind includes rooms provided with looking-glasses which allow the customer this little supplementary pleasure.

*　　*　　*

Infantilism and the opposite perversion, *gerontophilia,* may be included in the category of perversions of object, since individuals affected by these aberrations seek an abnormal love object: a child or someone old. It is the disproportion in age which here makes all the difference between the normal and the perverse.

While most aberrations have a psychical or psychological origin, infantilism is an aberration due principally to physiological disorders. It is obvious that psychic disturbances may be determined by an abnormal physical development, but in this case we are not concerned with those traumatic fixations which are found to be at the root of so many other perversions.

Infantilists are persons whose genital apparatus has not reached its full development, but has stopped at an infantile stage. In men it is the testicles, in women the ovaries, which most frequently show considerable atrophy. But infantilism, leading to perversion, is found chiefly in the male sex.

There are two kinds of men who are attracted by children: young men between twenty and thirty years of age, whose undeveloped physiological condition renders them similar in every way to little boys, and old men in whom that similarity is produced by a regression of sexual activity. To illustrate the first of these two types, we shall recall an observation of Magnus Hirschfield concerning a young man twenty-four years old, of bourgeois origin. He was condemned for indecent behaviour, after having been caught in the act with two little boys of nine and ten years. With these children, he indulged in reciprocal masturbation, which gave him complete satisfaction. In his case, puberty was delayed, and when, at the age of about seventeen, he became conscious of sexual needs, he found that his desires had no other object than children of from two to ten years of age. His perversion caused him moral torment, and when he heard of treatment which consisted in castration, he applied to the professor, in order to have the operation performed. The third week after the operation his perverse tendency grew weaker, and little boys no longer gave him anything more than æsthetic pleasure. Finally, this last pleasure also disappeared, and the young man was liberated from all sexual obsession*.

The annals of forensic medicine report innumerable cases of old men indulging in sexual acts with little boys and little girls. They are sometimes people with an honourable past, who are urged to immoral actions simply by disturbances in their sexual life. These disturbances are often accompanied by mental troubles which are all the more pronounced in the case of dipsomaniacs. The infantilism of old men, though in itself odious enough, is often rendered still more horrible by the addition of incest. His own children are often the easiest prey for a sufferer of this type, and the majority of these sad cases of incest which cause such a stir are caused by senile infantilism, aggravated in most cases by alcoholism. In the course of his long experience, Magnus Hirschfeld has had several cases of this perversion under observation; we shall quote the most characteristic. It was that of a man of fifty-six years, feeble-minded and a great consumer of beer. He had five children and was accused of indulging in incestuous practices with his youngest daughter, Martha, eight years of age. He tried to throw all the responsibility upon his wife, and gave the following description of his conduct:

'When the child was born, I was very fond of her. She was only one year old when I left the family, and I saw her again for the first time three years ago, when she was five years old. Circumstances for which my wife is responsible forced me to send away three of our children—this one among them—to have them educated in a catholic convent at B——. From that time, I did not see them again until

* *Editor's Note.*—It is important to point out that castration by no means always succeeds in curing the patient of the perverse tendency. Segregation may still be necessary, and in my opinion segregation is better than castration for such cases.—N. H.

January of this year, when I had them brought to Berlin. As a result of this separation, they had become perfect strangers to me, and this, I admit, troubled me very much. I could not explain what urged me to act as I did. I blame my wife for what has taken place; for various reasons, she has done all she could to lead me into this trouble, first of all by making me sleep in the very bed where the child slept between her mother and me, and also by leaving me alone with her. I believe it was in the month of July that I first played with the child's sexual organs. I was at this time extremely excited, and at times I did not know what I was doing. Afterwards, I regretted my act, and I resolved never to repeat it. But I cannot control myself, and I have repeated it four times in all, which I regret sincerely. It would be impossible for me to explain how this happened, for while acting in this way I was always so excited that I did not know what I was doing, and I did not realise it till afterwards, when I blamed myself most bitterly. But the way she has behaved makes it perfectly clear that the mother intended to ruin me. She herself said the time was coming when she would have her revenge on me. All that I have done is to play with Martha's sexual organ with my finger.'

Gerontophilia is a tendency similar to infantilism, but with the difference that the object of desire is a much older person.

Apart from physiological causes, this perversion, according to Freudian theories, has a psychological origin. It is well known that this school attributes to children sexual love for parents of the opposite sex, a phenomenon known by the name of 'the Œdipus complex'. If the development of infantile sex life does not proceed normally, the subject, while detaching himself from the object of his desire, may retain a preference for older persons. Thus the young man would feel himself attracted by women who reminded him of his mother.

Jean-Jacques Rousseau, in his *Confessions*, admits, with his customary sincerity, the attraction which women of a mature age had for him. In the monumental work of Dr. Hirschfeld, we also find a very interesting observation concerning gerontophilia. From his earliest years, the subject felt himself attracted by men of from fifty to sixty years. One day he made the acquaintance of an aged man, whose fine head, adorned with an imposing beard, immediately inspired him with passion. As the object of his desire made no response to his advances, the young man, in order not to break off all relations with him, took the course of marrying his daughter. He continued to pay attention to his father-in-law, and even got so far as to exchange kisses with him. His wife left him absolutely indifferent, for all his sexual desire was concentrated on the old man. That, of course, was a case of homosexual gerontophilia.

It would be a mistake to see evidence of gerontophilia in the relatively numerous marriages in which the difference in age is very marked. Here, the only perversion is an exaggerated love of money. But it is none the less true that adolescents, and even young men of over twenty, are frequently attracted sexually by elderly ladies. On the other hand, young girls sometimes show evidence of an analogous perversion. While unmoved by the attractions of young men of their own age, they are excited in the presence of white-haired old men. But it is nearly always a temporary aberration of little consequence, which disappears as the woman develops.

We now come to *necrophilia**, which, of all perversions, is the most repugnant, on account of its lugubrious character.

Attempts have been made to explain in many ways these

---

* *Editor's Note.*—Sexual attraction for corpses.—N. H.

sad sexual predilections for dead bodies. The Freudian school sees in necrophilia memories of childhood, of the love felt for the sleeping mother, and the fixation of the first sexual feelings aroused by this spectacle. Other experts attribute these pathological tendencies to a certain sexual laziness, which leads one to seek a docile partner, incapable of offering the least resistance.

A classical example in the annals of medicine is that of Ardisson, who dug up the corpse of a little girl, hid it in a garret, and went every night to violate it until the day when the poor little outraged body fell into putrefaction.

Sexual pathology reveals cases of men who indulge in coitus only with sleeping women, and necrophilia would seem to be an analogous perversion, carried to greater lengths. Magnus Hirschfeld tells the story of a man who, having begun by practising the former of these perversions, was quite naturally driven to the practice of necrophilia:

'He had relations with his wife during eight years of marriage, but he preferred her to remain absolutely calm and inert during the act, without saying anything and without showing any feeling. In 1924, his wife died of pneumonia, and it was then that his visits commenced. With great difficulty, he dug an underground passage from his garden to his wife's tomb, a piece of work which kept him busy for about two months. He went on paying visits to his wife by means of this passage until he was discovered. Nothing would make him confess what he did in the tomb. He simply said that his visits took place regularly every day, and that he made a present of flowers or fruits to the corpse. Later on, he had also brought perfumes, which, however, were rather for his own use, as the smell in the tomb had become intolerable. The coffin showed signs of having been opened. According to what he said, the visits lasted from ten to fifteen minutes. No traces of violation could be observed on the corpse itself, which was in an advanced state of putrefaction. Concerning his sentiments, F. S—— could only say that his stay in his wife's tomb produced in him an extremely agreeable sensation, and that in his bed he had never felt so happy as by the side of his wife's coffin.'

Some authors confuse necrophilia with *vampirism*, which latter is a variety of sadism. The truth is that the vampire's pleasure consists only in murdering the woman he desires, while the necrophile is attracted by the inanimate body. Nevertheless, it should be noted that the necrophile, when unable to procure the object of his desire, may be led to kill, for the craving to possess a corpse is so strong in him that it may blind him to the extent of making him commit a crime. It is possible that the vampires of Düsseldorf, Muy, etc., were only degenerate necrophiles.

The most striking case, studied by many psychiatrists, is that of Sergeant Bertrand. It was first described in 1849 by Krafft-Ebing. He was a morbidly erotic individual, who during his youth masturbated seven or eight times a day, and while quite young indulged in day-dreams in which he evoked the corpses of little girls. He soon began to realise his dreams, first by cutting up the bodies of animals and at the same time masturbating. Then, carrying his cruelty still further, he caught live dogs and disembowelled them. Finally, he began to frequent cemeteries in order to disinter and mutilate women's bodies. He himself describes his sensation as follows:

'I cannot describe how I felt at that moment, but all the pleasure I have ever known with a living woman is as nothing compared with that. I kissed the woman on every part of her body. I pressed her against my heart as if I wanted to crush her; in short, I did everything to her that a passionate lover can do to his mistress. After being intoxicated by this body for about a quarter of an hour, I cut it up into pieces and disembowelled it as I had the other victims of my passion.'

But let us repeat that necrophilia is not necessarily associated with sadism. The individuals afflicted by this perversion are not always daring enough to violate dead bodies. Usually they are content to imagine that they are dealing with a dead woman when they are confronted with a sleeping one, and they urge their partner to remain motionless and with her eyes closed during the sexual act. The sight of cemeteries and funeral processions is capable of exciting them, and this excitement, though of pathological origin, may, however, be satisfied in a normal way. Dr. Hesnard describes this lugubrious tendency in the following terms:

'The cases in which necrophilic tendencies are most pronounced are those in which sexual excitement increases when the subject is in the presence of death. One of our patients who was obsessed by religion, and whose practical sexual life was exclusively auto-erotic, was greatly grieved to find that he was sexually excited in churches and cemeteries, and that liturgic chants celebrating death and the pomp and music of funerals aroused in him a kind of mystic exaltation, tainted with erotism. This strange mixture of grim emotion and erotic excitement is not rare among neurotic people, who are always more or less haunted by the idea of death, and whose grief at funerals often contains a strain of voluptuousness.'

In order to cater for the most bizarre tastes of their clientele, tastes not uncommon among sexually abnormal people, the managers of certain establishments have conceived the idea of fitting out funeral rooms, with a whole paraphernalia of coffins, black cloths, candles, etc., where the necrophile finds, laid out in a coffin, a woman showing the rigidity and the colour of a corpse. By means of cosmetics and subtle lighting, a perfect illusion is created. Failing a real corpse, the pervert is enabled to give his tendencies full scope with a venal creature, ready to play any part whatsoever, so long as the fee is paid.

*   *   *

The habit of attributing an erotic value to some peculiarity or physical detail in the person loved, even to an inanimate object belonging to that person—a phenomenon which Havelock Ellis includes in the category of erotic symbolism —is not always a matter of sexual pathology. Readers who have followed us through this volume will have noted, in the chapters devoted to sexual attraction and the way it leads up to the selection of a love-object, and directs passion, that a decisive part is often played by details. A woman becomes attached to a certain man on hearing his voice; a man is, without knowing it, in love with a brown hat that a chance meeting has fixed in his subconsciousness. But, in these cases, the voice, the colour and the shape of the hat are only intermediaries which lead to love in the complete and normal sense of the word.

It is not quite the same as regards the habit—dear to unrequited lovers—of keeping as souvenirs locks of hair, dried flowers, *billets doux,* or perfumed handkerchiefs which have belonged to the loved one. These substitutes sometimes go so far as to play the part of erotic stimulants, and a disappointed lover who sighs before locks of hair sometimes experiences an erotic excitement which such an object would not normally inspire. Obviously it is difficult to draw a line of demarcation between inoffensive and quasi-normal erotic symbolism, which comes within the limits of the normal, and *fetichism*, which is a sexual perversion. At all events, in all the cases we have just mentioned, the object had no value beyond the radiance of the person to whom it had belonged. The fetichist proper experiences a sexual emotion on seeing the object, though there is no precise association of ideas in his mind. 'This tendency', says Havelock Ellis, 'becomes abnormal if it is exclusive and general, and it constitutes a characteristic deviation when the fetich itself, in the absence of the person, suffices entirely to provoke not only tumescence, but also detumescence, so that it suppresses all desire for sexual intercourse.'

This definition leads us to distinguish, on another plane, two kinds of fetichism. In the first, the object merely plays the part of a stimulant, an indispensable prelude to coitus (this in itself is a characteristic perversion); in the second, the object becomes in some way the corollary of the normal sexual act, the pervert either accompanying that act with an evocation of the person desired (in this case, the object is a makeshift), or finding in the fetich a perfect stimulant and form of satisfaction (this being the most complete form of the perversion).

Experts, especially psycho-analysts, have been greatly pre-occupied with the origin of fetichism. Some attribute it to a trauma or to an outstanding incident dating from child-hood or from puberty, while others, though they admit the possibility of this, do not accept it without reservation, and in some cases are convinced that fetichism has a con-genital origin. This amounts to saying that an individual may be born with a morbid predisposition which determines in him an erotic tendency for a certain object.

Havelock Ellis develops the first theory, while admitting the part played by predisposition:

Sexual precocity is unquestionably a condition favour-able to such a deviation; a child who is precociously and abnormally sensitive to the presence of persons of the opposite sex, before puberty has established in him the normal channels of sexual desire, is especially likely to become a prey to the vagaries of symbolism. In this symbolism all degrees are possible. While the average insensitive man perceives nothing of it, the symbols constitute, for the more imaginative lover, a fascinating element in the high tension process which crystallises his passion. As soon as such symbolism is firmly implanted in an exceptionally nervous man, he regards it as an absolutely essential factor in the charm of the person whom he loves. Finally, for the morbid individual, the symbol becomes generalised, the fetichist no longer desires a person at all; he regards the person as being a mere appendage of the symbol, and one which he may even be able to do without altogether; only the symbol is desired, and it is quite sufficient in itself to give complete sexual satisfaction. If we regard as morbid the need of a symbol, which becomes an essential element in the charm of the desired person, it is still only in extreme cases, when the symbol comes to be quite sufficient in itself, that we have a completely morbid variation. In less complete forms of symbolism, it is still the woman who is desired, and the aim served is that of procreation. But when the woman is ignored and the mere symbol is sufficient, or even preferred as a stimulus for detumescence, the pathological state has become complete.

Although the objects capable of becoming fetiches may vary infinitely, it is principally details of the body or of the clothing that are called upon to play this part. In the first category, the eyes, the hair and the feet hold the record. Hair fetichism has quite a long history. Who has not heard of those cutters of tresses, whose field of activity has necessarily been restricted by the fashion of wearing the hair short, but who not very long ago abounded, chiefly in Paris? All experts who have had occasion to study forensic medicine, mention these lovers of hair in their works or their reports. The mere fact of cutting the tresses gives the fetichist a voluptuous thrill, coloured perhaps with sadism, but the rôle of these petty thieves does not stop at this point. The hair fetichist uses the hair for the purpose of masturbation, and indulges in all sorts of queer practices in order to recall the first thrill. In most cases these hair-cutters are not capable of normal sexual intercourse, and their passion for hair is so exclusive that it leaves no place for any other sexual activity. One of them made the following confession to M. Macé, a former chief of police:

'It is a passion. For me, the child does not exist. It is her beautiful, fine hair that attracts me. I could often take it at once, but I prefer to follow the little girl and take time; it is my satisfaction, my pleasure. Finally, I come to a decision, I cut the ends of the curly locks and I am happy.'

As we see, tresses are not the only things coveted by the hair fetichists; the taste of these perverts may vary from heavy tresses to little kiss curls. Needless to say, the method of using them varies from one individual to another.

Fetichism is an almost exclusively male perversion. Women, though not indifferent to fine hair, have not supplied the medical annals with typical hair fetichism. On the contrary, sexologists have noted in the female sex a tendency to make a fetich of bald heads.

Apart from the hair of the head, hair in general may be the object of a kind of erotic symbolism. The hair of the body is capable of attracting some and repelling others. That depends, not only on individual taste, but on the customs of the country. It is known that hairy men have a certain attraction for women, though this does not imply fetichism proper.

More interesting, perhaps, than hair fetichism is foot fetichism, and the somewhat peculiar form of it which applies to shoes. Some writers see in it only an expression of the masochist tendency, a leaning towards the subjection which sees in the foot a symbol of violence, ill-treatment and trampling. This interpretation has perhaps the defect of being too one-sided, for many physicians have known individuals, especially men, whose character was perfectly manly and who showed no masochist tendency, but whose capacity for sexual excitement was aroused in a way quite beyond what may be considered normal by the sight of a pretty foot, well shod. The foot is considered one of the chief attributes of feminine charm, and, in the same way as the eyes or the hair, it may at times play a more important part than all the other elements of seduction. Besides, as with every erotic fetich, the part played by the foot may be due to an incident dating from childhood, when it was associated with the first sexual sensations.

One of the most curious examples of foot fetichism is that of Restif de la Bretonne. From his earliest childhood and during all his life, he showed an unusual sensitiveness to women's pretty feet. The face of the woman was of little importance to him. To inspire love in him, it was sufficient to have pretty feet. His first memory of fetichism dated from the time when he was only four years of age. Later on, his father had him apprenticed to a printer at Auxerre. Seduced by the feet of his employer's wife, young Restif was preoccupied with quite another matter than that of learning the printing trade. He placed his first *billet-doux* in the shoes of his beloved.

As the foot is rarely seen bare, but nearly always covered with a shoe, the worship of this part of the body becomes confused with that of the shoe, which we shall have occasion to mention when discussing the part played by clothes in fetichism.

The hands, being more often uncovered than the feet, and being so much less mysterious, exercise a fetichistic attraction much more rarely. Still, cases are known in which the hand, bare or gloved, has constituted a first-rate erotic element for neurotics who were indifferent to all other attractions.

We have just enumerated the principal parts of the body that appeal to fetichists, but it must be remembered that any detail of the face or of the body may play a similar part. Physical imperfections, and even deformities, are capable of inspiring erotic sensations. There are men and women who go into ecstasies at the sight of scars and warts, and everyone knows the success achieved by lame people and hunchbacks among individuals of special tastes*.

A more accentuated form of fetichism is that in which it is not a part of the living body that takes the place of the entire person, but in which an inanimate object, recalling a region of the body, is called upon to play an erotic part. It is easy to understand that it is objects or parts of the clothing directly associated with the sexual organs, or which recall them by their form, that are adopted as fetiches. In

---

* *Editor's Note.*—There exists in London a weekly Journal on sale at all newsagents and bookstalls, the main purpose of which is to supply thrilling articles about various fetichistic peculiarities. A special feature is made of the correspondence columns. I suspect that some of the letters are written by the members of the Journal's staff, but many of them are written by readers of the paper, some of whom I number among my patients. Among the most popular fetiches are the following: tattooing, ear-rings, nose-rings, tight corseting, dressing males in female clothing, clothes made of corduroy, female underclothing, long hair, garments made of rubber or other waterproof material. Bodily deformities recently gave rise to a large correspondence from persons who are attracted to one-legged girls, as well as letters from some one-legged girls themselves. This seemed extraordinary enough, but it was capped by a letter from a girl who had lost *both* legs, and who claimed that a large number of men fell in love with her especially on that account. I am surprised that the paper has not been suppressed by the police authorities; though actually, in my opinion, it serves a useful purpose, for it affords a channel for fetichists of all sorts to find a harmless satisfaction for their fetichistic tendencies, by writing and reading articles and letters in which they may express their fantasies. It acts as a lightning-conductor, so to speak.

the works of Freud, we find a long list of objects which may
thus, in dreams, stand as symbols for the genital organs.
Havelock Ellis reports the observation of Dr. Jeliffe, whose
patient, Zenia X——, 'had been haunted by phallic
symbols from the age of thirteen. Since that time, but
more frequently the last few years, when the struggle has
become more consciously sexual, and consequently more
violent, I have been obsessed by symbols, especially by
those of the phallus: a watering pipe or a jet of water, long-
shaped fruits, especially pears, the pistil in the center of
a flower, a stick or any object of the same shape pushed into
a round hole, the lobe of my ear, with which I have played
since my birth, my teeth, and my tongue, which I pressed
nervously against my teeth until I got tired, a finger with
which I repeatedly pointed in front of me several times, as
if to suppress a sudden sexual idea, and which I afterwards
pulled back quickly and folded between the others as if to
correct it; the thumb, which involuntarily, in an effort of
repression, I pressed inside my fingers, certain letters of the
alphabet; these are some of the symbols which obsessed
me continually, rushing before my eyes and recalling the
effective contact of the male and the female organs'.

Among articles of clothing, it is naturally underwear
that holds the record in the lists of fetiches. The fact that it
recalls nudity and that it is associated in thought with
erotic scenes seems to make it destined to play the part of
a fetich. The silk articles, ornamented with lace-work,
displayed in shop windows frequently attract male spectators, whose interest in such exhibitions is not always free
from a sexual element. Some go so far as to maintain that
such a display of underwear is indecent, which betrays their
abnormal attitude towards these objects*.

* *Editor's Note.*—Among the lingerie-fetichists who have come under
my care, there is a clergyman in the forties, a highly respected member

But if silk and laces are excellent fetiches, combining as they do æsthetic and erotic elements, psychiatrists know of cases in which, on the contrary, it is coarse underwear that exerts a fascinating influence over the fetichist. We have been able to observe this curious anomaly of taste in a young student, who, through having love affairs with servants, came to show a very marked affection for coarse and inelegant underclothes. Without being a fetichist in the true sense of the word, he could never afterwards become accustomed to finer clothing, and forced his mistress to wear underclothes of the coarsest kind.

Dr. Hirschfeld tells of a divorce case in which the woman was the plaintiff. Ever since their wedding night, her husband had urged her to wear a cotton petticoat. 'On conceding to this strange desire the bride had felt humiliated: "If at least he had asked me to wear silk underclothing," she cried angrily. ". . . But no. His taste was exclusive." . . .'

A railwayman, also known to Dr. Hirschfeld, was in the habit of looking in windows behind which he expected to see women undressing; he would then get into the houses and steal the underclothes, the sight of which had brought him a moment of excitement.

A rather peculiar case is that in which corsets and belts play the rôle of fetiches. Many writers maintain, and not without reason, that we are here concerned with a form of

of society, and the father of a family. He has never been unfaithful to his wife, nor committed any of the more usual sexual irregularities, but for many years he has made a habit of buying ladies' fashion journals, and other papers containing pictures of female underclothing, which he cuts out and pastes in his scrap-books. He now has an enormous collection of these, and obtains sexual pleasure, culminating in an orgasm, by contemplating them. I met him at a luncheon party and he asked me so many questions about the sort of underclothing my female patients wore, that I was able to diagnose him as a lingerie-fetichist. I asked him bluntly if my diagnosis was correct, and after some hesitation he admitted that it was, and gave me full details of his peculiarity.—N. H.

sadism rather than with genuine fetichism. Men who are attracted by corsets give free play to their perversion by lacing the corset of their partner very tightly, and not being satisfied until she cries out with pain. These practices call up so much pleasure that the mere sight of the corset soon suffices to arouse voluptuous sensations, and from that they proceed to fetichism.

Less intimate garments are also, though less frequently, erotic fetiches. Charcot and Magnan report a rather strange case, one which is probably unique. We quote from Dr. Chapotin:

'At the age of fifteen the subject caught sight of a shining white apron which was drying in the sunshine. He approached, took hold of it and fastened the string around his waist. From that day, aprons held an attraction for him, and he could not restrain himself from taking them. Several times this man was arrested and condemned for stealing white aprons. His desire attained such a degree of intensity that, not only did he voluntarily submit to being kept for long periods under observation, but he would even expose himself to great dangers in order to succeed. Succeed in what? In the conquest of a white apron! He has been punished several times, but remains incapable of controlling himself. He had tried heroic means. He has gone to sea; he has taken refuge in a monastery. But no sooner has he disembarked than he begins again. No sooner has he left the cloisters than he rushes off to buy white aprons. It is a destiny which pursues the unfortunate man and affects his whole existence.'

Everybody has heard of the sentimental and innocent habit of keeping a perfumed handkerchief belonging to the loved one, but it is much less known that these pieces of linen may be first-rate sexual stimulants. The same thing applies to hats, night-caps, and even to garments made of rubber*. Medical annals record the case of a waterproof-coat fetichist, who fled from shop windows where these articles were displayed, knowing that he could not escape strong sexual excitement and even an orgasm. Lastly, velvet articles and furs are in great favour, perhaps because they remind the pervert of the softness and the hairiness of the female skin. Krafft-Ebing records the case of a neurotic for whom the sight and contact of fur, while not being a condition *sine qua non* of excitement, is a powerful sexual stimulant. Even illustrations representing fur clothes have the greatest interest for him, and the mere word ' fur ' acts like magic.

' Fur ', he says, ' is an object of so much sexual interest to me that a man who wears a fur makes a very disagreeable impression on me; it is horrible, scandalous, like the impression any normal individual would get on seeing a man in the costume of a ballerina.'

Women are much less inclined to make fetiches of clothes. Still, it is curious to note that everything pertaining to the military exerts a certain erotic influence on those with a perverse predisposition. The uniform of officers, especially during the war, when an officer was a demi-god to the woman deprived of her usual sexual partner, became in some way an erotic symbol. Fashion journals and pornographic pictures furnish a good illustration of partial fetichism.

But of all the forms of fetichism associated with clothes, shoe fetichism is the most widespread, and the object of the most assiduous observations on the part of specialists. This perversion is often connected with love of the foot, as we have already seen, and its origin may lead back to a childhood memory.

---

* *Editor's Note.*—A long and vivid correspondence on this subject has appeared in the weekly journal referred to in a previous foot-note.—N. H.

Here is a case observed by Dr. Biswanger and quoted by Havelock Ellis:

'Gerda, while still a child, had acquired the habit of sitting on her heels, with her shoe pressed between the vulva and the anus. This attitude produced stimulation of that erotogenic zone, and the girl derived pleasure from urinating (perhaps because that was a means of producing detumescence). The shoe became her friend, her lover, her beloved; she protected it amorously and prevented other people from looking at it. The foot, especially when shod, being confused with sexual ideas, became representative of the phallus, and even, as amongst primitive people, the symbol of fertility. In the course of time, phobias and other symptoms developed on this basis, concealing and to some extent weakening the other manifestations.'

Another interesting case is recorded by Krafft-Ebing in his *Psychopathia Sexualis*. It was that of a diplomat, a descendant of the old Polish aristocracy. Having been seduced in his youth by a school-mistress who flirted outrageously with him, but would not permit the sexual act, he was one day struck by the sight of some very elegant boots belonging to the temptress he so ardently desired. Since then, nothing had excited him so much as the sight of shoes. Bare feet left him more or less indifferent. A shoe, even when not being worn, as, for instance, when displayed in a shop window, roused in him a state of irresistible sexual excitement. The doctor he consulted advised him to marry. This treatment met with little success. In the presence of his wife he felt guilty, and did not dare to approach her. But he continued to associate with prostitutes, with whom he could make free use of his fetich. At length he conceived the idea of buying a pair of very elegant boots, and hiding them, unknown to his wife, in their double bed. For some time this trick enabled him to perform his marital duties.

Shoe fetichists have not much difficulty, especially in European capitals, in satisfying their strange tastes. The enterprise of Prostitution has made provision for this case, as well as for so many others, and certain *filles de joie* have an imposing collection of footwear, ranging from the low-cut dancing shoe to the high boot, and showing as much variety in colour as in form—all this to anticipate the desires of their customers. The professor visited a house of assignation in Tauentzienstrasse, Berlin, noted for prostitutes who make a point of catering for customers who are boot fetichists. One prostitute, on being questioned, stated that she possessed twelve pairs of boots, each of which was worth, on an average, 1,200 francs. Her customers were numerous and her business prospering. Visitors were very faithful and came to see her from distant provinces. One of them, an officer, was a fetichist of a masochist type. He asked the girl to welcome him, every time he arrived, by insulting him, and to this treatment he replied by kneeling and kissing her boots. Then, still on his knees, he followed her across the room, begging her to kick him. His sexual appetite never really manifested itself except when there was contact between her heel and his body.

In the collective work entitled *Sexual Perversions*, we find another case of boot fetichism, that of a man whose whole life was spoilt by this cruel perversion:

' G. S——, 44 years of age, a merchant, consulted us and asked for a medical certificate for use in connection with his divorce case. S—— was married at the age of twenty. From the beginning of his married life he knew that he had a marked preference for a certain kind of footwear, i.e. for ladies' high boots. His wife, knowing her husband's taste, wore only boots of that sort, even during the sexual act. In the course of time, this abnormal tendency became accentuated. S—— realised that his wife's boots were more important to him from the sexual point of view than his wife herself. She began gradually to inspire him with repugnance, and this became so pronounced, that at length he began to neglect his marital duties. Then, instead of copulating with his wife, he contented himself with masturbation. It was his wife's boots that gave him the desire to perform masturbation. He took those boots to bed with him, pressed them against himself, wore them himself and kept them with him all night. S—— possessed no less than fifty pairs of ladies' boots, of all colours and shapes, but always of the same height. He finally became unable to endure life with his wife, and decided to be separated from her.'

In Dr. Chapotin's book there is a story of a humble postal assistant, Mademoiselle R——, a story so extraordinary that it might be taken for pure fiction if it had not been known to Dr. Julou. The strange perversion of this person is due to disturbances associated with the menopause, which in women, and especially in old maids, gives rise to the most unexpected sexual aberrations. The lady in question fell in love with a gendarme's boot which she caught sight of in an old clothes shop in Bordeaux. At the sight of that boot she felt the blood boiling in her veins. She experienced a strange sensation which impelled her to acquire the coveted object, regardless of the price. She took the boot to the village where she worked, laid it in a cradle, and put a child's bonnet on it. Her perversion was a strange mixture of boot fetichism and suppressed maternal instinct. She took care of the coarse shoe and doted upon it as if it were a baby; she polished it carefully, for the reflection of the polished leather gave her untold joy. This aberration of the sexual instinct died down as soon as the menopause came to an end. Mademoiselle R—— no longer felt any attraction for the gendarme's boot.

Another patient, no less curious, and known to Dr. Garnier, describes in a picturesque manner his customary performance with boots. We quote him word for word:

'I put on my pink underpants and my boots. I get up on two chairs, with my legs apart, and I partly open the mirror door of my wardrobe so as to get a back view of myself, by means of the reflection in the mirror by the fireplace.

'I keep my eyes fixed upon my boots. At this moment, I feel that I could love myself. At other times, I rub myself with one of my boots, while keeping my eyes on the other one, to see the light reflected on it; but nearly always I put each one on a chair near the window, turned in such a way that they shine as much as possible, and then placing myself at a certain distance, I try to reach them. From this performance I derive a sense of triumph which is due to the enormous enjoyment it affords me.'

Fetichism has a curious counterpart in the inverse perversion, which consists in an invincible repulsion at the sight or touch of certain objects. Anti-fetichists show as much diversity as fetichists. One of these perverts had such a horror of breasts that every object which, by its shape, recalled that part of the body, disgusted him. He could not eat pudding, and he could not pass before a door with a Roman arch without evoking the idea of breasts and shivering with disgust.

We shall not give further examples of anti-fetichism, because it would lead us far beyond the scope of this chapter. Suffice to say that in the eyes of a pervert any object may constitute a fetich or an anti-fetich. A list of them would be too long ever to be completed.

*   *   *

Another kind of perversion is Zoophilia, i.e. the capacity of being sexually attracted by animals. This phenomenon has been given a different name by the different writers who have studied it. Among other terms, those of *sodomy** and *bestiality* have been used, shades of meaning having been established between all these expressions. Once again we must draw the attention of the reader to the fact that affection for animals cannot in every case be classed as a perversion. In this case, as always, the line of demarcation between the normal and the abnormal is not clear. Literature supplies us with numerous accounts of deep affection springing up between a human being and an animal; we mention, for instance, the legend of Leda, the *Animal* of Rachilde, and, quite recently, the *Cat* of Colette, in which an innocent feline is the cause of a family tragedy.

As far back as human memory reaches, sentimental and sexual relations between man and the animals have always existed, and it is not necessary to see in this one of the consequences of the dissolute ways of modern civilisation. According to a legend of the ancient Hebrews, the goat was often the companion of a woman. Voltaire pleads wittily for the cause of these women who were zoophiles in spite of themselves:

'I shall say in justification of the Jewish ladies who wandered in the desert, that they could not wash themselves owing to the lack of water. They could not change either their clothes or their shoes; they had no chemises. So the he-goats of their country could very easily mistake them for she-goats on account of their smell, and that similarity might very well have given rise to some gallantry between the two species.'

Moreover, goatherds and cowherds in all ages, grazing

---

* *Editor's Note.*—The word sodomy is used in more than one sense in English. By some persons it is used in the Continental sense to denote intercourse with animals, which is better known as bestiality. By other persons it is used to denote anal intercourse between males, and its use should be restricted to this latter meaning.—N. H.

their flocks far from all human habitation, and forced by that fact to associate with animals only, have not been able to avoid gratifying their sexual needs with these companions. In the Middle Ages, copulation with animals was very severely punished, those who were guilty of such an aberration ending their life at the stake. Here is a song of one of the condemned named Vion:

> Je suis ce Vion que la foule
> Des pages, laquais et badauds,
> Vont voir mourir sur l'échafaud
> Pour avoir caressé sa poule.

(I am that Vion whom the crowd of pages, lackeys and idle spectators, are going to see die on the scaffold for having caressed his chicken.)

Here, evidently, we are to understand the word 'poule'* (chicken) in its literal sense.

With certain primitive peoples, sexual relations with animals are required by tradition. Dr. Hesnard mentions, by way of example, a regular custom in certain parts of Africa, which requires that young men shall have sexual intercourse with the first important game that they kill while hunting. If we are to believe a legend which is greatly credited in Northern Africa, the Arabs, before taking a hen to market, make use of it to perform the sexual act. A similar custom is often attributed to the Chinese. Mantegazza affirms that they cut the neck of a duck with a sabre in order to copulate with it afterwards.

'Bestiality' is often found in very primitive individuals whose state is bordering on idiocy. Cases are reported of intercourse with domestic animals in the country where peasants spend most of their time in the company of their

---

* *Editor's Note.*—The word *poule* is commonly used in France to denote a 'mistress', or as the Americans would say, a 'sweetie', and as we say in England, a 'bird'.—N. H.

cattle. Their psychological life is reduced to a minimum, and the sexual act comes to be a physiological act for which the female animal may very well take the place of a woman. The irresponsible attitude which usually characterises this aberration of the sexual instinct is well illustrated by the case of the German peasant who, when accused of sodomy and brought before the court, declared: ' My wife was absent for too long, and so I went with my sow '.

Besides the sow, whose pink and smooth skin perhaps counts for something in the rôle of sexual partner which she is made to assume by certain feeble-minded peasants, the she-goat, the cow, the ewe, the bitch, the cat, etc., have all at times been the chance companions of men in the country. Among the rarer animals, serpents, bears, crocodiles, not to speak of swans, have sometimes been favoured by ladies. Certain travellers affirm that in Central Africa the cohabitation of women with gorillas is fairly frequent.

The following case, reported by Dr. Feré, is disturbing. It shows how a perverse attraction to a dog, due to an infantile memory, ruined the life of an otherwise normal woman.

' A chance incident which occurred when she was only three-and-a-half years of age gave her the idea of her terrible perversity. Two dogs took to caressing her in such a way that she experienced an intense satisfaction. From that time onwards, she made dogs follow her into the woods. She was quite indifferent to young boys and girls. She lived only for canine intercourse. As a girl, she was terrified by her own mania. She married with the firm intention of founding a family. But her husband merely repelled her. She submitted to him with resignation. One day she shuddered: he had kissed her. Suddenly the idea of a dog came to her mind. It came like a thunderbolt, and brought an intense satisfaction, such as she had not known before. And in her future marital relationships she could not avoid the fatal association of ideas. She was anxious and ashamed when her husband approached her; she was in revolt and angry with herself, but could not get rid of the obsession. But she was destined to undergo still more cruel tortures. To her great joy, she became a mother. All went well until, one day, while she was suckling her child, she saw a dog pass. She experienced strong sexual excitement. And after that she could not suckle her child without immediately reproducing the association with all its consequences. The longer the child's meal lasted, the greater was her genital excitement. She fed him less frequently, she cut his meals short in order to avoid an orgasm; the child became sickly, he developed slowly. He died. She blamed herself for his death, attributing it to her sexual anomaly.'

The dog is perhaps the animal most apt in satisfying perverse women. Women of the lesbian type, who prefer a special kind of caress to normal coitus, sometimes train dogs or cats in such a way as to make them play this part. 'One of our patients,' writes Dr. Hesnard, 'an elegant, high-class courtesan, a drug addict and a nymphomaniac, had a very pronounced erotic tendency for big dogs, preferably of a reddish colour, which she used in lesbian fashion.'

It is a much discussed question whether sexual relations with animals is harmful to man. According to Forel, this should be one of the least offensive perversions. From a eugenic point of view, he judges it preferable that an idiot or a feeble-minded man should violate an animal rather than impregnate a young girl. Still, it is unquestionable that bestiality is fraught with danger of contagion for man. Tetanus, erysipelas and anthrax are the price most frequently paid for these particular caresses.

According to a fairly common superstition, amorous intercourse with animals may bring about the birth of monsters, half animal and half human. This belief has proved to be unfounded, for it has been scientifically demonstrated that the germ cells of human beings and those of animals are not capable of impregnating each other.

In short, although it is less harmful than certain perversions which urge a man to acts of unspeakable cruelty, zoophilia is of such a nature as to repel every normal person.

CHAPTER XXXIII

CONCLUSION

Other sexual anomalies. Satyriasis and nymphomania. Don Juan and Messalina. The effects of narcotics. Prevention better than cure.

THERE exist sexual anomalies which cannot be classified in either of the two great categories of perversion of subject and of object, for they are of quite a different character. We are concerned in the first place with a perversion of intensity which one might call *hyper-eroticism* or *erotomania*. But usually, two different terms are employed, according as to whether it is a question of masculine or of feminine perversion. The term *satyriasis* is used for men and *nymphomania* for women.

The causes of these sexual anomalies are most frequently physiological. A hyperactivity of the genital glands maintains the individual in a state of permanent sexual excitement, which takes possession of his mind, to the exclusion of every other occupation. Often, men suffering from satyriasis are veritable super-males, capable of making impressive records, and for whom coitus only serves to increase their sexual appetite. The phenomenon was known to mythology, where it is described in a legend about Hercules, one of whose twelve tasks consisted in rendering pregnant, in a single night, the fifty daughters of Thespios.

[486]

If we are to believe certain historians and chroniclers, Caligula, Nero and Tiberius, among others, were capable of robbing a hundred girls of their virginity in a few days. Even when we make allowance for exaggeration, it remains certain that at all periods there have been men whose virile potency was very much above the normal.

But an erotomaniac is not necessarily a Hercules. He is often the victim of an exaggerated sensibility, which gives rise to excitement at the sight of a woman even though she may be far from handsome. Most of these 'runners after women' would probably be very embarrassed if all the persons who inspire them with desire became their conquests. No doubt there are Don Juans whose erotic life is very rich, though in no way miraculous, but, as a rule, it is a question of rather timid individuals, whose sexual obsession may be explained by their very sexual insufficiency.

In speaking of hypererotism in men, it is important to distinguish clearly between erotic mania and the disease known by the name of *priapism*, which consists of a permanent and painful erection of the virile member. This affection is due to a nervous disease, and coitus, even when repeated, is unable to relieve it.

Erotomania in a woman is known by the name of nymphomania. This anomaly existed in all times, and the ancient history of Rome furnishes us with numerous examples of it. Roman ladies, in their greed for strong emotions, did not hesitate to have the ædiles enroll them on the list of prostitutes, in order that they might be able to satisfy their passionate temperament. There existed, at the same time, male brothels, in which wealthy ladies had legions of young men reserved for their own use, keeping them 'sealed' during the intervals between their visits in order to prevent them expressing their manhood elsewhere. To do this they used a system similar to that of the chastity belts of the crusaders' women.

Messalina, possessed by the demon of the flesh, led a life which was nothing more than an incessant orgy. Not satisfied with the feasts of the Court, where an unrestrained sexuality held sway, she went nightly to houses of prostitution as the courtesan Lycia. There, full of burning desire, she gave herself up to labourers and to the scum of the town, and was indignant when, one morning, the director dismissed her. After a night of amorous orgies, her lusts were not yet satisfied. She went away with tired limbs, but in no way satisfied. (*Lassata sed non satiata exit.*)

Juvenal describes the fury of another Roman nymphomaniac, Laufela, during the course of a religious festivity: 'Laufela laid down her crown, challenged the prostitutes themselves and took the prize in the art of inspiring voluptuous sensation. . . . They were not satisfied with a vain pretence; everything was carried out in reality. Then arose those warm desires which would not suffer delay. . . . And one single cry echoed through the vault: "The men. It is time for the men".'

Nowadays, physicians know of many men and women who, being continually obsessed by erotic thoughts, are incapable of leading a normal life and carrying on their vocational activities in a fitting manner. At every step, they exceed the bounds of decent behaviour, and being ostracised by everybody, they are the first victims of their own mania.

To exhaust so vast a subject as sexual pathology is not within the bounds of the present work. We have enumerated and briefly described the principal aberrations of the sexual instinct, but there are a great many others as well, for variety, in this domain, is almost infinite. We have intentionally refrained from mentioning those numerous pathological cases in which the sexual instinct is found to have deviated on account of an anatomical anomaly. This is the case with hermaphrodites, persons of indefinite sex. Having come into the world with male and female elements, it is evident that their sexual activity could not follow a normal course.

But apart from this extreme anomaly, the annals of sexual pathology contain accounts of abnormalities of the genital apparatus which condemn their victims to a life in which no love but that of a pathological nature is known. An analysis of these afflictions would be far too technical for us to undertake in a work of this kind.

Finally, the sexuality of the congenitally healthy man is threatened in modern times by the sinister influence of stimulants, an influence which is widespread in all countries that civilisation has reached. Alcohol, which does incalculable damage to the human organism, is the greatest enemy of normal sexuality. The statistics of all experts go to prove that perverts and sexual delinquents, if not themselves dipsomaniacs, are often descended from dipsomaniacs.

Stupefying drugs, such as cocaine, morphia and opium, which, despite the terrific struggle against them, do not in any way tend to disappear from present-day life, are one of the most important factors in the sexual degeneration of thousands of human beings. The close connection existing between these drugs and sexuality is illustrated by the fact that the establishments where the passion for these drugs may be satisfied are at the same time the scene of the most unbridled erotic orgies. Drug addicts who hope to find a new lease of life for their sexual activity by means of these practices are not long in finding that they have been mastered by these modern poisons. Sexual perversions, if not impotence, are the price one pays for this deplorable habit.

To conclude our chapter on sexual aberrations, it is worth

while devoting a few words to the problem of sexual delinquency. Legislation, in different periods and in different countries, has adopted various attitudes towards the question of sexual crimes. Excesses of an erotic nature which in one latitude are regarded as normal, are in other climes a matter calling for severe judicial measures.

In the course of this study, we have taken pains to insist on the pathological character of perversions, and the consequent irresponsibility of those who are affected by them. To punish these unfortunate people as criminals would be just as iniquitous as to allow them to give full swing to their morbid tendencies at the expense of their neighbours. The prison or the madhouse, as Magnus Hirschfeld rightly remarks, is not the right place for these freaks of nature. The prison would place them among ordinary wrongdoers, and would inflict punishment without supplying a remedy. To put a sexual criminal in an asylum would be equally futile, for in the majority of cases we are dealing with persons who are perfectly normal, apart from their morbid sexuality. It is medical science that should be responsible for this class of delinquent. Modern therapeutics already has at its disposal several methods that we have been led to mention, and which not infrequently bring about satisfactory results. In certain cases, several writers recommend castration and sterilisation, drastic though these methods may be. However, one must not be discouraged by a few setbacks, for the interest of society is at stake. We have a gigantic task before us; namely, *that of preventing sexual aberrations, so that we may not be called upon to cure them.*

BOOK VI

VENEREAL DISEASE

BOOK VI

CHAPTER XXXIV

GONORRHŒA

*Gonorrhœa in antiquity and the Middle Ages. Superstitious beliefs.
The first discoveries. The problem of contagion. Clinical picture of the
development of gonorrhœa. Gonorrhœa in the man and in the woman.
The effects of gonorrhœal infection. Gonorrhœal ophthalmia and
Créde's method.*

GONORRHŒA was already well known in antiquity. An
Egyptian papyrus, dating from the sixteenth century B.C.,
mentions urethral inflammation in men and leucorrhœa
in women. The Old Testament contains several allusions
to this disease, and in Pompeii surgical instruments were
discovered which could only have been used for treating
gonorrhœa.

Ivan Bloch has stated that the ancients did not differentiate spermatorrhœa (involuntary emission or ejaculation)
from prostatorrhœa (pathological discharge of prostatic
liquid) or from chronic gonorrhœa (gleet). They included
all three disorders under the generic name of blenorrhœa.
Yet Hippocrates's pupils had already noticed cases of acute
gonorrhœa, the inflammatory character of which did not
allow them to be classified as blenorrhœas.

The Middle Ages made notable progress in diagnosing
gonorrhœa. Its contagious nature was soon detected, and
its origin traced to unclean sexual intercourse; the pathogenic agent of the disease remained unknown, although

the Arab school, so derided in the past, was already sus-
pecting it.

Once venereal diseases had been found to be infectious,
prophylactic measures were taken to prevent their spreading.
It was all the more urgent in view of the fact that houses
of prostitution, which it was not considered shameful to
visit, were then enjoying great popularity. Kings and
princes were conducted to them in state by the town
councillors, and the wantons fawned upon the noble
visitors in the hope of being ransomed by them. These
brothels, accessible to anyone possessed of a few crowns,
were hot-beds of infection. At an early date they were
put under the supervision of the town council, the women
were examined by doctors, and those who were guilty of
having infected a customer, or even of having themselves
caught the infection, were severely punished. Immediately
one of the women was found to be diseased she had to leave
the town. This was, of course, a double-edged law, because
the expelled women, faced with starvation, copulated,
extramuros, with any stray passer-by, and this constituted
an equally great danger to the city. In towns where the
penalty for venereal infection was death, the prostitutes
did everything they could to conceal their illness—and they
frequently succeeded—so that their condition grew worse
while they spread the infection.

This was all the more to be regretted because at that
time no distinction was made between gonorrhœa and
syphilis. Practitioners did not prescribe urethral injections,
because they thought that the purulent discharge represented the natural elimination of the syphilitic toxins, and
ought not to be stopped lest the infection become more
acute. If eventually barley-, rose-, plantain- or lime-water
injections were given, it was always after the primary
period, in order not to interfere with the escape of the

poison. A frequent prescription was that of red wine
injections, one still favoured by contemporary charlatans,
those good people who, rather than imitate modern scientific
methods, prefer to revive old formulæ exhumed from dusty
tomes.

The real character of gonorrhœa became known only at
the beginning of the eighteenth century, when it was
defined as a blenorrhœa (catarrhal inflammation) of the
mucous membrane. Ricord's researches (1800–1809) proved
beyond question that syphilis has no connection with
gonorrhœa and that the former can never induce the latter.

The pathogenic agent in gonorrhœa is a microscopic
bacillus which its discoverer, Neisser, called gonococcus.
This bacillus is found in the purulent discharge peculiar
to the disease in its acute stage; it has a circular shape and
the power of penetrating into the white corpuscles, where it
multiplies rapidly. Yet gonococci are not always found in
gonorrhœal pus, the globules of which may be germless or,
after prolonged treatment, contain extremely degenerated
bacilli; their detection then requires an involved process of
cultures and reactions to distinguish them from inoffensive
microbes.

A method has recently been evolved which is somewhat
similar to Wassermann's reaction for syphilis, and may
prove quite helpful in diagnosing gonorrhœa. The patient's
blood is tested in the following manner: the blood taken
from a vein of the arm is treated by complex chemical
reactions which cannot be described here in detail. A
positive reaction alone is conclusive, as it constitutes a
definite proof of the presence of gonococci. A negative
reaction would be better termed doubtful, since it affords
us no certainty either way. This reaction is superfluous
in the case of an acute gonorrhœa, which can be diagnosed
by much more immediate and reliable means; but when

the patient suffers from subsidiary troubles or specific complications, like epididymitis or arthritis, which may be either gonorrhœal, rheumatic or tubercular, it gives valuable information. If the reaction is positive, one can nearly always diagnose a gonorrhœal infection; if it is negative, the question remains open and other diagnostic methods must be resorted to. Researches are at present being carried on in laboratories, and we may expect results that will greatly improve our present knowledge of gonorrhœal infection.

Cultures and reactions are a great help when it is a question of ascertaining whether an individual who has had gonorrhœa may safely marry. The time is drawing near when a prenuptial medical certificate will be enforced in every country and will be given only after a test for venereal disease.

When a gonococcus is placed on a mucous membrane, it remains on the surface for a time, multiplies, and then burrows; gonorrhœal infection takes place in a few hours. A germless infection is an impossibility and there is no foundation for the idea that it can be caught by passing water against the wind or through irritation of the mucous membrane. In the great majority of cases gonorrhœa is the result of sexual intercourse, during which the bacilli are transferred from one diseased mucous membrane to the other. Direct sexual contact is not necessary, infection being possible by a hand that has touched the infected genitals. Transmission by lavatory seats, linen, or injection nozzles is very unlikely in practice, although theoretically possible.

The time elapsing between the moment of infection and the appearance of the first symptoms varies; it usually ranges from two to five days; the symptoms are: itching, burning sensation in the urethra, purulent discharge, lymphatic nodules along the canal. It may appear as soon as 24 hours after intimacy took place, while there have been cases where incubation lasted as long as four weeks. This period, during which the patient is unaware of his contagious state, is, together with that of partial cure, the most dangerous for all concerned.

Fortunately, with the exception of a very few criminally irresponsible individuals, it is most improbable that a diseased person will contaminate anyone during the acute stage of gonorrhœa. But it is possible to be actually infected and not know it; so that one may in all good faith have sexual relations with a healthy partner to whom one will thus bring disaster. Gonorrhœa is contagious as soon as contracted, and almost every physician's consulting hour brings a wife whom her husband has unintentionally contaminated. This distressing accident is especially frequent among working people; the man often drinks a little too much on pay-day and thus becomes an easy prey to a diseased prostitute; the next victim is the wife, and when the man realises that he is ill, it is too late and the mischief is done.

It is, however, a mistake to believe that every urethral discharge is due to gonorrhœa; other discharges with a yellowish or greenish tinge may appear after sexual intimacy, which yet have nothing in common with gonorrhœa. Such catarrhal affections are usually due to local irritation, or to the action of microbes favoured by lack of cleanliness, and may require as long a treatment as gonorrhœa. To diagnose the specific origin of such discharges needs a trained physician's experience. As for the dreaded blenorrhœal filaments found in the patient's urine, they are no proof of a gonococcal infection; they may be the remains of a cured gonorrhœa or merely the outcome of an irritation of the mucous membrane.

It is essential to distinguish between gonorrhœal and blenorrhœal symptoms, because the treatment of gonorrhœa is wholly different from that of mucositis; the former needs drastic treatment, while the latter must be handled with great gentleness. The similarity of their respective symptoms is widely exploited by quacks, who always diagnose gonorrhœa and then point to the infallible promptness of their methods.

To give a clinical picture of the evolution of gonorrhœa is very difficult, if not impossible, because it may last only a few days, or it may persist for months or years. If taken in hand early, the chances are that it will be cured quickly; a fairly mild case treated within 24 hours of infection is often cured in three days; an older infection takes two to six weeks, or even months; if complications, like orchitis or cystitis, have set in, the duration of the treatment cannot be forecast.

With patience and perseverance—those are essential points—any gonorrhœa is curable, even the so-called chronic gonorrhœa which is such a popular bogy. In fact, chronic does not mean incurable, but of long standing, and to give up treatment on the pretext that a chronic infection is hopeless, is worse than foolish. Physicians to-day have at their disposal a large number of instruments, besides vaccine-therapeutic, urethroscopic and electric methods, that can deal successfully with what were formerly regarded as desperate cases. Of course no practitioner can undertake to cure gonorrhœa within a limited time; just as in the equine world there are nags, hunters and race-horses, so we find among gonococci various grades of virulence; thus, of two patients treated alike, one will be cured in a fortnight, while the other will develop orchitis, arthritis, or other complications. In addition to the virulence of the microbes an important part is played by the patient's personal resistance; in this resistance the constitution of the genito-urinary organs, the size of the vesical sphincter, previous infections, and a number of as yet ill-defined factors, come into account.

Rationally treated, gonorrhœa usually takes the following course: the discharge lasts from twelve to sixteen days, then only one drop appears, finally the filaments disappear from the urine and the cure is soon complete. Unfortunately this regular course may be subject to a number of deviations. If the bacilli ascend the genito-urinary system, that is, if the infection passes backwards from the urethra into the bladder, whence it can spread to the prostate and along the vas deferens to the testes, matters may become critical. Spasms of the bladder may occur, accompanied by extremely painful micturition; abscesses may form in the inflamed prostate, which has to be massaged through the rectum and sometimes calls for an operation; epididymitis, orchitis and swelling of the testes may set in, in which case the patient must keep to his bed until the complication is over. The most unfavourable aspect of gonorrhœa is the infiltration of the blood by the germs through the urethra and the kidneys, because the whole organism is then affected. Inflammation of the knee-joint with subsequent stiffening, and gonorrhœal rheumatism, are well-known disorders. The gonococci may even lodge in the heart muscle, in which case pericarditis follows, or even septicæmia, with fatal results.

Gonorrhœa can thus be anything from a mere indisposition to a fatal illness, according to circumstances and the individual. It is therefore the duty of every infected person to seek medical advice on the slightest suspicion, for his own sake as much as for that of others.

Whereas a man is usually aware when he has contracted gonorrhœa, in a woman the symptoms are slower to appear.

There are several reasons for this. It is the urethra which becomes infected in a man, and it may be the urethra in a woman, but her genital organs are more frequently contaminated; the vagina, however, contrary to common belief, is not susceptible to gonococcal infection except in the part adjacent to the uterus, or, more exactly, in the cervix. If her urethra is affected, the woman also feels itching and a burning sensation when passing water. If the cervix is the centre of infection, there is usually no pain; but, as the infection progresses, leucorrhœa appears. But so many women suffer from this innocuous trouble that they do not interpret it as an early sign of gonorrhœa.

As for the burning sensation in the urethra which we have just mentioned, it is seldom suspected; women usually attribute it to cystitis, to a chill on the bladder, or to too many iced drinks. The disease is then allowed to drag on for weeks and months. Sometimes it disappears, because a strong organism can to some extent fight down the infection; but in that case the bacilli only withdraw into the deeper layers of the uterus, where they may lie dormant for a very long time. It is safe to say that 80 per cent. of infected women are not aware of their condition, and believe themselves absolutely sound, until they infect a man or the trouble makes itself apparent, as, for instance, in the case of childbirth. A physician himself often finds it difficult to detect gonorrhœa in a woman if the germs are hidden in the remoter parts of the genital system; they only appear very rarely, for example, after menstruation or through some exceptional circumstance. One or two examinations, therefore, do not suffice for a definite diagnosis where women are concerned; an honest physician will not assure his patient that she is perfectly healthy unless he has had her under observation for some time; the most he can say is that so far he has found nothing.

The two following cases, taken from our records, are characteristic. A lady patient was in a nursing home on account of a serious fracture; an association of circumstances led us to place her under observation for a possible gonorrhœa, but without positive results. It was only after seven months that gonococci were detected in her uterus. The second case is that of a woman who had become infected with gonorrhœa in 1912, and after three months' treatment had been discharged as cured. She married in 1913; in 1917 she developed salpingitis and infected her husband, with whom she had been living for four years without the slightest accident. This was therefore a relapse of the incompletely cured gonorrhœa of 1912.

We stress this hidden aspect of the disease because many men who have become infected seem to think that the woman should have known that she had the disease. She often has not the least inkling of it; hence the danger of relying on a woman's statement that she was declared healthy after a medical examination. Even when she has been treated, a patient may still be contagious, because it is only in very exceptional cases that the woman has the patience to continue her visits to the doctor for weeks, which is the *sine qua non* of a complete cure.

The development of gonorrhœa in women, as in men, may take a variety of forms. Between a mild urethral catarrh which is cured in four weeks, and the most acute organic disturbances, there are a number of intermediate stages. Cystitis and its consequences are comparatively harmless; much more dangerous and unfortunately fairly common are the cases in which the infection reaches the uterus (gonococcal metritis), then the fallopian tubes (salpingitis), the ovaries and the peritoneum (gonorrhœal peritonitis), by which time the damage is practically beyond repair.

Even if the patient recovers, she may be left with a crippled organism and handicapped for the rest of her life.

Gonorrhœa is not only dangerous for the woman herself, but also for any children she may have, for the bacillus may attack the eyes of the child. The purulent infection begins with an inflammation of the eyelids (conjunctivitis), then spreads to the cornea and finally to the internal parts of the eye. Unless treated early, it gives rise to blindness.

The havoc caused by gonococcal ophthalmia among children is evident from an examination of the statistics of infantile blindness due to hereditary taint. Up to 1880, over 30 per cent. of the inmates of Homes for the Blind had lost their sight shortly after birth; the number dropped to 19 per cent. in 1895 and 12 per cent. in 1912; more recent figures show a continued improvement.

Venereal blindness can now be prevented, thanks to Crédé's idea, dating from about 1880, of instilling silver nitrate (or argyrol) in the eyes of new-born babies. Were this practice made compulsory, infantile blindness would doubtless disappear entirely.

* * *

The treatment of gonorrhœa has lately been greatly improved. Whereas it used to last for an eternity, nowadays the cure can be completed under favourable conditions in a short time. The injections given are practically painless, and vaccinotherapy has become a valuable weapon in the fight against the disease.

Vaccinotherapy consists in inoculating the patient with the virus of his own disease; the patient is given a subcutaneous injection of gonococci which have been previously killed; this starts a process of reaction, in the form of antibodies created by the organism against the foreign elements introduced; those antibodies attack not only the inoculated virus, but also the active gonococci, and destroy them. The difficulty lies in preparing an adequate virus in which the bacilli, while non-virulent, are not too neutralised. Experiments are now being made with live germs and good results are anticipated.

In the case of a particularly tenacious infection, resort is made to inoculating with the germs of malaria; although somewhat drastic, this method is about the most efficacious known to modern therapy. Malarial inoculation is followed by high fever; after five or six induced attacks, the result is astounding. Whether it is the high temperature, or other factors, that produce the effect is still uncertain.

A suitable mode of living is essential to the cure of gonorrhœa. For some as yet unknown reason, a very light diet is indicated as having a definitely favourable influence on the disease; experience has proved that privations greatly assist the specific treatment. On the other hand, the patient should drink enormous quantities, but not a drop of alcohol; fresh fruit juice, mineral but not sparkling waters, and especially milk, at the rate of from two to three quarts a day, constitute the liquid diet. Savoury dishes, spices and acid aliments must be avoided.

The regularity of the bowel-movements is also essential; the rectum must be kept empty to avoid pressure on the internal genitals.

The strict observance of this *modus vivendi* cannot alone cure gonorrhœa, but it will help to avoid complications.

CHAPTER XXXV

SYPHILIS

How one catches syphilis. The primary, secondary and tertiary stages. Five indications of syphilis. Syphilis is curable. Treatment of long duration. The truth about mercury. The advantages of salvarsan, silver and bismuth. The reward of patience. The Wassermann reaction and its value in diagnosis. Should a person suffering from syphilis be allowed to marry?

THE specific agent of syphilis is an organism known as the *spirochæta pallida*, discovered in 1905. Through contact with someone whose skin or some part of the body carries this organism, as in the case of syphilitic ulcers, a healthy person's skin or mucous membrane may become infected and the disease thereby introduced into the system. It would be a mistake to think that the infection can penetrate only through a large sore; the spirochætes are extremely active and can penetrate through the slightest abrasion. Contagion is, of course, most frequent through sexual intimacy and the microbe may then be transmitted by the genital parts, as well as by the lips, the mucous membrane of the mouth and the tonsils. Practitioners who treat ulcers, without knowing their specific nature, run the risk of being infected through their fingers.

Contagion being possible through any contact, direct transmission from the diseased person is not necessary, and the germ may be acquired by handling an object or drinking from a glass which has previously been used by a syphilitic. But infection by such means is very rare.

The infection does not at first manifest itself externally; the spirochætes multiply in the blood, and only when it is 'saturated' does the first external sign appear in the shape of the hard or true chancre. This takes from three to five weeks, during which time no physician can possibly detect the disease; even then, the diagnosis is difficult because the hard chancre is not easily distinguishable from a soft one. Nor is the information obtained from the patient very enlightening either; if intimacy took place two days previously with a partner who was suspect the latter cannot be held responsible. But if it took place four weeks before the appearance of the chancre, syphilis is most likely to be the cause. Such certainty, however, is rare, because in the meantime other sexual acts may have occurred, so that it would be arbitrary to attribute the infection to a four-week-old affair.

This latent character at the beginning of syphilis is, as in gonorrhœa, one cause of the extraordinary way in which it spreads, even among married people. A husband who has had extra-marital sexual relations does not know that he has contracted the disease until three or four weeks later, and during that time he may have had several opportunities of infecting his wife.

Fortunately, connection with a diseased person does not always involve infection. Careful hygiene can eliminate the organisms deposited on the skin before they penetrate it, especially if contact was neither deep nor prolonged. Also, here, as in everything else, chance plays its part.

A layman has no means of detecting syphilis without the help of a physician, who should be consulted on the least suspicion, so that the disease may be fought as soon as possible after its inception.

In addition to chancre, the primary period of syphilis is characterised by adenopathy or affection of the lymphatic ganglia. This lasts three to five weeks; it then extends to the skin and the mucous membranes, thereby entering on its secondary stage.

The symptoms of secondary syphilis are so complex that a full description of them would require volumes. They may include roseola, erythema maculosa (confined to the body but not touching the face); sometimes erosion does not occur, but it may take very unsightly forms or assume a furunculous appearance. These manifestations may be followed by such general disorders as fever, acute headaches, angina, falling hair, and the formation of ulcers in the anus and the genital parts (vagina). Practically no organ escapes the disease. This period lasts five to seven years.

In the tertiary stage syphilis passes from the external organs to the vital internal organs. The ulcers may spread to the bones; fistulas, suppuration and gummæ may appear, and cachexia set in. One of the best known signs of the final development of syphilis is aneurism of the aorta; needless to say that, when allowed to follow its course, this terrible scourge is fatal.

Happily there are many exceptions to this classical course of the disease. The chancre may heal without further repercussion, and people may live to an advanced age without knowing that they ever had syphilis; others are afflicted with syphilitic blindness in their youth.

*   *   *

There are other disorders which, although not direct consequences of syphilitic infection, are greatly intensified by it and must therefore be mentioned here.

Such are arterio-sclerosis and cardiac affections. In a syphilitic subject these assume a particularly serious form and sometimes lead to premature death. Of exclusively syphilitic origin are tabes dorsalis (locomotor ataxia) and softening of the brain. The former is often followed by blindness and paralysis; the patient walks haltingly and suffers from stabbing pains in the abdomen and the legs; paralysis of the bladder and the intestines is not infrequent, and soon leads to death. But the end may come slowly. Tabes drags on sometimes for as long as twenty years, during which the only outward sign is the ataxic gait. The most unfortunate victims of syphilis are those who remain unaware of their infection for seven years—the average period of development—and are then suddenly afflicted with blindness.

The following are two cases taken from our records:

Mr. R. when twenty years old suffered from a slight eruption, which was cured in four weeks by cauterisation; at twenty-five he married and had two healthy children; at thirty-six he began complaining of headaches; one day, eighteen years after the appearance of the first symptoms, he became paralysed on the right side and lost the use of his speech. He is still alive but will remain a complete invalid until the day of his death, which I foresee in about three years' time.

Baron M. became infected when twenty-two years of age and had mercury treatment. When forty-eight he suddenly became deaf, was taken to a nursing-home and died in eight weeks.

Softening of the brain often takes the form of unusual behaviour in the affected person. A miser becomes a spendthrift, a staid father a rake; symptoms of dementia and megalomania appear, and the patient may declare himself to be God, the Emperor and Devil all in one; from that time, his days are numbered.

The question of syphilitic contagion is one of the highest importance. During the primary and secondary stages, the disease, although latent, is infectious. With the onset of the tertiary period, it is concentrated on the internal organs and is no longer transmissible except by heredity.

With regard to the inheritance of syphilis, it can be transmitted to the children only by the mother; naturally if the father is the infected party the children have every chance of being tainted, but it will be through the medium of the mother. If she is not infected, the children will also be spared. This does not mean, however, that the descendants of a syphilitic father will be wholly unaffected by his disease; the semen of a syphilitic man cannot produce such sound progeny as that of a healthy man. For instance, the interrogation of a patient suffering from organic disorders will often reveal the fact that his father was treated for syphilis. Nevertheless, the children of syphilitics are frequently healthy and long-lived. The victims of inherited syphilis are few, because, fortunately, they usually die in the fœtal stage and are expelled by the mother at an early stage of pregnancy. If treated in time, hereditary syphilis presents characteristics similar to those of tertiary syphilis; the patient may live for a long time without any serious disturbances arising, but he may also die suddenly of cerebral disorder.

A physician is often asked how a layman who wants to avoid venereal contagion can detect whether his partner is diseased. We can only answer that the manifestations of syphilis are so varied, from harmless-looking pimples to the most repulsive erythema, that a true diagnosis is impossible to anyone except a trained practitioner. There are, nevertheless, a few small signs which may serve as danger signals; although not always of syphilitic origin, it is wiser, once they are noticed, to avoid sexual intercourse with the suspected person. In such a case caution must be the guiding principle. The signs are as follows:

I. All ulcerations, wounds, scratches, and abrasions in the region of the genital parts and the anus are suspect.

II. Any pink or brown eruption on the abdomen, the breasts or the hips is suspect, though open pimples, especially on the back or the legs, are generally harmless.

III. Swollen glands on the neck or in the groin are suspect.

IV. Also all abscesses and ulceration of the lips and the head are suspect.

V. Beware of a hoarse voice which is accompanied not by a sore throat but by a headache.

The careful observation of these five points will prove a fair safeguard. Several of my patients have brought me women whom they suspected on those counts, and their diagnoses have proved correct.

*   *   *

Syphilis is essentially curable; this statement cannot be broadcast too widely. Not only is it curable, but the treatment is painless and in no way interferes with personal habits or professional occupations. But for a cure patience is essential. Medicine has at its disposal definite means of checking the disease, but none of them is radical enough to remove the infection at one stroke. A patient who undergoes syphilitic treatment must be prepared to keep it up for a very long time; once he has made up his mind to this his cure is assured. The only exceptions are those cases in which infection took place several years ago, and even then, provided the nervous system is not affected, there is still hope; a complete cure may not be possible, but the terrible consequences of syphilis may, at any rate, be avoided.

Naturally, the success of the treatment depends to a great extent on the time when it is begun. Syphilis which is taken in hand when its only external manifestation is a chancre, and when the Wassermann reaction is still negative, has a much better chance of being cured comparatively rapidly, than if it has been allowed to reach its secondary or tertiary stage.

The three drugs most widely used in the treatment of syphilis are mercury, arsenic (606 and 914), and iodine; more recently silver and bismuth have been added to the list. As regards mercury, it has been the object of much ill-founded superstition and has been accused of causing disorders which are in reality due to syphilis itself; as a matter of fact, mercury is eliminated by the kidneys and not a particle of it remains in the organism. Moreover, patients treated by mercury for other diseases never developed the symptoms imputed to its use, while syphilitics who were not treated by mercury suffered from the very disorders which were imputed to it. The most that injections of mercury may do is to cause diarrhœa and irritation of the mucous membranes; these, however, can be avoided by prudent dosage, care of the mouth, and abstention from tobacco. There are also, on the other hand, cases in which mercury is not tolerated, and in these a different drug has to be used.

Salvarsan, the active element of which is arsenic, was discovered in 1909 and has proved extremely valuable. Administered with due care, the injections present no danger whatsoever and their action is quicker than that of mercury. Salvarsan has not escaped irrational objections, and it is true that tolerance to it is variable, but it has resulted in so few accidents that patients must not be discouraged. Treatment with salvarsan is not more dangerous than a train journey, where catastrophes can also happen. The real danger lies in choosing a clinic where patients are treated one after the other, without provision being made for individual peculiarities.

Iodine is generally used in cases of tertiary syphilis; its effects cannot be compared in rapidity with those of mercury and salvarsan. Intolerance takes the form of various eruptions and catarrhs, which may call for interruption of the treatment.

Silver and bismuth, the former of which is used in combination with salvarsan, have not yet been tried to the same extent as the other drugs. Bismuth has, however, been used, particularly in France, for other treatments, and the results seem to warrant its wider application in the case of syphilis.

As an illustration of the perseverance required of the patient to achieve a complete cure, we quote the following two cases:

Two friends, A. and B., had been infected the same evening by the same woman. Four weeks later, when a chancre appeared, they came to me and treatment was begun in May 1916; they continued to have treatment until July, when a Wassermann test proved negative in both cases. It was, of course, understood that the injections would be continued. A. continued to come to me regularly, and in October he was completely cured. On the strength of the negative Wassermann test, B. discontinued treatment and did not come back until 1917, when he had syphilitic ophthalmia. In spite of prolonged treatment his blood still contains spirochætes.

Until fairly recently, medicine was completely helpless against the most terrible consequence of syphilis: paralysis, which was considered incurable. The methods used in the treatment of syphilis were not powerful enough to avoid this complication, unless it were due to a somewhat different spirochæte. Recently, light has been thrown on the subject; chance observations led to the discovery that an infectious fever tends appreciably to improve a paralytic state. The patient is usually inoculated with malaria, and the high fever thus induced (which is ultimately checked by quinine) soon gives satisfactory results. The process has, however, not been definitely perfected.

* * *

Great progress in the struggle against syphilis was made by the discovery of Wassermann. The specific reaction which bears his name has enabled physicians to connect with syphilis a number of disorders, the origin of which was hitherto unknown and the treatment therefore impossible.

This reaction does not, however, constitute an absolute diagnosis, because only a positive result is conclusive, while a negative one does not give any certainty that spirochætes are not present in the blood. It not infrequently happens that a week after a negative Wassermann test the patient develops indisputable symptoms of the disease, or that patients who had considered themselves cured on the strength of a negative reaction fail to escape the terrible effects of syphilis. On the other hand, a Wassermann test is positive in certain cases of malaria, frambœsia, leprosy, and even scarlet fever, but in those cases the test remains positive for only a few weeks.

With this reservation, it must be stated that three Wassermann tests at intervals of fifteen days establish conclusively a syphilitic infection. To ascertain definitely whether a patient whose specific reaction was negative is cured, it is advisable to perform a lumbar puncture. This enables the physician to carry out an examination of the brain and the spinal cord, and to avoid possible repercussions of the disease on the nervous system. If the least trace of infection is found, one must resort to every possible measure, to protect the patient against the dangers of cerebral affections and those of the spinal cord and the nervous system.

The negative result of Wassermann's reaction at the beginning of syphilis is often due to a localisation of the organisms in some remote part of the system, from which they will later be carried by the blood-stream. It is therefore safer to begin treatment without waiting for definite signs of infection; this will greatly hasten the cure.

However deceptive the Wassermann test may be, its merits are nevertheless enormous. How often headaches, eczemas, lung troubles, and disorders of the liver, or of the urinary and intestinal tracts, not to mention nervous diseases, have been cured thanks to this test. It is a simple thing to have a blood test made at the first suspicion, and it is far preferable to face the enemy than to ignore his presence.

A vital question is that of knowing at which stage of his illness a syphilitic may marry. Obviously, anyone displaying active symptoms is barred from marriage; he may only consider it when discharged by his doctor, and after the Wassermann test has been negative for one or two years. Cases in which, despite all efforts, it has not been possible to render the blood free from the virus, present a delicate problem. Although in the tertiary stage there is no danger of contagion, the next generation must be considered. In this regard it is necessary to distinguish between a man and a woman. A man who has been treated and who shows no symptoms, but whose blood still retains traces of infection, can hardly be forbidden marriage; but a woman in the same condition, if allowed to marry, must give up all idea of having children. In such a case, the artificial interruption of pregnancy is justified.

CHAPTER XXXVI

PREVENTION OF VENEREAL DISEASES

Propagation of venereal disease. Some eloquent figures. Fallacy of trusting domestic remedies and the panaceas of charlatans. Prophylactic measures. Cleanliness the fundamental principle. Injections and washing with soap. Unpopularity of the condom. Prevention of gonorrhœa. Three processes to be recommended. Prevention of syphilis. Some efficacious measures.

To understand how necessary it is for everyone to protect himself against venereal disease, one must realise the frightful spread of the scourge and how easily one can be infected.

As a matter of fact, the general public has no conception of the prevalence of these diseases, because they have always been considered 'shameful' (as though honesty consisted in not contracting anything during sexual intercourse), and those who find themselves infected hide the fact from their family, and it is therefore the exception when one learns of it. Nevertheless, according to reliable statistics, the average man living in a big city, whether he be rich or poor, has been infected at least twice in his life by venereal disease. That is to say, if one man escapes contagion in the course of his life, his neighbour has been infected four times. I may further state from long experience, and in agreement with all the specialists, that practically every woman who has had sexual relations with several men is afflicted with venereal disease.*

According to statistics, in France alone, for example, approximately 140,000 cases are treated every day. It remains to be known how many receive no treatment whatever or are in the hands of charlatans. The following figures on the incidence of the disease in various professions is interesting. Soldiers, approximately 3 per cent.; workmen, 8 per cent.; employees and tradespeople, 16.5 per cent.; students, 25 per cent.; waiters in cafés and restaurants, 26 per cent.

Out of a hundred men and women suffering from venereal diseases, 65 per cent. have gonorrhœa, 18 per cent. soft chancre, and 17 per cent. syphilis. In a big city like Paris 43 per cent. of the men under the age of fifty contract syphilis.

We have already told how common the disease is among women who make a practice of what is euphemistically called 'free love'. Very often men contract the disease from their 'regular mistress'. As German students are fond of putting it, gonorrhœa is often caught from one's *petite amie*, because the precautions one takes with a casual acquaintance are often neglected with a permanent one. Many married women are also infected, most frequently by their own husband. If we are to credit the statement of Professor Baisch, seventy out of a hundred sterile marriages are attributable to an early gonorrhœal infection in the husband, and out of a hundred babies stillborn, forty-five are due to syphilitic ancestry.

It is, of course, among registered prostitutes that the

* *Editor's Note.*—The moral prejudices of the author of this article have here destroyed his scientific objectivity. There are many people who think that a woman who has sexual relations with a number of men *deserves* to catch venereal disease, but every sexologist knows that many highly promiscuous women escape infection, while many quite 'pure' women are infected by their own husbands.—N. H.

highest percentage of venereal disease is found. It is a mistake to think that they are not infected because they are subjected to frequent medical examination. We shall see further on how difficult it is to detect venereal disease in women, even if they submit to a minute examination. It is not our intention to frighten our readers; we restrict ourselves to facts and we emphasise once more that, fortunately, every person so infected is not necessarily permanently contagious, nor does it follow that every connection with a diseased person leads to infection.

Thirteen out of every hundred syphilitics eventually become cripples or die of the disease. It is also a fact that in the Homes for the Blind in France 20 per cent. of the cases have a gonorrhœal origin.

Generally speaking, the propagation of venereal diseases in small villages is less than in large cities. It is, however, significant that after the demobilisation of the army and the return of the soldiers to their homes, this ratio was considerably modified.

There are two other causes of the frequency of these diseases. The first lies in the nature of the malady itself, often so insidious that the afflicted person has no suspicion of it for years, and during that time he may have intercourse with perfectly healthy individuals and transmit the germ to his partners.

The second cause is alcoholism. A large percentage of infections—some statisticians say as much as 65 per cent.—can be traced to inebriety. Experience has shown that alcohol, while deadening the intellectual faculties, increases sensuality to a certain extent. Married men who, when sober, would be incapable of marital infidelity, fall, when drunk, into a prostitute's snares and forget to take the ordinary precautions, thereby contracting venereal disease. * * *

Before describing the rational methods of venereal prophylaxis, we must denounce the harmful practices of laymen and charlatans.

As regards the former, it must be understood that, although it is not necessary to consult a physician for such a slight infection as a cold in the head, which responds to home treatment, there is not a chance of checking a serious infection of the internal organs by such simple means; at best one can only succeed in making some of the symptoms disappear. For instance, in the case of gonorrhœa, there are remedies which stop the discharge; for syphilis, certain powders and salves clear up the eruptions; but these must not be considered as cures. On the contrary, they only drive the disease back into the system by checking its normal course and, what is more important, the precious time needed for its proper treatment is lost.

No less sad is the fate of those who have entrusted their health to quacks. Usually, the latter are people with no knowledge of medicine, who prescribe only specific remedies. They know that the discharge can be stopped by certain injections, but they do not take the trouble to find out whether the discharge is due to gonorrhœa or to catarrh, for the latter can also suppurate freely. Moreover, they are not interested in curing the patient, but solely in stopping the discharge so that they may gain his confidence for a time. Physicians know only too well the victims of these quacks; they come to them after a prolonged treatment because their relief was only temporary. The situation is further complicated because there are no means of combating the disastrous activities of these charlatans. Only the parents of minors can take legal proceedings against them for having given their child injurious treatment without their knowledge.

* * *

Before giving any prophylactic advice, we wish to call the attention of our readers to the fact that, although tested by numerous experiments on both men and animals, the precautions which we recommend cannot be *guaranteed* to give immunity. Such an ideal remedy does not exist. For example, before having sexual relations it is well to smear the penis with 30 per cent. calomel ointment, a sure protection against syphilis. But can one be positive that no small portion of surface remained unsmeared through which the infecting germ might gain entrance? The way in which precautions are carried out is, like everything connected with man, subject to mistakes and imperfections.

Cleanliness is the finest protection against venereal diseases. To wash the genital parts with plenty of soap both before and after the sexual act, and also to urinate immediately after it, are a better guarantee than antiseptic injections. We know that gonorrhœa is caught through transmission of the bacilli from an infected mucous membrane to a healthy one. Therefore the man who wishes to avoid contagion will have to choose between several methods which are open to him. First he should try to sterilise the woman's vagina. But obviously this gives only a relative degree of certainty, because not only the vagina but the urethra may be the source of infection. Even when this has been washed by urinating prior to the sexual act, there still remains the uterus, which may contain the germs, and which, by its contractions at the moment of the orgasm, may expel secretions infected with gonococci. Notwithstanding these reservations, it is always wise to diminish the danger of infection as much as possible by seeing that the partner's genital organs have been disinfected. It is well to advise the woman to douche with permanganate of potash; mercuric and soapy solutions should not be used. Antiseptic suppositories can be used instead of a douche. When all this advice has been followed one has a maximum of guarantee against contagion.

Another method consists in hindering the transmission of the gonococci by the interposition of a protective barrier, such as a condom; this should be of the best make, otherwise it is practically useless. In removing it, great care should be taken not to allow the part that has been in contact with the feminine organs to touch the orifice of the urethra. The condom has the advantage of being a protection against all venereal infections. On the other hand, it is not very popular because it deadens sensation.

Those who do not care to have recourse to condoms, or who do not happen to have one handy, may apply the method which consists in disinfecting the urethra immediately after intercourse. Here too it is imperative to exercise the greatest care. It must also be remembered that there is no pharmaceutical preparation capable of killing the gonococci without irritating the mucous membrane of the urethra. There are nevertheless some which are practically innocuous. The choice of a preparation depends on the taste and tolerance of the individual. We offer several:

I. Inject into the urethra, having widened the orifice with the fingers, one or two drops of a very concentrated antiseptic like a 20 per cent. solution of silver albuminate (protargol). For the purpose, a small syringe or tube can be procured at any chemist's. Hold the liquid in the urethra with the fingers for the space of two minutes; do not urinate during that time.

II. Introduce into the urethra small bougies of cocoa-butter containing some kind of antiseptic. These soon melt; nevertheless they should be retained for five minutes.

III. Injections into the urethra are also recommended. These should be of warm water to which an antiseptic has been added. The nozzle should be adapted to the orifice of the urethra and care be taken not to allow the liquid to enter the bladder.

The other methods are much too complicated for home use and should it become necessary to use them it is best to consult a specialist. Generally speaking, it is well to see a physician as soon as possible after any suspicious sexual connection. This precaution has checked the disease more than once.

In the case of a woman wishing to protect herself from infection, she must be sure that the man has no discharge. The slightest discharge is suspicious and should be a warning. Nevertheless it is well to know that a small transparent drop is harmless, whereas a whitish or yellowish secretion is probably a symptom of disease. What we have said above about detecting the disease applies also in the case of a woman.

Whereas a man, in order to protect himself against a gonococcal infection, has only to concern himself with his penis, the question of prophylaxis for a woman is much more involved owing to the complexity of the female genital organs. The germs of gonorrhœa can, in fact, penetrate the folds of the vagina or the urethra, making it extremely difficult to control. Therefore a woman should also advise her partner to disinfect his urethra before intercourse. Nevertheless, an injection which can destroy the gonococci in the urethra cannot reach the actual seat of chronic gonorrhœa in men, viz., the glands.

Sheaths or condoms are a precautionary measure for women as well as men, because they prevent the possibly infected secretions from reaching the feminine organs, besides avoiding contact between the skin and the mucous membrane. A woman should also thoroughly wash her vagina, and urinate immediately, after coitus. The douche-bag should be held high enough to let the water assist the chemical action of the injection. The most commonly used antiseptic is permanganate of potash. Suppositories introduced into the vagina after coitus also act as antiseptics. They should be retained from two to three hours; other suppositories are introduced before the sexual act and should be retained for an hour afterwards.

Syphilitic prophylaxis aims at preventing the spirochætes from penetrating the skin of a healthy person. Here are the methods employed to that end (it being assumed that the infection results from sexual relations, which it most frequently does):

I. The penis is anointed with calomel ointment, which may be free from grease, according to Meissers' method, or greasy according to Metchnikoff's. The two preparations insure the same excellent result, as has been proved by experiments with monkeys. Naturally, the penis should be cleaned as soon as intercourse is over.

II. It is also possible to prevent the penetration of the spirochætes, as in the case of gonococci, by the use of a condom. If it does not break, it is an excellent preventative against syphilitic infection.

III. One of the best known measures consists in destroying the germs soon after exposure to infection. Although this method is not quite so good as the first two, it has proved practicable in experiments on animals. In this case also the penis is smeared after intercourse with one of the above-mentioned ointments. This operation takes about five minutes, for it is imperative to cover the whole penis and the testes as well. Previous to this the parts should be thoroughly washed with soap. If preferred a disinfectant may be used, although it is much less efficacious. Solutions of permanganate of potash or bichloride of mercury answer the purpose.

For a woman prophylaxis is a much more delicate matter than it is for a man. Granted that condoms are a mutual safeguard, it is dangerous to restrict oneself to their use. As for injections, they only affect the spirochætes deposited on the surface. It is advisable for a woman to smear herself, before intercourse, with calomel ointment, because the entrance to the vagina, with its delicate mucous membrane, is an ideal seat of infection. In this way the grease of the vaseline forms a mechanical obstacle to the bacilli, while the calomel serves as an antiseptic. In recent years, a preparation known as stovarsol has succeeded in gaining public confidence. Stovarsol contains salvarsan, but instead of being injected, it is made up in tablet form to be taken internally. It seems to have a great future in store.

Let us briefly state the principal precautions necessary. Soaping and micturition head the list. The condom offers a considerable safeguard to both man and woman. In addition, we advise:

For the man: *before* sexual intercourse, protecting the penis with the ointments mentioned; *after* intercourse, urination, soaping, urethral injections and another layer of ointment.

For the woman: *before* intercourse, protection of the vulva with calomel ointment and the introduction of an antiseptic suppository into the vagina. *After* intercourse, urination and an antiseptic douche or the use of suppositories.*

---

* *Editor's Note.*—In England it is a criminal offence for any person, other than a legally qualified medical practitioner, to treat venereal disease. This law is an excellent one. It is also an offence for any chemist to sell any preparation as a preventive of venereal disease, though he is quite at liberty to sell the same substance so long as he does not describe it as a preventive of venereal disease. This is obviously stupid.—N. H.

CHAPTER XXXVII

OTHER DISORDERS OF THE SEXUAL ORGANS

Maladies of a sexual nature not acquired through sexual intimacy.
Difficulty of distinguishing them from venereal symptoms. Urethral
catarrh. Causes and treatment. Verruca acuminata or 'fig-wart'.
Balanitis. Cause and treatment. Phimosis and paraphimosis. The
advantages of circumcision. Crabs.

THE maladies which we are about to describe also seem to
have a sexual character, with, however, this difference:
that, unlike the diseases which we studied in the previous
chapters, they are not acquired through sexual intimacy.
The origin of these other troubles varies, but they all have
one element in common, they leave no after-effects. A
physician must nevertheless be consulted at their very first
appearance, for it is quite impossible for a layman to
differentiate them from actual venereal symptoms.

First comes urethral catarrh, a form of blenorrhœa
which is usually diagnosed as such and which is non-
infectious. We have already seen that it has nothing to
do with gonorrhœa. It is usually nervous people who
are affected by it. There appears at the meatus (mouth of
the urethra) a discharge, often accompanied by itching.
As a rule, it is not a profuse discharge, but rather a thick
drop that forms when the penis is squeezed; in colour it is
usually light grey, rarely yellow. It is especially noticeable
in the morning, when long or short filaments are found

in the urine owing to accumulation in the urethra during the night. Many people are alarmed, quite unnecessarily, by those filaments; if the doctor has ascertained that it is not a gonorrhœal symptom, but merely a urethral discharge, there is no cause for anxiety. It is not usually contagious, nor can it become serious.

The cause of this catarrh can be a chill or over-exertion during sexual intercourse, or the use of excessively strong disinfectants or soaps. It can also be due to uncleanliness, or to the use of a rubber sheath which irritates the mucous membrane.

The treatment is not so simple as one might expect for such a simple disorder. There are cases of urethral catarrh which will not respond to treatment, but disappear spontaneously, sometimes to recur just as unexpectedly. The patient should be very particular in avoiding all pressure on the urethra at any time, even as a means of testing the presence of matter; this practice is the most frequent cause of a chronic infection and as such must be strictly controlled, even though it involves restraining the natural tendency of an already nervous patient.

The *verruca acuminata*, or ' fig-wart ', when collected in a close group of small warts, resembles a cauliflower head. It is generally quite painless, but if not properly treated may become moist and suppurate. In men, these warts form under the foreskin; in women, on the vulva. They may assume such a size that they conceal the sexual organs.

They are mostly due to an irritation of the parts when moist. If a woman, for instance, who is suffering from acute leucorrhœa neglects to keep herself clean and dry, the verruca grows alarmingly. It is often a sign of gross negligence and, since it thrives in moisture, it appears in badly tended cases of gonorrhœa. Although it may have no immediate connection with the latter disease, it constitutes a warning to be more careful.

These warts practically never disappear of their own accord. If there are only a few, cauterisation or drying powders applied by a physician will cure them; if they are more spread or developed, they should be removed by electricity. But the chief cure consists in seeing that the parts are kept dry, otherwise there will be a relapse.

Balanitis is not due to gonorrhœa. It manifests itself by a copious purulent secretion, easily identified by the smallness of the prepuce through which it flows from the urethra or that region. Whereas in gonorrhœa the urethra is attacked, in balanitis the purulent inflammation is located in the glans and the foreskin. It affects men with a narrow prepuce, owing to the difficulty in keeping clean. Strong perspiration in summer often causes it. The process of infection is as follows: the substances secreted under the prepuce decompose (specific odour); the product of this decomposition irritates the sensitive skin of the glans and causes still more copious secretion, which, in its turn, decomposes. The result of this vicious circle is acute inflammation, soreness of the glans, and suppuration.

The treatment is extremely simple: strict cleanliness and care in keeping the parts dry. The penis must be repeatedly washed during the day, preferably with a solution of permanganate of potash; then, a fine layer of antiseptic cotton-wool should be worn under the prepuce. so as to avoid direct contact between the foreskin and the glans. Dusting with boracic powder is also recommended. Some men are particularly susceptible to this affection; after any exertion or during the hot season, a white secretion immediately appears. In addition to cleanliness, antiseptic cotton wool worn constantly as indicated above is a necessity for such individuals. It should be remembered that sores offer a ready entry into the system for more virulent bacilli; neglect therefore entails a serious risk and may even lead to infection with syphilis.

Other unpleasant consequences of a narrow prepuce are *phimosis* and *paraphimosis*. In the former the opening of the foreskin is too narrow, sometimes so much that not only does it refuse to retract, but becomes so tight that micturition is hampered. This naturally renders the suitable treatment of gonorrhœa and the like almost impossible. In this case, circumcision is indicated, and is performed either by clipping the foreskin or by removing it altogether.

In paraphimosis, the foreskin is not so abnormally narrow, and retraction is possible, but it may suddenly refuse to come back into place; it locks itself at the base of the glans and resists all attempts to bring it back to cover the latter. This is by no means an easy case; the tip of the penis, being, so to say, constricted, swells and thereby makes matters worse. Immediate medical intervention is necessary in order to avoid stoppage of the blood supply to the glans and its ensuing gangrene. The trouble may be cured without operation under suitable medical supervision.

These various complications resulting from a quite superfluous foreskin explain why a wise legislator instituted the prophylactic practice of circumcising children. A physician can only endorse this measure because, apart from avoiding the troubles just mentioned, a glans without foreskin offers more resistance to venereal infection.

Finally, one more harmless sexual trouble—vermin. This takes the form of *crab-lice* which fasten on the genital parts. These small parasites are generally acquired through unclean sexual intercourse or from suspicious bedding or unhygienic toilet-seats. Only one or two of them are usually transferred, and are hardly noticed; but they lay their eggs on the pubic hairs or those of the perineum and fourteen days later the first brood hatches and itching becomes acute; a fortnight later a new brood is born and itching becomes unbearable. It is particularly acute at night and sores may be caused by scratching.

The most careful washing does not help much, as it merely destroys the lice but not the eggs, to exterminate which chemicals must be resorted to. The best known is the mercurial salve commonly called 'blue ointment'. Still better is conscientious washing with a 1 per cent. solution of bichloride of mercury, which radically destroys the eggs in two or three days. As a measure of precaution, the process may be repeated a fortnight later, when one can rest assured that extermination is complete.

CHAPTER XXXVIII

AT THE GYNÆCOLOGIST'S

The repercussions of female complaints. Leucorrhœa and suspicious discharges. Displacement and dropping of the organs. Cancer of the internal genital organs. How to prevent cancer. The ' dangerous age '. Inflammation of the ovaries and the fallopian tubes. Cysts and fibroids. Ovarian deficiency. Painful periods. Constipation in the woman and its causes. The treatment of varicose veins. The effect of gymnastics on the genital organs. Advice on hygiene.

In the previous chapter we studied maladies which, although they are not acquired as a result of sexual intercourse and do not always affect the genital organs, must be classed with disorders of the genital apparatus. We shall now examine diseases of the feminine genital organs which are not the result of contagion, but which have an enormous effect on the other organs and on the general health of the woman.

If a woman suffers from heart disease, gall-stones or any other chronic disease, she may nevertheless feel well, look well, and even enjoy life, provided she is not suffering from an attack involving pain. It is altogether different with a woman who has pelvic trouble; no other disorder can so severely affect the spirits of the patient, destroy her joy in life, and make her look prematurely old and worn. I have known tubercular patients, women, who were taken to be ten years younger than they were; but when I see coming into my consulting-room a patient who is obviously prematurely aged, I know what is the matter with her: her sexual apparatus is out of order. Serious psychoses are frequently due to diseased ovaries—the term hysteria is derived from a Greek word which means uterus—and such an illness needs not only advice and sympathy, but the help of a gynæcologist. The female organs have the multiple function of regulating menstruation, assuring procreation, stimulating vitality, and increasing the joy of living and the desire to live. Women from whom the ovaries have been removed become obese and indolent; nothing pleases them, they vegetate and are constantly occupied with their ailments; they lack energy, to say nothing of sexual desire. In brief, they are old and tired before their time.

The other disorders of the genital organs are not less formidable. They cause weakness, depression, discontent, which, while not exactly painful, make a woman nervous and exhausted by their persistency; headaches, backache and oppression, fainting attacks, shortness of breath and general fatigue are other symptoms.

In what follows we shall describe the most frequent female diseases and indicate how they may be prevented.

Out of ten women who consult a gynæcologist, nine complain of leucorrhœa, and the tenth has not noticed it. This symptom actually reveals or conceals the most harmless urethral catarrh as well as the worst kind of inflammation; it is often difficult for the most experienced specialist to diagnose the trouble at the first examination.

Most women have a certain amount of discharge which is nothing more than a kind of perspiration or secretion which keeps the parts moistened and supple; it is the counterpart of saliva and tears; if this moisture becomes more copious, it takes the form of a yellowish discharge, and one is then face to face with a case of leucorrhœa. It is frequently not easy to calm the patients and explain to them what is wrong. They have been frightened through reading certain announcements in the press or have listened too seriously to the gossip of their friends. They fear the worst, and the most logical explanations are futile to allay their anxiety. If their physician refuses to give them anything but sympathy and reassurance, they rush off to another one who has a better idea of business than of professional ethics.

In other cases the discharge is due to the general state of health, anæmia or weakness, and here the layman is liable to mistake the cause for the effect; in fact, the albuminous content of leucorrhœa is far too small to cause weakness; anæmic girls, city dwellers, practically always suffer from some such discharge; if the general system is toned up, the trouble automatically disappears without the aid of injections or any other remedies.

Fair women are more susceptible to this than are dark ones, while red-haired women are still more susceptible— though the reasons for this are not known.

Among discharges which are not innocuous, that due to gonorrhœa must be mentioned; this has already been studied in a previous chapter, and here we shall only insist once more that no woman, even with the help of a whole technical library, is capable of diagnosing the nature of her discharge; this has to be left to a physician, who, even though a specialist, is frequently unable to diagnose the origin of a discharge of long standing.

Thanks to the common use of the douche, uncleanliness nowadays is rarely the cause of leucorrhœa*; the reverse is more common, the irritation being the result of excessive douching with strong disinfectants. One day a woman in a

* *Editor's Note.*—Unfortunately this is not true in Anglo-Saxon countries, where many women—even those who are otherwise very cleanly in their habits—neglect the hygiene of the sexual organs to a shocking extent. So, too, do many Anglo-Saxon men.—N. H.

state of acute anxiety came to consult me; a few days after intercourse, she had observed a yellow discharge and she had resorted to drastic douching with ten tablets of bichloride of mercury to a quart of water (one tablet being the correct dose); following a negative examination, this clearly explained the matter. Extreme sensitiveness to rubber can explain the irritation which sometimes occurs after the man has used a sheath; one woman invariably suffered from leucorrhœa after intercourse if a condom were used, but not if intimacy took place without it.

Any displacement of the uterus, exhaustion, or depression, may result in leucorrhœa. The position of the uterus is definitely determined in the abdominal cavity, and it is kept in place, and also at the same time protected, by the ligaments which anchor it to the pelvis; the relaxation of these ligaments by some cause, hereditary or other, may give rise to the displacement of even a relatively large uterus; as a result, the blood-vessels which supply the uterus are pulled out of place and disturbances in the genital organs follow.

If the discharge contains blood it is a more serious symptom; in a young woman, it may be due to inflammation or to an early miscarriage; in an older one, to a growth.

Let us examine the first case. If the dislodged ovum is completely expelled, the discharge stops; but if some of the uterine contents remain, the uterus cannot contract sufficiently and the bleeding continues. This is the normal development: menstruation does not appear, the woman is pregnant; some days later, that is after the date on which menstruation was due, a copious bleeding begins, this is the miscarriage; it is accompanied by slight labour pains even after the flow has subsided if the uterine contents have not been wholly expelled.

[531]

The causes of miscarriage are many and varied. It may be the result of a fall or of a clumsy movement, which dislodges the ovum from its niche in the wall of the uterus; the latter then expels the released ovum with the accompanying hæmorrhage. As a result, the ovum is destroyed—this is the miscarriage—and is expelled through the vagina. If pregnancy is not far advanced, a miscarriage may occur and pass unnoticed with the bleeding. Even without external causes a miscarriage may occur. In some families there is a tendency for it to occur. With women of weaker constitution, miscarriage is, of course, more common. One patient of mine had twelve miscarriages, each time during the fifth month. There was no apparent cause for it. Later, when her uterus was removed for some other reason, the examination revealed that the uterus contained a growth. The ovum developed, but so soon as it touched this growth a miscarriage immediately occurred.

If, during pregnancy, a protracted bleeding occurs, abortion must not be delayed. It is most frequently for this reason that a surgeon decides to curette. There is no need to fear this operation. In the hands of a skilled and experienced surgeon, it is absolutely painless and requires no more than ten minutes time. In a few days there is complete recovery. In this case, the doctor is entitled to perform this operation, for he merely completes an interrupted pregnancy. The interruption of pregnancy on other than health grounds is forbidden in this country.

Since one knows that cancer is one of those diseases which is never cured without surgical treatment, and that its neglect is fatal, one can understand how urgent and necessary a prompt physical examination can be. It is common knowledge nowadays that, when diagnosed early, cancer is curable. The danger of placing trust in incompetent quacks cannot be over-emphasised. The time that is wasted in consultation with such charlatans may destroy all hope of success in future treatment with a specialist.

It is important before all else to stress the fact that, at first, cancer looks like a local affection. It must be examined immediately and treated by a physician of repute. We are still uncertain as to the cause of this scourge, whether it is due to the mode of living or to bacteria, the latter theory being the more probable. But one point to be noted is that cancer may appear wherever there has been repeated and continual irritation of the skin or mucous membrane. Cancer of the lip in the case of smokers and cancer of the mouth from decayed, sharp teeth are both well-known phenomena. Cancer of the external sexual organs is relatively rare. Some of the sufferers have stated that they had suffered for a long time from a discharge, and that the sore, in spite of douching and powdering, continued to develop. If it is a case of cancer, the physician quickly recognises the malignant nature of the growths. The first symptom of disease of the uterus is irregularity of the periods. Naturally, not all such symptoms point to cancer. Nevertheless, no time should be wasted in consulting a doctor.

To recognise cancer of the breast is not at all difficult for an expert, especially if the more usual symptoms are present, i.e. that of a hard tumour situated on the nipple, either visible or perceptible to the touch. In this case an operation is essential. If the growth is in another part of the breast, it is permissible to await developments, although the patient should consult a doctor. As regards treatment, surgical operation or X-ray give the best results. Only when an operation is impossible is treatment with radium or X-rays resorted to. Recently, the results of operations have been very encouraging. The majority of patients operated on, in the early stages, for cancer recover.

Finally, a few words about prevention: the chief point to observe is the avoidance of all friction or irritation of the skin or mucous membranes. There should be a special hygiene for the genital organs. By special hygiene, we mean washing the external genital region every day and douching frequently with salt solution or with soapy water. It is often stated that constant douching irritates the mucous membrane; that is scarcely true, for there are women who are accustomed to douche daily and who have no trouble in that respect. On the contrary, prostitutes who douche themselves several times every day never suffer from irritation of the genital organs due to the practice. Two points, however, should be stressed with regard to douching; first, the solution should not be too strong nor the pressure of the fluid too great. Secondly, one should also douche during the menstrual period because it is during that time that the vagina is most susceptible to infection.

These means of prevention, which were advocated principally by Professor Albert of Dresden, have contributed largely to diminishing the incidence of disease of the genital organs. Nevertheless, many thousands of women contract cancer in this country every year, of which only a small proportion are cured. Unfortunately, the majority of cases arrive too late for treatment. Professor Jaschke, in Giessen, has shown that only one-fifth of all cancer cases come for treatment during the first few weeks after symptoms occur; a second fifth come after two or three months, and a third fifth after six months. It is difficult to give statistics of the remaining two-fifths.

So long as the cause of cancer remains unknown, women must be doubly careful. Rather listen three times to the doctor saying 'It is nothing', than once to the reproach: 'Why did you not come sooner?'

One last word concerning the hygiene of menstruation.

This subject has been the butt of countless superstitions. The cause of menstruation we have already described. During the period frequent washing daily with tepid water is not only harmless but advisable. A quiet régime and abstention from all unnecessary exertion are also recommended. The unæsthetic aspect apart, intercourse during the period is not dangerous, although many physicians condemn it. Some women have an especially strong craving for intercourse at this time. Women who suffer from painful or excessive menstruation should remain in bed for a day, or even longer, according to their suffering. If very intense, a doctor can prescribe an appropriate remedy.

Many young wives complain shortly after their marriage of indisposition. This, for the most part, is psychogenic in origin and can be traced in the majority of cases to two factors: the way in which the man initiates the woman on the wedding night, and his efforts to persuade her to renounce her desire for children. Although the woman may appear to conform to his wish, the unquenchable longing nevertheless remains. In such a case the woman will develop phantasies as compensation for her repressed instinct.

The less notice a woman takes of her period—and that requires a good deal of self-control—and the less the man is made aware of it, the better for both of them. A woman can so cleverly conceal the exigencies of this time that the man remains unconscious of it. She should avoid giving the impression of having had a sleepless night, and should take care to keep the bed-linen perfectly clean. This is possible if she places a sufficiently large piece of soft material on the bed before she retires.

If the woman takes care of her general health, especially during the menstrual period, she will not run the risk of offending her husband with body odours, etc. The personal odour of both partners should be mutually agreeable. It often happens, however, that a man and a woman who are strongly attracted are nevertheless disgusted by the odour which they notice the first time intimacy takes place. Perfectly clean and hygienic people, men as well as women, have their own personal body odour, which emanates principally from the sexual organs, and the sweat glands, the mouth and the hair.

In order to guard against any unpleasant odour, let us suggest these precautions:

The odour of the body constantly varies. A woman, for example, may normally have a very pleasant odour, but, owing to exhaustion or some slight illness, she may lose it and acquire an unpleasant one. It is, of course, obvious that dirty linen is a frequent cause of disgust, and that special care should be taken with regard to stockings. We need not repeat here the dangers which carelessness in such matters can bring about.

A good influence is exerted on the abdominal organs by daily physical exercises. These are of great assistance to general health, provided they are performed sensibly, and not exaggerated to the point of exhaustion or over-exertion. The exercises should be strenuous but not fatiguing.

Special mention must now be made of certain disorders, the importance of which has only recently been fully recognised. We refer to disturbances of the internal secretions. The ovaries may present a perfectly normal appearance yet fail to function in the way required by the body. The symptoms of defective ovarian function are as follows:

1. The periods become gradually less and, in certain cases, cease altogether.

2. The woman, in spite of a normal diet, becomes much more corpulent.

3. Sexual desire grows weak and sometimes the woman becomes frigid.

These symptoms are not necessarily typical of every case. Sometimes frigidity is the only characteristic, sometimes corpulence. But in every case the menopause is premature.

Women suffer in this way for years from the most distressing complaints and depression. Observing such cases, from day to day, one is forced to admit that this disorder seems to be on the increase. Whether this is the result of degeneration is difficult to say, since the primary cause is still unknown.

The treatment of such cases was until recently impossible, but to-day, thanks to the experiments of Steinach, Zondek and Aschheim, a remedy has been found which is capable of compensating for the secretory deficiency. Obviously, this does not mean that we have a preparation with which success is absolutely certain. But in most cases a woman who has been under medical observation for some time, and has been treated with this preparation, experiences decided relief.

And now let us consider the ovaries. The disorders to which they are most susceptible have many causes. Sometimes they are due to the fact that the ovaries lie near the appendix, and are thus subject to any inflammatory process in that organ. Secondly, the ovaries, by means of the fallopian tubes, the uterus and the vagina, are in direct contact with the external world and consequently exposed to infection. Thirdly, forming part of the female sexual apparatus, they are far more heavily taxed than the sexual organs in man. Nevertheless, one of the most frequent causes of inflammation of the ovaries is gonorrhœa. In many cases the gonococci remain in the vagina at the mouth of the uterus, but unfortunately, only too often, they make their way from the vagina to the uterus and through the fallopian tubes to the ovaries, where they set up inflammation.

Whatever the causes of inflammation of the ovaries, the disorder gives rise to many weeks of suffering and may even lead to peritonitis. At other times the inflammation slowly abates, in which case the women complain of painful and irregular periods, discharges, etc. Such women are characterised by premature old age and extreme lassitude.

If taken in time, the illness is soon cured. It is not enough, however, merely to douche or use suppositories. The skill of a doctor is required to combat it effectually.

Ovarian cysts are relatively rare. The female genital organs are much more subject to such tumours, however, than are those of the male. On the other hand, tumours of the stomach and the intestines are more common among men. Uterine fibroids are not dangerous and require a comparatively simple operation.

Other female complaints have their sources in the bladder. Here there is less pain, but the frequent need to urinate is most disturbing. If there is no gonorrhœal infection, these disturbances are generally due to a chill, and can be controlled with suitable treatment in a few days.

The physician often hears during his consultation hours that disorders in the genital region are the result of a chill. To be exact, one must first understand just what is meant by 'chill'.

We know that a sudden drop in the temperature, which causes a contraction first of the small blood-vessels of the skin and then of the mucous membrane, plays havoc with sensitive organs.

Besides these chills, which appear in the form of catarrh and inflammations, there is another group of disorders which can trace their origin to a sudden change of temperature. How this comes about is not yet clear, although we know that rheumatism and neuralgia are two of the consequences.

But the decisive fact in every chill is the individual reaction, and this differs in different people. It is possible systematically to train our bodies, 'hardening' or 'strengthening' them, as it is called, to resist the bad effects of sudden changes of temperature. Participation in sports, rub-downs, cold baths, all help to diminish the risk of catching a chill.

After this brief examination of the word chill, what kind of chills are we to expect in the genital region? The internal organs like the stomach are well protected. The bladder, however, is susceptible to chill, although the phenomenon manifests itself only when bacilli already exist in the membrane of the bladder.

Is it possible for the internal sexual organs of a woman to be so affected by a chill that they develop some disorder? Yes, indirectly. A sudden increase of blood in the blood-vessels supplying the sexual organs may be fraught with serious consequences, affecting the ovaries, or interfering with menstruation. These results are not serious, but they may be if the chill is met not with full vigour but with exhaustion and fatigue.

It is different with women who suffer from chronic inflammatory disorders, whether of the uterus, the ovaries or the duct. Here a chill, whether direct or indirect, may cause a relapse.

The reason why women are more subject to constipation than men is not known. Some attribute it to the difference in the construction of the abdominal organs; others (and I am inclined to side with them) maintain that it is due to carelessness. Neglect to defecate regularly gives rise in a few weeks to constipation, and the longer one allows it to continue, the worse it becomes. Women then turn to strong purgatives, which irritate the intestine and finally exhaust it.

The danger arising from such irregularity is far greater than is generally believed; for the excrement which fills the rectum takes up too much space in the body and interferes with the movements of the intestine.

To combat constipation, the first essential is regularity. The intestine, which in man is adapted to evacuation at least once in every twenty-four hours, must be re-educated. Patients must train themselves to go to the lavatory at the same hour every day.

It is not necessary to lay particular stress on the diet. Whether one eats meat or farinaceous foods has nothing to do with bowel-movement. On the other hand, it is good to eat a great deal of fruit, especially in the evening, and, if possible, to drink milk.

But in addition to these local measures, more general treatment ought to be undertaken. We ought to escape more frequently from our unnatural mode of living and, through a more intimate contact with nature, find and appreciate the bounties of good health. It is not necessary to go to such extremes as nature-healing, sun-, water- and light-cults, but to balance the enforced condition of civilisation, it is necessary to leave the streets behind and to wander in the woods.

I have mentioned among the consequences of constipation varicose veins; these are due to enlargement and twisting of the vein through interference with the circulation between the abdomen and the heart. The blood accumulates at certain spots in the legs, and the veins, enlarged and twisted, form knots under the skin. Other factors conducing to the formation of varicose veins are a sedentary mode of life, tight garters, etc.

The inconvenience caused by varicose veins is not only of an æsthetic order; this trouble causes itching and an extraordinary feeling of fatigue in the legs. In the long run, the skin of the legs, rendered less resistant through defective circulation, becomes more susceptible to inflammation and eruptions, which often degenerate into abscesses and varicose ulcers, the latter one of the greatest problems which medicine has had to solve. True, one can prescribe complete rest in bed for several months in order to give time an opportunity to effect a cure, but how many women can observe this regime long enough? Even after the ulcers are healed a relapse is always to be feared. In short, varicose veins have an extremely depressing influence, causing those who suffer from them to lose their joy of living and their capacity for work. Here again, as always, prevention is better than cure.

The very cause of varicose veins indicates their treatment; regular movement of the bowels, systematic exercise, and eventually massage of the affected limb to stimulate the circulation and tone up the tissues. Above all, no garters.

But once the varicose vein is there it is necessary to bandage the affected leg with an elastic band about five yards long. The leg is dressed like this in the morning while the patient is still in bed, so that it is thoroughly rested and has not begun to swell. Rubber stockings, although effective, are not recommended because of the perspiration which they induce.

Varicose veins in the anus are known as hæmorrhoids, and are due to enlargement of the veins in the recto-anal region. A distinction is made between external and internal hæmorrhoids, whether they are situated in the anus or in the mucous membrane of the rectum. A sedentary life and horse-riding stimulate the formation of hæmorrhoids;

[541]

some people whose veins are especially weak are particularly susceptible to this disorder.

The effects are local and general. Locally there is pressure, itching, soreness, pain and bleeding. If the nodules are very large they may burst and thereby bring relief, but infection of the open wound thus caused may result in the formation of abscesses. In some cases the patient is unable to think of anything but his trouble, and becomes melancholy.

The serious effects produced by hæmorrhoids render it necessary to have medical attention. The physician, having first diagnosed the cause of the trouble, will devote himself to regulating the intestinal functions and relieving the liver by suitable remedies; he will also try to purify the blood and regulate the circulation. The local treatment, which in former times required a fairly severe operation, has been much simplified. A local anæsthetic is given, after which a concentrated solution of some drug is injected which makes the veins contract. This can be done in the doctor's consulting room without much inconvenience to either party, and can hardly be called an operation.

*   *   *

Once a year everybody who can afford it ought to undergo a 'regenerating cure', the chief factor of which is fruit. This cure is done in two stages: a week of 'dry cure' to combat illness, and two weeks' 'wet cure' to eliminate the possible remaining toxins.

The dry cure consists of the following diet: in the morning, a stale roll or rye bread with marmalade, according to taste. For lunch, rice, porridge, or other cereal, a plate of vegetables and stewed fruit. For dinner, again a stale roll of rye bread, and four ounces of Gruyère cheese. Every other day a quart of fresh milk.

After a week of this dieting, one resumes his normal diet, adding to it before each meal a pint of grape juice, or fresh apple juice (non-fermented), slightly iced; one can also take the juice of six lemons, sugared, with or without water.

It is essential also to take the rest which modern life has reduced to a minimum. As night follows day, rest must follow every expenditure of energy. Eight hours' sleep is indispensable; feather beds should be avoided; during spring, summer and autumn, it is essential to sleep with open windows because the whole system requires fresh air.

When possible, people should leave the city for a few weeks every year, but they should avoid fashionable resorts, which are often, and wrongly, recommended to nervous people on the ground that they offer distractions. A city dweller on his summer holiday should seek quietness, and this he will find only in small places.

Patients often say that they cannot endure loneliness; just like morphomaniacs or dipsomaniacs, city people claim that they cannot live without their poison. That is nonsense. They are the very people who need complete rest; and if for the first few days they find it a little lonely, they will soon become accustomed to their solitude.

On the other hand, an agriculturist or a landowner who spends all the year in the country needs to take his holiday at a popular resort, so that he may have a period of stimulation.

We must not forget, either, that the care of the skin plays an important part in the treatment of all disorders. Baths have been and still are about the best remedy, and if one can bathe every day in the sea, it constitutes an ideal cure. Failing this, cold showers or friction with a sponge or a rough glove will successfully replace the invigorating action of the sea.

People with a weak constitution should have a warm shower every day. Anyone who has exposed his body every day to a strong force of water, followed by an energetic rub-down, feels himself regenerated and renders his system immune to infections and illness.

INDEX

Embryos, 259
Emission, 83, 87, 100, 104, 112, 113, 114,
  122, 140, 147, 149, 185, 199, 223, 320, 339,
  413
Emission, involuntary, 91, 92, 150, 151,
  208, 209, 302, 493
Emission, nocturnal, 151
Emissions, 152
Endocrine, 398
Endocrine balance, 388
Endocrine glands, 301, 327
Endocrine secretions, 399
Endocrines, 392
Enema, 260
Enemas, 265, 346
Engelmann, 57
England, 280, 316, 375, 397, 455
England, Elizabethan, 376
Enlightenment, 336
Environment, 341, 451
d'Eon, Chevalier, 451
Eonism, 451
Epididymes, 329
Epididymis, 13, 16, 303
Epididymitis, 495, 499
Epilepsy, 99, 110, 255, 307, 315
'Equus eroticus,' 432
Erection, 78, 83, 94, 103, 104, 113, 114, 147,
  149, 150, 178, 186, 224, 301, 319, 320, 321,
  322, 324, 325, 326, 328, 373, 380, 389, 390,
  399, 414, 487
Erection, angle of, 222
Erection, centre of, 148
Erections, 152, 383
Erectile nerves, 321
Erectile tissue, 103
Erectile tissues, 380
Ergot, 136, 278
Eros, 7, 362, 370
Erotic action, 176
Erotic activities, 346
Erotic atmosphere, 323, 371
Erotic biting, 188
Erotic books, 206
Erotic capacity, 314
Erotic dreams, 385
Erotic effect, 376
Erotic effects, 381
Erotic element, 472
Erotic elements, 474
Erotic enjoyment, 412, 421
Erotic excitement, 459, 466, 467
Erotic imagination, 375
Erotic impressions, 173, 174
Erotic influence, 175, 362, 476
Erotic inspiration, 368
Erotic mania, 487
Erotic manifestation, 340
Erotic needs, 340
Erotic orgies, 489

Erotic phantasies, 385
Erotic power, 176
Erotic practices, 432
Erotic purpose, 179
Erotic recipes, 367
Erotic rôle, 368
Erotic scenes, 473
Erotic sensations, 104, 472
Erotic stimulants, 467
Erotic superstitions, 376
Erotic symbolism, 467, 470
Erotic tendency, 468
Erotic thought, 488
Erotic value, 217, 369, 467
Erotic vanity, 419
Erythema, 508
Erythema maculosa, 506
Eskimos, 162
Esther, 374
Ether, 385
Ethyl-chloride, 385
Eugenics, 287
Europe, 586, 588
Europe, Central and Southern, 382, 385
European capitals, 478
European countries, 275
Evans, 365
Evans, Dr., 179
'The Evolution of Sexuality and of Inter-
  sexual States,' 449
Excitant, 426
Excitants, 175, 379
Exhibitionism, 411, 412, 416, 417, 418, 438
Exhibitionism, phallic, 413
Exhibitionist, 407, 413, 415, 419, 420
Exhibitionist, psychology of the, 414
Exhibitionists, 411, 412, 413, 414, 416, 418,
  419, 421
Exhibitionistic tendencies, 419
Exocrines, 392
Exorcisms, 360
Eyes, 187, 230, 231, 469, 471, 502

F

Faculty of Leipzig, 363
Fallopian fringes, 284
Fallopian tube, 132
Fallopian tubes, 229, 234, 283, 284, 298,
  299, 304, 308, 501, 537, 538
Faradisation, 380
Fear, 135, 210, 213, 214, 215, 216, 226, 235,
  246, 267, 324, 325, 326, 341, 347, 348,
  350, 415, 419
Fear of action, 419
Fear of being hurt, 225
Fear of castration, 419
Fear of contagion, 153, 154, 325
Fear of death, 155
Fear of disease, 347, 349

Genital system, 134, 233, 320, 500
Genital tract, 313
Genital zone, 26
Genitals, 321, 496
Genito urinary organs, 499
Genito urinary system, 383
Germ, 293, 504, 518
Germ, female, 238
Germ, male, 238
Germany, 136, 371, 376, 435
Germ-cells, 296, 380, 485
Germinal cells, 163
Germinal 28th, 255
Germs, 299, 499, 500, 518, 521
Germs, female, 240
Germs, male, 240
Germs, live, 503
Gerontophilia, 459, 462, 463
Gerontophilia, homosexual, 463
Gestation, 232, 233, 234, 246, 257
Gland, 392, 397
Gland, endocrine and exocrine, 393
Gland, grafted, 397
Gland, hypertrophied, 390
Gland, implanted, 398
Gland, salivary, 392
Gland, sex, 386
Gland, sexual, 386
Glands, 113, 132, 149, 150, 199, 391, 392, 398, 509, 520
Glands, ductless, 451
Glands, endocrine, 301, 327
Glands, endocrine and exocrine, 397
Glands of external secretion, 392
Glands of internal secretion, 111, 122, 123, 248, 392
Glands, gastric, 391
Glands, genital, 123, 138, 146, 198, 291, 297, 314, 315, 386, 486
Glands, interstitial, 122, 398
Glands, lachrymose, 392
Glands, lymphatic, 392
Glands, mammary, 234, 391
Glands, monkeys, 394
Glands, pancreatic, 391
Glands, puberty, 122, 398, 399
Glands, salivary, 391
Glands, sex, 122
Glands, sweat, 269, 391, 392, 536
Glands, vestibular, 179, 199
Glandular bodies, 396
Glandular cells, 392
Glandular disturbances, 148
Glandular extracts, 390
Glandular functioning, 251
Glandular organs, 391
Glandular secretions, 186, 220, 298
Glandular system, 254, 392
Glans, 14, 103, 189, 221, 224, 378, 515, 526
Godard, 46

Godemiché, 86, 87, 321
Goitre, 307
Gold mine, 328
Goncourt, Edmond de, 56
Gonococci, 495, 498, 499, 501, 502, 503, 518, 519, 520, 521, 537
Gonococcus, 495, 496
Gonorrhœa, 59, 298, 325, 493, 494, 495, 496, 497, 498, 499, 500, 501, 502, 503, 505, 515, 517, 518, 520, 523, 524, 525, 526, 530, 537
Gonorrhœal infection, 496, 538
Gonorrhœal inflammation, 329
Gonorrhœal peritonitis, 501
Gonorrhœal rheumatism, 499
Gonorrhœal symptom, 524
Gonorrhœal symptoms, 498
Goodchild, Dr., 54
Gourmont, Remy de, 165, 405
Graafian follicle, 19, 136, 284
Graafian follicles, 296
Graft, 395, 396, 401
Grafting, 299, 300, 390, 394, 400
Grand Guignol, 427
Grassel, Dr., 35
Gratz, 284
Great Britain, 240, 427
Greco-Roman times, 427
Greece, 147, 439
Greece, Ancient, 340
Greece, idea of love in ancient, 7
Greek philosopher, 163
Greeks, 97, 98, 143, 373
Group marriage, 5
Gualino, 91
Guesquel, 377, 378
'Guignolet,' 361
Guillotine, 111
Guilt, sense of, 104, 105
Guilt-feelings, 196
Gurnemanz, 371

H

Haberlandt, 317
Hæmorrhage, 115, 129, 220, 222, 258, 262, 266, 274, 426
Hæmorrhages, 204
Hæmorrhoids, 541, 542
Hagen, 374
Hahn, Dr. Desider, 73
Hair, 121, 138, 146, 173, 180, 187, 194, 217, 231, 374, 430, 467, 469, 470, 471, 472, 506, 536
Hair fetichism, 469, 470
Hair fetichist, 470
Hair fetichists, 470
Haire, Norman, 26, 95, 103, 104, 107, 111, 112, 118, 133, 208, 209, 226, 231, 240, 244, 246, 263, 284, 289, 293, 304, 319, 328, 346,

["

Sellheim, 288
Selwyn, George, 587
Semen, 15, 16, 17, 108, 109, 112, 179, 383,
 291, 303, 304, 308, 310, 320, 328, 329, 330,
 348, 384, 508
Semen, stag's, 363
Seminal ejection, 204
Seminal emission, 423
Seminal fluid, 146, 199, 202, 293, 303, 329,
 360, 399
Seminal immunisation, 287
Seminal percussion, 202
Seminal secretion, 87
Seminal vesicle, 399
Seminal vesicles, 14, 15, 16, 94, 150, 329
Semination, 204
Seminiferous tubes, 13
Senile decay, 394, 400
Senility, 391, 394, 398, 399
Senses, 172, 173, 183, 359, 432
Senses, over-stimulation of the, 376
Septicæmia, 279, 499
Sergeant Bertrand, 465
Sewing, 248
Sewing machine, 82, 95
Sex, 192, 193, 230, 231, 236, 237, 238, 239,
 240, 259, 294, 295, 332, 333, 335, 336, 338,
 341, 344, 370, 371, 377, 381, 413, 415, 418,
 429, 439, 443, 444, 448, 451, 452, 454, 455,
 462, 468, 489
Sex abnormality, 342
Sex appeal, 172, 173, 174, 175, 180, 217, 351
Sex equality, 591
Sex hormones, 320
Sex hunger, 350, 603
Sex initiation, 197
Sex life, 309, 341, 388
Sex morality, 332
Sex preparations, 386
Sex reactions, 379
Sex urge, 389
Sexological Institute of Berlin, 87
Sexual abnormalities, 325, 406, 407
Sexual abnormality, 334
Sexual act, 30, 32, 82, 84, 85, 92, 140, 182,
 184, 185, 186, 192, 194, 195, 197, 198, 201,
 203, 211, 213, 246, 268, 283, 286, 302, 308,
 310, 311, 313, 320, 323, 329, 331, 339, 345,
 353, 358, 389, 402, 408, 410, 424, 425, 432,
 433, 449, 450, 452, 466, 468, 477, 478, 483,
 518, 521
Sexual activity, 122, 125, 126, 157, 193, 322,
 343, 369, 393, 425, 460, 470, 489
Sexual aim, 345, 408
Sexual anæsthesia, 339, 342, 394
Sexual anomalies, 297, 486
Sexual anomaly, 484
Sexual apparatus, 239, 356, 359, 531
Sexual appetite, 147, 151, 385, 478, 486
Sexual asthenia, 394

Sexual athletes, 338
Sexual athleticism, 218
Sexual attitude, 424, 448
Sexual attraction, 467
Sexual attractiveness, 389
Sexual beauty, 172
Sexual characters, 121, 123, 145
Sexual chemistry, 342
Sexual connection, 126, 182, 520
Sexual contact, 193, 496
Sexual control, 356
Sexual decadence, 337
Sexual deficiency, 425
Sexual degeneration, 489
Sexual delinquencies, 390
Sexual delinquents, 489, 490
Sexual desire, 103, 104, 112, 124, 160, 161,
 180, 320, 359, 389, 411, 463, 469, 529, 537
Sexual development, 119, 121, 126, 128, 454
Sexual differentiation, 445
Sexual disorders, 352
Sexual element, 421, 455, 473
Sexual emanations, 179
Sexual energy, 149
Sexual enjoyment, 161, 246, 347, 349, 376,
 419
Sexual enlightenment, 33, 50, 53, 54, 58,
 61, 62, 64, 82
Sexual ethics, 155, 356
Sexual evolution, 162
Sexual excesses, 297
Sexual excitation, 173, 174
Sexual excitement, 82, 179, 186, 207, 211,
 220, 325, 349, 380, 410, 413, 424, 466, 471,
 477, 484, 486
Sexual experience, 213, 223
Sexual expression, 195
Sexual faculties, 365, 385, 391
Sexual feelings, 134, 224, 269, 410, 464
Sexual fright, 419
Sexual function, 365, 366
Sexual functions, 359, 366, 369
Sexual gland extracts, 386
Sexual habits, 292
Sexual harmony, 194
Sexual happiness, 196
Sexual idea, 473
Sexual ideas, 477
Sexual ideal, 173
Sexual ideals, 8
Sexual ignorance, 129, 364
Sexual impulse, 69, 70, 80, 121, 151, 407,
 424, 443
Sexual indifference, 343
Sexual inhibitions, 356, 357
Sexual initiation, 152, 153
Sexual instinct, see Instinct, Sexual
Sexual insufficiency, 487
Sexual interest, 269, 476

INDEX

Sexual intimacy, 149, 210, 245, 246, 497, 504, 523
Sexual intercourse, 37, 71, 75, 76, 77, 92, 103, 113, 117, 124, 140, 142, 143, 150, 151, 152, 193, 202, 208, 209, 210, 213, 245, 267, 268, 269, 273, 275, 318, 326, 329, 349, 389, 399, 425, 446, 459, 468, 470, 482, 493, 496, 505, 514, 522, 524, 526, 528
Sexual irregularities, 474
Sexual irritation, 390
Sexual laziness, 464
Sexual life, 75, 97, 98, 116, **117**, 122, 124, 142, 147, 148, 151, 152, 167, 170, 176, 185, 210, 214, 234, 291, 292, 324, 331, 333, 339, 353, 361, 387, 388, 425, 461
Sexual life of the child, 69, 70
Sexual matters, 145, 186, 358, 409
Sexual, meaning of the term, 24
Sexual maturity, 91, 147, 155, 170, **387**
Sexual needs, 334, 460, 482,
Sexual neurosis, 326
Sexual object, 444
Sexual obsession, 487
Sexual organ, 426, 462
Sexual organs, 33, 34, 89, 93, 116, 124, 128, 129, 146, 174, 232, 367, 372, 379, 412, 421, 430, 462, 472, 524, 530, 533, 536, 537, **539**
Sexual orientation, 172
Sexual orgies, 368
Sexual partner, 350
Sexual parts, 79, 105, **106**
Sexual passions, 376
Sexual past, 197
Sexual pathology, 65, 339, 382, **464**
Sexual periodicity, 151
Sexual personality, 139
Sexual perversion, 320
Sexual pleasure, 172, 214, **276**, **389**, **474**
Sexual pleasures, 332
Sexual point of view, 479
Sexual potency, 356, 384
Sexual power, 314, 327
Sexual practices, 70
Sexual precocity, 123, **468**
Sexual predilection, 464
Sexual pride, 419
Sexual problems, 248
Sexual question, 196
Sexual reactions, 190
Sexual reason, 412
Sexual reform, 155
Sexual relations, 149, 159, 161, 180, 182, 190, 195, 201, 210, 218, 220, 235, 246, 267, 291, 294, 299, 323, 324, 325, 326, 332, 335, 337, 343, 358, 367, 373, 410, 450, 481, 482, 497, 505, 515, 518, 521
Sexual relationship, 152, 269, 423
Sexual relief, 152
Sexual satisfaction, 210, 246, **469**
Sexual sensations, 185, **471**

Sexual sensitiveness, 332, 363
Sexual shame, 419
Sexual stimulant, 399, 476
Sexual stimulants, 355, 357, **359**
Sexual stimulation, 179, 295, **379**
Sexual subjection, 431
Sexual surrender, 351
Sexual system, 202, 365, 372
Sexual tendency, 344, 438
Sexual touch, 179
Sexual trouble, 526
Sexual troubles, 118
Sexual union, 126, 160, 289, 309, **358**
Sexual urge, 152, 161, 164
Sexual vigour, 396, 431, 452
Sexual weakness, 409
'Sexual education,' 223
'Sexual Perversions,' 321, 324, 327, **478**
Sexuality, 88, 93, 98, 121, 123, 125, 163, 193, 335, 347, 459, 488, 489
Sexuality, allo-erotic, 121
Sexuality, auto-erotic, 121
Sexuality, difference between human and animal, 161
Sexuality, dual, 157
Sexuality, female, 150
Sexuality in children, 23, 24, 25, **26, 27, 32**
Sexuality, independence of, 161
Sexuality, morbid, 490
Sexuality, normal, 449
Sexuality, physical, 126
Sexuality, psychological, **126**
Sexuality, woman's, 347
Shakespeare, 176, 442
Shame, 215, 216
Shaw, Bernard, 351
Sheath, 347, 524, 531
Sheaths, 520
Sheik Neffzawi, 350, **367**
Shock, 254, 273
Shoe, 471, 477, 478
Shoe fetichists, 478
Shoes, 470, 471, 477
Shunamite, 381
Shunamitism, 381
Sight, 172, 177, 408, **444, 477, 487**
Sight-seeing, 272
Silver, 510, 511
Silver albuminate (protargol), 519
Sin, 72, 98, 106, 166, 193, 276, **349**
Sin of youth, 71
Sins, 587
Sins, carnal, 349
'Sins of youth,' 69
Skin, 336, 362, 372, **373**, 378, 426, 483, 504, 505, 520, 521, 533, 534, 538, 540, **541, 543**
Skewer, 378
Skewers, 279
Sleep, 349
Sleeplessness, 338

[563]

INDEX

Syphilis, 59, 272, 274, 295, 298, 307, 325, 373, 494, 495, 504, 505, 506, 507, 508, 509, 510, 511, 512, 513, 515, 517, 518
Syphilitic, 505, 513
Syphilitic blindness, 506
Syphilitic contagion, 507
Syphilitic infection, 506, 521
Syphilitic prophylaxis, 521
Syphilitic treatment, 509
Syphilitic ulcers, 504

T

Tabes dorsalis, 507
'Tableau de l'Amour conjugal,' *see* Venette
Tablet, 386
Tablets, 531
Taste, 172, 176, 177, 183, 217, 349, 360, 474
Tattooing, 379
Templars, 441
Testes, 189, 297, 327, 329, 392, 394, 397, 398, 499, 521
Testicle, 12, 13, 15, 16, 20, 103, 122, 390, 396, 397, 398
Testicle grafting, 394
Testicles, 314, 316, 367, 387, 390, 393, 400, 460
Testicles, bull's, 366
Testicles, dog's, 393
Testicles, hare's, 363
Testicles, stag's, 363
Testicular extract, 386
Testicular grafting, 400
Testicular matter, 399
Testicular transplantation, 397
Tests for blood grouping, 397
Tests of endurance, 120
Theory "Rhythm," 318
Thighs, 336, 446
Thirst, 244, 259, 262
Thirst for cruelty, 426
Thrombosis, 265
Thumb-sucking, 25, 28, 29
Thymus, 123
Thyroid, 122, 298, 392
Tiberius, 487
Tillier, 76
Tilt, 57
Timidity, 110, 125, 126
Tolstoy, 176
Tongue, 179, 473
Tongues, 184, 223
Tongues, Goose, 366
Totis, Dr., 9, 59
Touch, 172, 179, 180, 182, 183
Townsend, 83
Trauma, 218, 342, 468
Traumata, 214
Traumatic experience, 328
Traumatic fixation, 460

'Traité de Sexologie normale et pathologique,' 407
Transvestism, 451, 452, 455
Transvestist, 452
Transvestists, 452, 454, 455
Tribade, 439
Triplets, 67
'Tristan and Isolde,' 176
Trobriand Islands, 77
Tube, 168, 169, 229, 230, 299
Tubes, 304
Tubal blockage, 304
Tuberculosis, 110, 280, 306, 322
Tuileries, 409
Tumour, 234
Tumours, 297, 300, 312
Tumours, fibroid, 260, 288
Turds, hen's, 363
'Twilight sleep,' 262
Twin births, 259
Twins, 67, 259, 274

U

Umbilical blood vessels, 230
Umbilical cord, 230, 274
Unborn child, 236, 240, 251, 253, 294
Unconscious, the, 168, 170, 173, 215, 341
Unconscious ego, 348
Unconscious ideal, 170
Unconscious impulses and instincts, 168
Unconscious means, 269
Unconscious memory, 31
Unconscious movement, 346
Unconscious need, 126
Unconscious phenomenon, 170
Unconscious protest, 351
Unconscious resistance, 214
Unconscious revolt, 325
Unconscious scruples, 326
Unconscious urge, 289
Unguents, 179
University of Kazan, 332
University of Moscow, 332
'Uranism,' 438
Urethra, 14, 15, 16, 313, 326, 327, 383, 393, 496, 499, 500, 518, 519, 520, 523, 524, 525
Urethral catarrh, 429, 501, 523, 524
Urethral discharge, 497, 524
Urethral inflammation, 493
Urethral injections, 494, 522
Urethral secretions, 186
Urination, 99, 522
Urine, 78, 178, 232, 243, 265, 383, 390, 432, 497, 499, 523
Urine, bull's, 363
Urine, human, 364
Urine, retention of, 99
Uterine cavity, 291, 308, 310
Uterine contents, 274

[565]

Uterine contraction, 257, 258
Uterine contractions, 188, 200, 245, 256, 258, 261
Uterine fibroids, 538
Uterine lining, 132
Uterine mucosa, 308, 312
Uterine mucous membrane, 230
Uterine muscles, 256, 295
Uterine orifice, 311
Uterine suction, 283
Uterine syringe, 303
Uterine tumours, 292
Uterine wall, 19, 132, 230
Uterus, 18, 19, 20, 131, 132, 134, 136, 188, 199, 201, 202, 204, 229, 230, 231, 239, 248, 256, 257, 258, 259, 260, 265, 266, 267, 268, 273, 274, 275, 284, 285, 291, 292, 295, 298, 299, 300, 301, 302, 303, 304, 307, 308, 311, 312, 314, 500, 501, 518, 529, 531, 532, 533, 537
Uterus, contractions of the, 262, 273, 291
Uterus, neck of the, 257
Uterus, perforation of the, 279
Uterus, stricture of the, 260
Uterus, vaginal part of the, 202
Uterus, vaginal portion of the, 204, 206
Uterus, vaginal region of the, 204

V

Vaccination, 293
Vaccine-therapeutic, 498
Vaccinotherapy, 502
Vacher, 431
Vachet, 321, 448
Vagina, 18, 20, 87, 114, 115, 131, 137, 138, 139, 140, 141, 143, 186, 197, 198, 199, 200, 207, 218, 219, 220, 221, 229, 232, 238, 240, 256, 258, 261, 273, 283, 281, 292, 293, 294, 297, 299, 302, 303, 308, 310, 311, 312, 313, 329, 330, 336, 339, 345, 348, 373, 450, 500, 506, 518, 520, 521, 522, 532, 534, 537
Vagina, artificial, 84, 85, 454
Vagina, stricture of the, 260
Vaginal canal, 241
Vaginal cavity, 238
Vaginal constriction, 351
Vaginal contractions, 200
Vaginal dilators, 226
Vaginal injections, 279
Vaginal muscles, 218, 348
Vaginal part of the uterus, 202
Vaginal portion of the uterus, 204, 206
Vaginal pocket, 85
Vaginal pulverisers, 314
Vaginal secretions, 200, 240, 241, 266, 298, 304, 313, 329, 360
Vaginal secretions of a sow, 363
Vaginal syringe, 314

Vaginismus, 187, 291, 351, 358, 378, 380
Valentino, 176
Valera, 457
Vampire, 384
Vampire of Dusseldorf, 431
Vampires, 465
Vampirism, 465
Van de Velde, 176, 179, 182, 214, 221, 295, 296, 297, 299, 301, 302
Van Swieten, 348
Varicose veins, 232, 243, 307, 540, 541
Varicose ulcers, 541
Vas deferens, 13, 15, 20, 314, 393, 398, 499
Vasoligature, 398, 399, 400
Vatiacs, 142
Vegetable extracts, 373
Vegetable juices, 360
Vegetable oils, 374
Vegetable origin, 359
Vegetable products, 363
Vegetables, 367
Venette, 323
Venereal blindness, 502
Venereal contagion, 508
Venereal disease, 66, 298, 310, 496, 514, 515, 516, 522
Venereal diseases, 65, 110, 154, 493, 514, 515, 516, 518
Venereal infection, 526
Venereal infections, 519
Venereal prophylaxis, 517
Venereal symptoms, 523
Venereal taint, 301
Venus, 147, 322, 327
'Venus in a fur coat,' 422
Verlaine, 442
Veronal, 263
'Verruca acuminata,' 524
Verville, Beroalde de, 375
Villa Gomez, Pedroda, 358
da Vinci, Leonardo, 188
Virgin, 141, 143, 213, 220, 223, 295, 373, 381
Virginity, 126, 139, 140, 141, 142, 143, 215, 239, 381, 469
Virgins, 371, 381
Virility, 289, 320, 321, 328, 338, 360, 381, 400, 448
Vitamin, 296, 365
Vitamins, 296, 297, 365
Vitrey, 270
Voice, 175, 417, 467, 509
Voice, break of, 145
Voltaire, 4, 481, 557
Vomiting, 242, 243, 274, 307
Voronoff, 393, 395, 396, 397, 400, 401
Voyeurism, 408, 409, 411, 438, 459
Vulva, 17, 115, 137, 186, 232, 258, 297, 351, 360, 477, 522, 524
Vulvo-vaginal glands, 18